A CELEBRATION OF POETS

NORTHEAST
GRADES 4-12
FALL 2011

creativeCOMMUNICATION
A CELEBRATION OF TODAY'S WRITERS

A CELEBRATION OF POETS
NORTHEAST
GRADES 4-12
FALL 2011

AN ANTHOLOGY COMPILED BY CREATIVE COMMUNICATION, INC.

Published by:

PO BOX 303 · SMITHFIELD, UTAH 84335
TEL. 435-713-4411 · WWW.POETICPOWER.COM

Authors are responsible for the originality of the writing submitted.

ISBN: 978-1-60050-471-6

FOREWORD

In January of this year, I was watching the Miss America Pageant. I thought of all the accomplishments that culminate in this one ending competition. These outstanding women had decided what they wanted, paid the price and now were reaping the rewards of their hard work. While watching the pageant, the finalists were on stage and a few of their accomplishments were written across the screen. For Miss Arizona, Jennifer Sedler (who ended as 3rd runner-up), one of her accomplishments was having a poem published in 5th grade. In checking our records, it was our company, Creative Communication, that published her poem "Hawaiian Seas" in the Fall of 2002.

Jennifer wrote to us about the experience of being published:

> "I had a poem published by Creative Communication in 5th grade, and I will never forget how special and inspired it made me feel. I have since gone on to win numerous essay contests, many which earned me scholarship money for college, and I may have never believed in myself if it wasn't for Creative Communication. And as Miss Arizona, I write pages and pages of creatively-written updates for all of my followers. Now of course I still take time on my own to read, study, and write poetry. When you choose to be an active learner and writer, I think you will find, just as I did, that truly anything is possible."

When a poet enters our writing contest, they are students like everyone else. As they move on in life, talents are developed. A 5th grade student becomes Miss Arizona. Another student, novelist Angela Bishop, also wrote to me the following:

> "My name is Angela Bishop, and almost ten years ago you selected one of my poems to be published in the Southern edition of your book. I was 15 and it was the highlight of my young life. Although it has been nearly a decade, I just wanted to finally express the thanks I have felt all these years. I cannot thank you enough for accepting my work and publishing it. I have been writing since I was a child and have continued to write. I am currently working on my second novel. So, thank you, thank you, for the confidence you unknowingly gave me in 1999. I plan to keep writing for as long as I possibly can. Your poetry contest is a wonderful thing, and you open a window for tomorrow's great writers to find their way through and gain the confidence in their work. Keep it going, you are making dreams into realities."

To both Jennifer and Angela and the students in this anthology, I am glad that we are here for you. We helped you in creating an accomplishment that you can be proud of and add to your resume. When students wonder if they should enter a contest, I give a strong affirmative. You may not be accepted to be published, but if you don't enter, there isn't a chance of being published or being a Top Ten winner. Sometimes you have to take a risk and enter a contest. It may change your life. Just ask Jennifer and Angela.

I hope you enjoy the poems that are included in this anthology. We are pleased to help provide the spark that makes lifelong writers. Each of these students took a risk in entering and has the potential to achieve great things in their lives. Good luck.

Tom Worthen, Ph.D.
Editor

WRITING CONTESTS!

Enter our next POETRY contest!

Enter our next ESSAY contest!

Why should I enter?

Win prizes and get published! Each year thousands of dollars in prizes are awarded throughout North America. The top writers in each division receive a monetary award and a free book that includes their published poem or essay. Entries of merit are also selected to be published in our anthology.

Who may enter?

There are four divisions in the poetry contest. The poetry divisions are grades K-3, 4-6, 7-9, and 10-12. There are three divisions in the essay contest. The essay divisions are grades 3-6, 7-9, and 10-12.

What is needed to enter the contest?

To enter the poetry contest send in one original poem, 21 lines or less. To enter the essay contest send in one original non-fiction essay, 250 words or less, on any topic. Please submit each poem and essay with a title, and the following information clearly printed: the writer's name, current grade, home address (optional), school name, school address, teacher's name and teacher's email address (optional). Contact information will only be used to provide information about the contest. For complete contest information go to www.poeticpower.com.

How do I enter?

Enter a poem online at:
www.poeticpower.com
or
Mail your poem to:
Poetry Contest
PO Box 303
Smithfield UT 84335

Enter an essay online at:
www.poeticpower.com
or
Mail your essay to:
Essay Contest
PO Box 303
Smithfield UT 84335

When is the deadline?

Poetry contest deadlines are August 16th, December 6th and April 9th. Essay contest deadlines are July 19th, October 18th and February 19th. Students can enter one poem and one essay for each spring, summer, and fall contest deadline.

Are there benefits for my school?

Yes. We award $12,500 each year in grants to help with Language Arts programs. Schools qualify to apply for a grant by having 15 or more accepted entries.

Are there benefits for my teacher?

Yes. Teachers with five or more students published receive a free anthology that includes their students' writing.

For more information please go to our website at **www.poeticpower.com**, email us at editor@poeticpower.com or call 435-713-4411.

TABLE OF CONTENTS

STATES INCLUDED IN THIS EDITION:

NEW JERSEY
NEW YORK

Fall 2011
Poetic Achievement
Honor Schools

*Teachers who had fifteen or more poets accepted to be published

The following schools are recognized as receiving a "Poetic Achievement Award." This award is given to schools who have a large number of entries of which over fifty percent are accepted for publication. With hundreds of schools entering our contest, only a small percent of these schools are honored with this award. The purpose of this award is to recognize schools with excellent Language Arts programs. This award qualifies these schools to receive a complimentary copy of this anthology. In addition, these schools are eligible to apply for a Creative Communication Language Arts Grant. Grants of two hundred and fifty dollars each are awarded to further develop writing in our schools.

Al Ghazaly School
Jersey City, NJ
Javairia Ahmad*

All Saints Catholic Academy
Albany, NY
Janice Smircich*

Bartle Elementary School
Highland Park, NJ
Mrs. Fernstaedt
Janet Garnett*

Bayonne High School
Bayonne, NJ
Deirdre Hurley*

Bishop Ford Central Catholic High School
Brooklyn, NY
Sr. Mary Towers*

Caroline G Atkinson School
Freeport, NY
Wendy Jackson*
Mr. Wall*

Catherine A Dwyer Elementary School
Wharton, NJ
Rebecca R. Mears
Nancy Reeves
Sandra Struble
Mrs. Webster*

Clinton Public School
Clinton, NJ
Barbara J. Shaffer*

DeSales High School
Geneva, NY
Doreen DeSain*
Beryl Tracey*

Dickinson Avenue Elementary School
East Northport, NY
Erin O'Connor*
Robert Shertzer
Michele Terranova

Ethel M Burke Elementary School
Bellmawr, NJ
Kathy Vespe*

Fox Lane Middle School
Bedford, NY
Paul Cullagh*

Golda Och Academy
West Orange, NJ
Hope Aronoff*
Julie Schwarzwald

Great Meadows Middle School
Great Meadows, NJ
Anita Holochwost*

Hammarskjold Middle School
East Brunswick, NJ
Nancy Davidson
Michele Green*

Harold D Fayette Elementary School
North Merrick, NY
Joyce Kelley
Christine Talbot

Hawthorne Christian Academy
Hawthorne, NJ
Erin Mulford
Joan Tortorello

Hillsborough Middle School
Hillsborough, NJ
Bill Dixon*

Hillside Elementary School
Montclair, NJ
Lisa Frankle*
Pamela Gerdes
Betsy Stout

Holy Cross High School
Delran, NJ
Thomas Gowan*
Pamela Tosto

Holy Family School
Flushing, NY
Jennifer Browne*
Linda Corrigan

Holy Innocents School
Neptune, NJ
Jill Uhden*

Hommocks Middle School
Larchmont, NY
Ray Betti
Loraine McCurdy-Little*

John G Dinkelmeyer Elementary School
North Bellmore, NY
Tillie McNamara*

Keyport High School
Keyport, NJ
Judith Zdanewicz*

Little Falls School #1
Little Falls, NJ
Jean Ermenville*

Manhasset High School
Manhasset, NY
Anthony Blyskal
Roseanne Buckleman
Candyce Kanengeisser
Robert Novak
Loretta Schuellein
Marcia Untracht

Maud Abrams Elementary School
Cape May, NJ
Margaret Swanson*

New Egypt Middle School
New Egypt, NJ
Renée Hogan*

New Providence Middle School
New Providence, NJ
Christine MacBurney*

New York Institute for Special Education
Bronx, NY
Pauline Burnett
K. Carragher
Rosemarie D'Amico

New York Institute for Special Education (cont.)
Bronx, NY
Nora Dupuy
Edward Flynn
Jill Klein
Nicole Korn*
Mrs. M. Leonard
Eileen McElroy
Liana Miller
Laura Nardi
Dr. Frank Raddock*
Melissa Reed

Noble Leadership Academy
Passaic, NJ
Dalia Ahmed*
Randa Saleh

Norman J Levy Lakeside School
Merrick, NY
Susan Molloy*

Oakdale-Bohemia Middle School
Oakdale, NY
Kay O'Rourke*

Our Lady of Good Counsel School
Staten Island, NY
Tracy Cunningham*

Our Lady of Mercy Regional School
Cutchogue, NY
Alicia Hunt
Miss McGoey
Nicole Salvo

Public School 114 Ryder Elementary
Brooklyn, NY
Mrs. Cozier
Elaine E. Rowe*

Public School 232 The Walter Ward School
Howard Beach, NY
Patricia Kander
Dr. Deborah Mayerson*

Raritan High School
Hazlet, NJ
Rory Clayton
Ada Marie Foley*
Laurie Skop

Regina Coeli School
Hyde Park, NY
Ann Dombroski*

Roosevelt Elementary School
Rahway, NJ
Natalie Polanin
Deborah Prakapas

Schuyler School
Kearny, NJ
Kerri Czech*
Joseph O'Neill

Slocum Skewes School
Ridgefield, NJ
Teresa Serafimov*

South Hunterdon Regional High School
Lambertville, NJ
Heather Damron*

St Clare School
Rosedale, NY
Mrs. Paladino*

St Mary School
New Monmouth, NJ
Mary Howley*

St Mary's Prep
Denville, NJ
Krista Kvist*

St Rose of Lima Academy
East Hanover, NJ
Aileen Lange*

St Stephen's School
    Grand Island, NY
        Miss Aprile
        Kristy Pasko*
        Daniela Schmidt*

St William the Abbot School
    Seaford, NY
        Mr. Harth
        Joyce Sackman*

Sts Peter & Paul School
    Hamburg, NY
        Jill Pallante*
        Mary Jo Sellers

Tecler Arts in Education Magnet School
    Amsterdam, NY
        Karen LaPlante*

Terence C Reilly School #7
    Elizabeth, NJ
        Kelly McHugh
        Lynn Rubin*

Townsend Harris High School
    Flushing, NY
        Joseph Canzoneri
        Aliza Sherman*
        Peter Wamsteker

Westampton Middle School
    Westampton, NJ
        Nancy Tuliszewski*

William Davies Middle School
    Mays Landing, NJ
        Lauren Kreifus
        Ms. La Torre
        Daniel Weber*

William R Satz Middle School
    Holmdel, NJ
        Jennifer Rogers
        Barbara Williamson

Language Arts Grant Recipients 2011-2012

After receiving a "Poetic Achievement Award" schools are encouraged to apply for a Creative Communication Language Arts Grant. The following is a list of schools who received a two hundred and fifty dollar grant for the 2011-2012 school year.

Annapolis Royal Regional Academy, Annapolis Royal, NS
Bear Creek Elementary School, Monument, CO
Bellarmine Preparatory School, Tacoma, WA
Birchwood School, Cleveland, OH
Bluffton Middle School, Bluffton, SC
Brookville Intermediate School, Brookville, OH
Butler High School, Augusta, GA
Carmi-White County High School, Carmi, IL
Classical Studies Academy, Bridgeport, CT
Coffee County Central High School, Manchester, TN
Country Hills Elementary School, Coral Springs, FL
Coyote Valley Elementary School, Middletown, CA
Emmanuel-St Michael Lutheran School, Fort Wayne, IN
Excelsior Academy, Tooele, UT
Great Meadows Middle School, Great Meadows, NJ
Holy Cross High School, Delran, NJ
Kootenay Christian Academy, Cranbrook, BC
LaBrae Middle School, Leavittsburg, OH
Ladoga Elementary School, Ladoga, IN
Mater Dei High School, Evansville, IN
Palmer Catholic Academy, Ponte Vedra Beach, FL
Pine View School, Osprey, FL
Plato High School, Plato, MO
Rivelon Elementary School, Orangeburg, SC
Round Lake High School, Round Lake, MN
Sacred Heart School, Oxford, PA
Shadowlawn Elementary School, Green Cove Springs, FL
Starmount High School, Boonville, NC
Stevensville Middle School, Stevensville, MD
Tadmore Elementary School, Gainesville, GA
Trask River High School, Tillamook, OR
Vacaville Christian Schools, Vacaville, CA
Wattsburg Area Middle School, Erie, PA
William Dunbar Public School, Pickering, ON
Woods Cross High School, Woods Cross, UT

Grades 10-11-12
Top Ten Winners

List of Top Ten Winners for Grades 10-12; listed alphabetically

Maria Capitano, Grade 11
Pittston Area High School, PA

Anna Daavettila, Grade 10
Houghton High School, MI

Anna Groeling, Grade 11
Arapahoe High School, CO

Arniecia Hinds, Grade 10
Germantown High School, TN

Sabrina Maus, Grade 10
Haynes Academy for Advanced Studies, LA

Erin McCune, Grade 10
Bellarmine Preparatory School, WA

Declan Routledge, Grade 12
Webber Academy, AB

Jacob Schriner-Briggs, Grade 12
Liberty High School, OH

Lianna Scott, Grade 11
Xavier College Preparatory School, AZ

Alexander Wimmer, Grade 10
Home School, GA

All Top Ten Poems can be read at www.poeticpower.com

Note: The Top Ten poems were finalized through an online voting system. Creative Communication's judges first picked out the top poems. These poems were then posted online. The final step involved thousands of students and teachers who registered as the online judges and voted for the Top Ten poems. We hope you enjoy these selections.

You

My day starts with you, the glow of your face.
I get lost in your eyes and start staring out into space.
There is nothing I love more than the sound of your laughter,
And I only hope to hear this now and forever after.
I love your flaws because they make you perfect,
I see the beauty in you and nothing you could say
Would ever make anyone else worth it.
Even with your crooked little nose,
I love everything about you because that's the way it goes.
I know you don't like when I mess up your hair,
But everything about it is so very rare.
I would walk a thousand miles
Just to see your beautiful smile.
The way you glow is like no other,
I get this feeling that we were made for each other.
I couldn't go a day without you.
You're the light that shines through my dark,
You will always be my little spark.
No matter how many girls I see,
At the end of the day,
I just want it to always stay you and me.

Douglas Deal, Grade 11
DeSales High School, NY

Anxiety

A breath too heavy,
The achy feeling in my chest
Slow. Slowly. Growing. It's here!
Oh, my old friend
Always around to accentuate my thoughts
Deeper, growing, how it bleeds, you're here.
No, I can't fight any longer. My expression dulls
It's crawling to my throat
Familiar friend, how pesky you are.
Always timely, consuming
My eyes turn red
You grow past my mouth,
Fight through my teeth and gums, numb my lips
My spine curves, my body vibrates
Pulsing through my veins, my muscles shake
Coming out of my skin through my pores
My friend, you aren't welcomed here
My posture crumbles as water flows down my face
What a grand entrance you have made but,
I never want to see you again
I can't fight any longer, you are here.

Christina Rodriguez, Grade 12
Purnell School, NJ

A Southern Girl

Once there was a girl who lived in the big city of Dallas,
In the even bigger state of Texas, who had a heart to match it.
She loved her family
And her friends,
And God too.
One day,
Her Daddy moved her away,
All the way across the country.
The Southern belle had to adjust
To the harsh Northern ways.
But her kind spirit brought her
Even more friends,
And even closer to God
Than she'd ever been before.
Sweetness does not equal weakness,
And soon the Southern princess
Will be moving on.
But lucky you,
At least you can say,
You were graced with
Just a touch of Southern charm.

Hannah Bishop, Grade 12
Holy Cross High School, NJ

What Destiny?

Last night destiny was completed
as I cut the strings attaching me to the stars.
No longer will I allow the placement
of explosions of light and gas
light years away tell me my fate.
I will not let horoscopes
have more meaning than knock-knock jokes,
the lines on my palm will be useful
only as a unique identifying marker of me,
(not a meeting with some Tall Dark Stranger).
Fortune cookies will just be a complimentary treat,
the sweet finale to Chinese cuisine.
If the winning lottery numbers come off
the back of a fortune the statistical chance of this can be calculated.
A crystal ball is just an empty snow globe
no one's gotten around to throwing away
and the tea leaves at the bottom of my cup
will not offer any more insight into my life
than that I don't drink coffee.
Last night destiny was completed
as I cut the strings attaching me to the stars.

Elizabeth Peets, Grade 11
Massena Central High School, NY

After Life

Life, it's lived once yet you live twice
The day of your birth then the afterlife
Your heart, mind, soul shouldn't be sold for a price
A soul shouldn't be left if you want to live right
So don't gain the world and lose your soul
Wisdom is always better than silver and gold

Think about your actions and what your future may hold
Don't wait until the end as everything unfolds
Your life becomes like a gun as everything unloads
Each bullet a problem only you can control

When it's time for death you will need insight
If you live your life right you will enter the light
Or continue on your path and live death in the night

So think about life, you die once but live twice
Keep that in mind when thinking about the afterlife
Jahmaya Charles, Grade 12
Progress High School, NY

The Sun

The hot intensity
Of the sun
Gives us warmth
Shows in the morning
Hides in the night
The sun, sun
Comes back every 24 hours.
Brings life to flowers.
Never goes out
But it floats about
In the sky from dusk
'til dawn.
Like a shiny light bulb
That never goes out
Ifeoma Ikejiofor, Grade 11
Bishop Ford Central Catholic High School, NY

God's Love

Many are those who are looking for love,
They should know that the real one is above.
Some are searching for love in a partner's heart,
But they always feel sad when they depart.

Surely, the love of God is eternal,
And human love is really temporal.
You can only feel it if things go well,
Otherwise all you get is a farewell.

God loves everybody on this planet.
God's love is similar to a magnet,
Attracting the good and wicked men.
God will love us when heaven and earth end.
Debora Chrispin, Grade 11
Bishop Ford Central Catholic High School, NY

Questioning

We are always questioning the many parts of life,
subconsciously, unconsciously,
but seldom consciously.
And we feign knowing these answers.

How high is up and how low is down?
How far is far and how deep is deep?
Where does it start?
And where does it begin?
What can we imagine?
And what can't we perceive?
Is what's there really there?
There is no answer to these questions.
The human mind creates imaginary solutions.

All we are consciously aware of,
is that at every moment,
we choose to live life to the fullest,
never allowing a moment to go by wasted.
These are the standards by which we all live.
Naomi Dilmanian, Grade 11
Manhasset High School, NY

Broken

I was strong
HAPPY, confident, determined, energetic, innovative
Even outgoing
I used to have vibrant dreams
Until I made one mistake
Now everything is falling apart and
The one person who is supposed to be there
And help put me back together is the one that's
BREAKIN' me

Now broken, MISERABLE, unsure, irresolute, lifeless, introverted
I now shed tears for what seems like eternity
My hearts breaks
My mind wonders
The beautiful dreams I once had
Are now nightmares
Shamyra Ming, Grade 12
Purnell School, NJ

Life

Life is harsh.
Isn't it bad?
You can never
Get what you want.
You pray every day
No matter what.
You keep faith
In yourself that
One day it will
Be better.
David Ni, Grade 10
Bishop Ford Central Catholic High School, NY

Friend Zone

I saw her down the hallway
Her figure was just right
She had the prettiest face
It was love at first sight

I started talking to her
Even her personality was great
We'd laugh and have fun
It felt like it was fate

One day I looked in her beautiful eyes
I went to kiss her 'til the end
She backed away from me
She just wanted to be friends

My heart was torn to pieces
I told her in a low tone
That I loved her
But I was in the friend zone

Michael Mendoza, Grade 10
Bishop Ford Central Catholic High School, NY

Up in Flames

The only thing he left
that damn lighter
covered with soot and the regret of a father that never cared
a nine-year-old kid waiting by the door every day, waiting
for him to come back, but he never did
the kid flicks the lighter open
and watches the flame burn, all
of the kid's hopes of having a normal childhood
gone with one flick of the lighter,
the flame smothered by the lighter's top
and the room goes dark.
The kid, left to sit and wonder
what he did wrong, why he wasn't good enough
still eight years later the kid carries that same lighter
to remember the dad he never got a chance to know
and inspire him to be the man that his father never could.

Jordan Smith, Grade 12
Holy Cross High School, NJ

Voices

Sound of our voices
soothes her pain
we sing for her every day.

"Ain't no mountain high enough, ain't no valley low enough,
ain't no river wide enough to keep me from gettin' to you"
brought a smile to her face every time,
she loved to hear us sing.

The day we all dreaded for these past couple months has
arrived; we shall sing for her in another life

Grace Burns, Grade 12
Holy Cross High School, NJ

Dream

Images with the freedom of choice
Our domain of eternity
A life beyond the natural borders
With opportunities that man cannot comprehend

We are the masters and the servants
To make our dream in its reality
Work and passion is the fuel
To dream that faithful dream

If darkness pierces through the shield
Then the life you dream will be for not
You must be the light to guide
The hopes of future peace beyond

Light will always triumph
With the right to live through every wish
To know how to live my life
I must dream that faithful dream

Matthew Orso, Grade 12
Paramus Catholic High School, NJ

A Promise to Our Black Ancestors

With each piece of injustice against our black ancestors,
An unspoken promise was made.
A promise for this generation to strive for greatness,
A promise to carry on what our ancestors fought for.
Young people, the new generation, keep your promise.
We have come too far, for you to have given up.

When people hear black,
They should think of success, a long way come.
When people hear black,
They should not think of drugs and guns.
I should not be ashamed to say I am black,
Because black is phenomenal.
As long as you all,
Young people, the new generation, keep your promise.
We have come too far, for you to have given up.

Danielle Williams, Grade 10
Townsend Harris High School, NY

Night

A world engulfed in illusion,
Where everlasting beauty uplifts the soul,
And air, fire, water, and earth dance in a circle of power,
Guided by gentle spirit.
Time goes on,
But this world remains untouched by its hands
And the dance for their divine audience continues
As they are illuminated by her beauty.
The more mysteries explored,
The more mysterious the world becomes,
For this is the essence of Night.

Stormie Simmons, Grade 11
Massena Central High School, NY

Beauty

Beauty is found
in the inner depths of a soul
in all shapes and sizes
in the way one portrays them self
in the way one views others

Beauty is hidden
in flaws and blemishes
in forever lasting scars
in the sound of a baby's laugh
in simple acts of kindness

Beauty is
learning lessons from mistakes
love shared and received
a drop of rain in a drought
a glistening rainbow after a storm

Achsah A. Thomas, Grade 10
Sewanhaka High School, NY

Vizard

Vizard.
It's something we all are,
something we all wear.
Feeling ashamed,
we wear one.
Feeling guilt,
we wear one.
Feeling sadness,
we wear one.
Feeling hurt,
we wear one.
Asked for honesty,
we give lies.
We wear one then, too.

Kristin Ho, Grade 12
West Morris Mendham High School, NJ

The Edge of the Cliff

The edge of the cliff is far off the ground.
From the city below comes not a sound.
The people within it appear real small.
If you can see them very clear,
you will fall.

Don't stumble, don't trip
or you will fly
off that cliff
that's way up high.

If you were me,
you'd stay away,
'cause I have a feeling
I might fall someday.

Julia Chiappelli, Grade 11
Middle Township High School, NJ

When They Went Away

I try to live my life but it's so hard, so hard, so hard
Every night praying to God, wishing on them shining little stars
Hoping that you're safe, Hoping that you'll be okay
Cant sleep at night, Twisting and turning different ways
Looking up at the sky thinking "Are they dead or alive?"
Hating the tears that I cry as they roll out my eyes
It's like visiting hours are over and I hate to say goodbye
It's torture seeing your face as I see sadness in your eyes
Coming to me telling me you're scared and you don't want to live here
Locking your door hiding your real fear
Not knowing if you're loved or even wanted here
Leaving your hopes and dreams behind with the sense of not making it there
But when I look in the mirror I can see my new life compared to my old life
The new addition is them being there without a doubt, without a fear
Now you can see the gates to their dreams wide open
And the doors to their fears disappeared
And no more tears in my eyes as I wipe them dry
No more fears in my eyes as I changed my life
Now I can fall asleep every night, Knowing you're safe
And knowing God put you by my side.

Samaria Carberry, Grade 11
Academy for Scholarship & Entrepreneurship, NY

Survival

This devoured soul is coping,
She tries but cries for she is hoping
This fear will fade away.
She asks, but her voice she lacks, "Someone, take the pain away."

This hopeless soul is reeling,
She's got hands clasped together, kneeling;
Someone take the pain away.
She stands and wipes the dirt from her lap, "Now memories, fade away."

This wide-open soul is feeling,
She's lost but she finds herself still breathing;
Now memories, fade away.
She smiles and nods her head, "This fear will fade away."

Erika Keeler, Grade 11
Wellington C Mepham High School, NY

Together We Stand

As one nation, we stick together
Through all the hardships that come along
Even though we lost so many on that fateful day
After that we were able to come together as one
No dividing by cultures or by races
But coming together to achieve a common goal
To celebrate and remember those we lost
Fathers, mothers, children and relatives will be remembered as those who died unwillingly
But coming together, will not let them die in vain
As 9/11 comes and goes we will remember when a great nation fell
But soon after that we were able to get back on our feet
As the great Abraham Lincoln said, United we stand and divided we fall

Rachael Adebayo, Grade 10
Baldwin High School, NY

The Pageant Child

Why are you vexed?
Why are you angry?
You have so much wrath
that you're losing your sanity.

Slowly, but surely, you must comply.
If not, soon, all you'll do is cry.

You nag and you brag.
All you do is annoy me, you wretched old hag.
You cook and bake
cookies and cake.
But you only allow me to savor their smell.

When will you see, that I'll never be
the person you force yourself to see.

Stop getting angry then sad and don't brag
or else we'll both become proper crazy and mad.
Dardalie Brooks, Grade 10
Brooklyn Technical High School, NY

Nightshade

Beautiful as the black mid of night,
fools seek me out with great delight.
I am but a flower, fragile and weak,
I urge you to sample, that I am what you seek.
But my siren's call is deadly, not a treat at all,
for my fair beauty, many will fall.
I call you in, simple and sweet,
begging you to love me, I am a wonderful treat.
Love is blind, or so they say,
but love me and you give your life away.
Death comes to those who dare,
to test my beauty, to see if I care.
I claim your life without sorrow or regret,
about you, I quickly forget.
I move on to the next fool in line,
How good, he asks. My fruit? Divine.
Cheyenne Wilder, Grade 10
Watertown High School, NY

Not Lost

Haunting me inside is the soul of you.
I can feel it inside of me
It's eating me up from the inside out
Only the master of this beast can tame it now
Save me from yourself and I'll save you from me
The beast has made its mark on me,
I can now never forget your face
It's built in my mind
Release it for me please, come and take the monster away
But leave what it was searching for, with me.
For I will need my heart to love you.
Jonathan Chirico, Grade 12
Maryvale Sr High School, NY

Addiction's Aftermath

I wake up to lines of wine, splattered on a canvas that is
not completely bare, but obviously defaced to deformity.
Repeated, overlapping lines —
I count 1-2-3-4-5-6-7, so far.
But I can't go on; I don't want to.
I am ashamed at the waste of wine,
embarrassed at such a misuse of canvas.

What have I done? My reasoning blurred
from the moment my brush hit the canvas,
sliding steadily across without hesitation.
This is not art; this is anger and sadness,
a silent scream, brought out by the closest medium, wine —
Dark red wine, such a contrast to its backdrop,
a stain that I cannot take back.

But no matter how tenebrous and esoteric,
no matter how badly imbedded in the canvas fibers,
the stain will fade — not over night,
but it will fade. It will become a distant memory,
dragged into remembrance when you ask,
"What happened to your canvas?"
And I will respond, "I simply spilled my drink."
Alyssa Ruhlen, Grade 11
Bayonne High School, NJ

Today Was the Worst

Today was the worst, my life had ended.
The sun was gone and the trees were faded.
My life was gone and the rules were bended.
Sadly it had all become outdated.

Yes it was all, all too good to be true.
And most of all I had something to fear.
I sadly had no idea what to do.
And the sound of cries was all I could hear.

When I looked down all I saw was the ground.
My eyes were closed, nothing is what I saw.
And how much I really hated that sound.
The sound in my head yeah it was my law.

So now my life has ended, yeah it was all done.
Too bad I couldn't say that it was all really fun.
Taylor Kuzma-LeBlanc, Grade 10
Brick Township High School, NJ

The Call of the Ancients

Emerald green with horns of azure,
is the goblin of the shadows that does dance before ruby red flames,
under the midnight like velvet and moon like quicksilver.
His dance has an origin that predates man's first breath.
None do remember this archaic rite but he that continues to live
as a primeval memory of a time before history did begin.
David N. Gelber, Grade 11
Yeshiva Derech Hatorah, NY

The Rebound Effect

Does it hurt you?
To hurt me
Do your words have a rebound effect?
Once they have succeeded in swelling my thoughts with pain
Do they bounce back to you?

Is it hard to watch me suffer?
Hard to watch my face mold into a plaster mask
With every shifted emotion a new crack surfaces

Do you empathize?

Or have you been robbed, of your skill to pretend
Pretend like the sharp daggers you throw at me don't pierce my skin

You believe that you're making the right choice
When you have a storm thunder over my peace of mind
I want you to know your rage snaps me in half
Like a frail, scraggly tree mangled in a hurricane

But I know you suffer too
When your words trail off, faltering with unease
It is my cue that the insults have completed their circle
The damage ends where it began

Are you strong enough?
To withstand the rebound effect

Charlotte Hoffman, Grade 10
Mamaroneck High School, NY

I Danced with Love

I simply hugged her
I always knew I'd love her
But it hit me now

I danced with my love
We waltzed with our gliding feet
Sliding on the floor

That was all I dreamt
Nothing more and nothing less
Just dancing with love

I woke to the same
What was before and not dreamt:
One who had not loved

O she was most real
And so was my love for her
But not hers to me

But still friendships last,
A dream of hugs and waltzes;
I had danced with love

Daniel Lang, Grade 12
North Shore Hebrew Academy High School, NY

I Am

I am unheard, I have no say
I wonder where this all will lead
I hear them yelling, my insides bleed
I see the pain in their eyes
I want to hide, to wear a disguise
I am unheard, I have no say

I pretend to feel no pain
I feel sometimes it's all in vain
I touch the space where there should be a heart
I worry it will all soon fall apart
I cry over emotions stirred
I am unheard, I have no say

I understand things will change
I say it's not my family I want to rearrange
I dream of the life I used to live
I try my best to stay positive
I hope everything turns out okay
I am unheard, I have no say

Raven Bonpietro, Grade 10
Comsewogue High School, NY

Love This Game

Basketball season is here
Sharp new sneakers, blue and gold
Running up and down the court
I can't get enough of this sport
Practice makes perfect
Dribble, shoot, pass
Defense and offense from the first shot to the last
Play with all your heart
Right from the start
Never give up, no matter what
And if you fail then try, try again
You've got to lose to know how to win
And every last second counts
Take chances, and believe in yourself because
Confidence is the key for everything
This sport is the love of my life, and I'll never stop playing.

Braedy Maher, Grade 11
DeSales High School, NY

Darkness

Darkness encases my soul in a blackness I can't explain in words
But I am writing this poem
And poems are made of words
And words are made of letters
And letters are made of love
But love doesn't exist in this empty world
Because you're not here
And I'm not here
There is only...
Darkness

Sarah Campbell, Grade 10
Monmouth Regional High School, NJ

A Weary Tale

She was starting to get a feeling that made her body gasp for some sort of irrelevant pleasure
She was in a gaze and couldn't figure out what was happening
Her thoughts were all over the place and her heart was fluttering with enchantment
Why would a girl in such despair feel so out of place?
She thought to herself "This couldn't be, I know this couldn't be"
She used this thought as her daily logic for a couple of days
Then she saw him and felt a feeling that she didn't seem to comprehend
"Why is my heart racing?" She said to herself
She felt his presence before he even walked up to her
She had seemed to lose the ability to speak the words that tortured her inner core
He stood in front of her and held her hand
She didn't know what to do but stare at the hand that held hers ever so gently
No words were said between the two
He took one brave step and introduced his forever loving lips to her misguided lips
With that kiss, He had opened up a girl that was forever lost in a pit of darkness
Now two hearts begin to flutter in harmony
His love to her was a dream she has yet to forget
He didn't really do much but in her eyes he freed her from astonishing pain she kept deep inside
He gave her meaning when while everyone else just gave her explanation
The girl has been taught to love again when all hope was lost
That boy has gained a treasure he will forever hold on to.

Diana Lewis, Grade 12
Clara Barton High School, NY

Untitled

last night I cried.
tossed and turned all night.
thinking about what could've been and what should've been.
I could've been yours and you should've been mine.
but you acted as if you just didn't have the time.
so now we is just me.
and us turned to rust.
so now my heart is shattered, because our love is battered.
I can't speak on the phone because you had a certain tone that made me feel like I wasn't alone.
so because of that awful goodbye causes my teary eye.
I'll let you leave, I shall not plead, but since you stole my heart that makes you a thief.
go on travel the world, just know you are leaving a beautiful pearl,
a pearl whose shine will never go down.
because yes, I am so profound.
so go on, do what you gotta do.
just know I will always love you.
soon my teary eye will dry and I will no longer cry.
the ending of you is the beginning of me, it just took a heartache to see.
so yes I must say, we did indeed have some beautiful days.
so I hope you do realize, or at least try, that this is the last time I will ever say goodbye.

Kendall Howe, Grade 12
Winslow Township High School, NJ

Hope for Our Time

The soul of the forgotten sunlight weeps in one's heart.
The soul weeps for the forgotten hope.
The soul wanders the world to find the one, with the heart of hopes, in this great time of worries.
The heart sings to the wandering soul to show the hope in their heart.
The sunlight shines down on the singing heart to show the world there is hope in our time.

Chevanese Mitchell, Grade 12
Dobbs Ferry High School, NY

Who Am I?

Walking through the hallways of my mind,
Wishing I knew who I was, and all that I could be.
I want to know where I came from, and where I could go.

I'm still a mystery to myself.

However, I am young,
I still need to find my place in the world.
I don't know where I'm going yet.

And I barely know where I came from.

Open doors, opportunities, possibilities, choices.
Putting my life in perspective as I go along.
Making it possible for me to go where I want to go.

Anything is possible, I can do what I want.

My life is my own but I don't know what I want to do with it
Suggestions, comments, concerns from all sides
People controlling where my life should go.

But it is my life, my choices.

If you can't be yourself,
Who can you be?
You can't live your life for other people,

You have to live your life for yourself.

Zelina Williams, Grade 12
Purnell School, NJ

Life

Opposing me
Is a sea full of troubles and doubt
Disorienting my path
From the one I cannot live without
To die or to sleep
To live and to wake
Perplexed by which road to take
Reconciling with troubles brought forth from the deep
Submerged in the entities of my own dreams
As life itself is torn apart from its seams
I am shown Mankind's true nature
And the wrath and greed we portray
We cause nothing but calamity and dismay
But I have been shown both tenderness
And beauty beyond belief as well
Puzzling me, shaking me to the very core
Leaving me with an unquenched thirst for more
Life is terribly good, and most bitter sweet
It's where success and failure meet
In life there is both good and bad to be shown
I live my life, you live your own

Javier Altamiranda, Grade 10
Raritan High School, NJ

My Words Were Stones

My words were stones,
Every single bad word,
I ever told you,
Have you ever heard,
"Sticks and stones may break my bones,
But words can never hurt me?"
But what if your words,
Were stones,
Would they still hurt?
Yes they would,
I threw words at you like
Rocks in a sling shot,
Every hurtful word was
Another rock being thrown
At your heart,
But I never meant,
To play the evil part,
My words were stones,
Thrown at you,
Carelessly and effortlessly,
My words were stones.

Natalie Rivera, Grade 10
Felisa Rincon de Gautier Institute for Law and Public Policy, NY

My First Wave

I feel my heart dancing within my chest,
And my stomach feels like it is upside down and backwards,
But that doesn't phase me at all.
I jump onto my baby-blue surfboard.
My cold body and my chattering teeth
Don't seem to distract me either.
I am too focused on catching my first wave.
I quickly paddle my way out into the turquoise ocean.
My wet and tangled hair whips across my face,
As I spot the picture-perfect wave.
I feel the wave lift me up,
And I spring onto the board.
I look around me, and at the foaming water,
As I ride the wave to the shore.
A wide smile quickly spreads across my face,
And a feeling of accomplishment,
Bubbles inside of me.

Olena Cardali, Grade 10
Manhasset High School, NY

Ode to My Pillow

As smooth as the skin of a new born after a warm bath
Attentive when I am speaking
Absolutely never callous like cold ice when I am weary
Like a soft tissue that will wipe away my tears
My head's number 1 fan
Is the boxing glove when playing pillow fight, BAM!
Instead of counting sheep
My pillow can sing a lullaby that will make me fall asleep.

Kirsten Meneses, Grade 11
Hawthorne High School, NJ

Regret

By now you probably know the truth
All the things I lied about, what I refused to confess to
'Cause I was ashamed and all I ever wanted to do was impress you
By day I think of the happier times and how bad I never wanted to let go
By night I'm haunted by the horrible things I did, of which I never wanted you to know
It was so easy to keep my secrets bottled inside, Yet so hard to fight the yearning of finding someone to confide in
Of getting it off my chest
Such a heavy burden to keep on one's shoulders
But I carried it as I became older, And as the world became colder
Wondering why I never opened my mouth
Asking myself why did I pile up lie on top of lie?
Realizing keeping these secrets wasn't worth the endless tears and sleepless nights
Nor the headaches, the yelling or the verbal fights
All I can keep telling myself is I should've let it all out
Let the ones I loved know what I was all about
But it's too late for all of that
What I chose to do, I can't take back
A clear understanding, is what I lacked
I let my pride keep me sidetracked
I can't rewind time, but if I could you know what I would do?
Work up enough courage to let go of my demons by telling you. I'm sorry.

Makeeba Lobban, Grade 12
Irvington High School, NJ

The Mysterious Spark

The
night was so quiet
and the birds were so tired.
An old man could not tell if the skies were black or dark blue.
But in this curiosity, he noticed that the sky had a weird spark. He tried to find out
what the spark was, but failed to get an answer. A bird flew to his shoulders. He looked at the bird
as if it knew the answer to his question. But unfortunately, it flew away in one glance.
Then the old man walked through the distant woods. Disturbed, helpless,
profound. Again he observed the sky. The weird spark stood on the
tale of the little dipper. The spark was different from all the others that
made the dipper. The old man walked a mile or so and found the spark at the
same spot. He quickly drove his car 20 miles   west and yet found it right above him.
Confused, he caught a woman walking   on the street and begged her to tell
him what the spark was.   At last, in the midst of
nowhere, with no one he   knew with nothing
to say, he   found out.

Laiba Shah, Grade 11
Bayonne High School, NJ

Restoration

Villains hug wrath and retribution tight,
Victims become paralyzed in the face of everyone.
Heroes dig people out of the ice in which life has coated them,
But writers are the ones who contact sorrow and loss like handling electricity with bare hands.

Villains invade the brittle composition of families and rip them to shreds,
Victims yield to the claustrophobia of life.
Heroes serve as medicine, cleansing the air we breathe,
Yet writers haul us back down to the pits of hell helping us mend.

Kelly O'Brien, Grade 11
West Morris Mendham High School, NJ

Knowledge of a Commoner

I do not know what lies beyond the rainbow
I do not know what lurks beneath the sea
I do not know where dreams may take you
I do not know where the road will lead

I do not know what the wind whispers
I do not know why miracles exist
I do not know why a bad thing will happen
To a good person who does not deserve it

I do not know why a heart is easily broken
I do not know why prayer can heal
I do not know why laughter is contagious
I do not know if monsters are real

I do not know much about the world
Or the forces that control it
But sometimes a little uncertainty
Is what makes life worth living

Christine Ramkarran, Grade 10
Forest Hills High School, NY

Dedication and Reward

Every morning I wake
Almost ready to break.
Any other's daily grind,
Can't compare to mine.
Though, there never seems to be
Enough for me
To eat in this damn place.
Going at a steady pace,
For six more years at least
In hopes of leaving the Northeast.
But because it hurts
It keeps me alert,
As to where I will be taken.
At any rate, look at all this bacon.
In a few hours I'll take the icy plunge
And all these feelings will be expunged.

Jack Long, Grade 11
Bayonne High School, NJ

Life Is But a Dream

Waking up from a dream that feels so real
An uncertainty of how I feel
What if dreams were reality
And reality were dreams?
Everything is not what it seems
Dreams are unpredictable, and can be scary
But so is life
So in a way, they're both alike
What if dreams were reality
and reality were dreams?
Everything is not what it seems

Olivia Villari, Grade 12
Holy Cross High School, NJ

I Imagine

It's so predictable that I'm adopted into a family,
Who fail to give me some security,
A sense of closeness that she gave me up for,
When I was empty.
I imagine life without anything,
How my life would've been like if I stayed with that
Dysfunctional woman?
Missing father figure who is totally out of the picture,
No brother, no sister,
Only child standing with two shoulders and some DNA missing.
I imagine myself raised out in the streets,
Or the calmness of a mother's love tap on my head
I imagine those things in one,
But I live this life God chose —
To choose not to conform,
Be an individual, not a fool.
I imagine a blackboard — the horizons, the sins all gone and remembered no more.
I imagine the tapestry hung when I was born,
A celebration of a baby girl into the world,
I can only imagine what it would've been like to live without knowledge!
Through all the chaos God stepped in at the right time to stop it.

Carla Beuthe, Grade 12
Monmouth Regional High School, NJ

Life

Such an unpretentious word
A simple word with a strong meaning
A powerful meaning many take for granted but few appreciate
Teaching us and showing us right wrong.
Testing our every move
Pushing and pulling us like a battle for survival
Watching as we live in this society
Happiness and love; sadness and hate
Changing the very person we are
Our time slowly but dissolutely ticks away
Burning away life a short fuse that makes us wish
Wish we had changed our ways making the most of our life
Living it to the fullest
Living in our paradise, our fondest dreams and fantasies
In reality we are far from this place
We are far from the life we once had or wanted
And sometimes we can forget how dear life is
And forget what it means to live
Forget what it means to love
Forget what it means to be human
The meaning of life is truly to find peace, happiness and love living life to its fullest

Cody Henehan, Grade 11
DeSales High School, NY

Mad

I finally found someone who makes me happy
Someone to love, who loves me back
This is the longest relationship I've been in
And yet the most stressful

As our relationship goes on
People in our lives feel the need to be mad
Most people of my generation call it "hating"

Not even my own parents want me happy
It's not my fault that they are miserable
Even my boyfriend's younger sister as well
It's not his fault that I can come over to their house
While she can't bring a guy over

So I feel that the solution to this problem
Is for me to show people just how mad I can be
Then the next thing I'll hear is
"Diamond, why are you being this way?"
And do you want to know what I'll respond?
I'll just respond
"It's people like you that make me regret letting people in"

Diamond Stevenson, Grade 12
High School of Graphic Communication Arts, NY

My Pop

He has a smile that brightens my day,
and stands tall with a twinkle in his eye.
A vibe that keeps friends from staying away
which makes me always hate saying goodbye.

He has stories that are far and beyond,
including his great fight through World War II.
I find this an amazing way to bond,
a creative way to learn something new.

We always like playing a game of cards.
Our favorites are Go Fish and Gin Rummy.
Since we play for fun they never seem hard
but when we lose it hurts our tummy.

I love my pop he is so great and true,
he has been there for me the whole way through.

Kaitlin Miller, Grade 11
Manhasset High School, NY

To Make the World a Better World

To Make the World a Better Place
People need to stop talking about every other race
Instead of fighting you should sit down and talk face to face
And not get on everyone's case
Just back up
Respect personal space

Edward Donnelly, Grade 11
New York Institute for Special Education, NY

Fixed Fate

Are you just afraid,
Of the inevitability of life?
You've been hiding behind what has been portrayed,
And now the truth cuts like a knife.

Are you scared, shocked, surprised,
That one day we all will die?
Everything in life that has been devised
Will not matter as it all flies by.

One day our hearts will stop,
Eyes will close,
Blood turn cold,
And tears forever run dry.

In the warmth, we hide in fear
From that long forgotten tear.
And in the cold,
Reality is all we know.

But our comfort is not predictable,
For the truth is that we are invincible.

Julia Maier, Grade 10
South Hunterdon Regional High School, NJ

Life

Screaming and tears now begin, you are now born.
Gazing eyes searching, now you're curious.
You crawl around like a checkerboard pawn.
No breakthrough, starting to get furious.

As life goes on, and you learn how to leap,
To the events that bring you much delight,
Realizing they're not fun, you start to weep,
Wanting to soar away into the night.

An image in your mind, a memory
It is happy, yet it's miserable.
Running through the fields, it's scenery
You're alone, at risk, and gullible.

Your life was tough, scary, yet you did pry
Open the doors fought it, you can now cry!

Destiny Marino, Grade 10
Miller Place High School, NY

Basketball

Basketball to me is everything,
It's not just a sport; it's a way of life,
Basketball is something I could do all day every day,
A gym is my sanctuary,
When I'm playing basketball it's like nothing matters,
Without basketball I don't know what I would do.

Thomas Kanaley, Grade 11
DeSales High School, NY

Perspective of Nick Carraway

The world they live in, is unlike mine
I am plain, average, less
They are perfect.

It is a fact, known by all
It says it on their clothing, homes, and cars
It is visible in their presence, and it is envied.

Our worlds collide, and soon I am trapped
Watching others lose their morals, their dignity.
It is disturbing.

We all spend time wanting, wishing
For happiness
My definition will not be achieved here.

Our worlds do have a commonality
Neither last forever.
It is your choice, where you want to stand.

Bridget Carratu, Grade 11
Manhasset High School, NY

If I Had Another Chance

If I had another chance,
Would I still be naughty?
Or would I still be careless about what I needed to do?
If I had another chance,
I believe the life I own may be different
But the truth is,
I don't have another chance
I can't do anything but regret what I have lost
I can't pay back the people who were hurt by me
It is gone, the things that you lost are gone
They can be called memory
But you can never turn back to them
If I had another chance,
I would like to start over again
So that I would not have shame when I look back
If I had another chance,
But I don't have another chance to go back to the beginning
I need to keep going on
Let the future move forward with no shame.

Yuhui Zhang, Grade 12
Purnell School, NJ

A History

Remembering our days:
We purged our homes of ancient trees
For aqueducts,
Fountains, rocks for roads,
Molding stoicism
And forgetting
Ourselves

Skinny-dipping in the glassy teal, dissolving into
Our sinning smoke-ring souls,
Knees soiled and scraped,
And yesterday always pounding in
Our chests

We are this, always this:
The weight of rubble, stony and
Sinking again
And again and again

Juliana Paterno, Grade 12
Purnell School, NJ

This Depression

Disappointment by the day
The color of the sun at bay
Growing weary by the week
Grayness flows into your soul fluidly as it seeps
Happiness slipping by the hour
A rainbow fades, taking you from your tower
This depression consists of many images
Speaks all languages
And can affect one's speech, their sentences
As this black plague has you in its grasp
You suffer from its tiresome attacks
Each and every morning
You find your strength slowly dwindling
Like a pulchritudinous flower in the process of dying
Buddy up with negativity
Like shaking hands with Satan himself
This depression...
Has taken over

Gabrielle Cohen, Grade 11
Absegami High School, NJ

Summer

I like summer
There are so many things to do
Swimming
In a pool, lake or river
Kayaking
Canoeing
Sailing
Going to water and amusement parks
Ride until they close
No worries about school

Andrew Merwin, Grade 10
DeSales High School, NY

Conflicting

If I were to write to you,
Saying the sky is blue,
Would it mean I was symbolizing,
My undying love for you?
But what if that wasn't true,
My feelings for you are hate,
But I am writing to another person,
So it must mean my undying love.
But what if this was a letter,
To you expressing my dislike,
I hate the way I smile,
I hate the way I break.
It's obviously my undying love.
But what if when you walk
Into the room,
I can't help but leave
Because I hate to see you.
How can you say
You know how I feel?
I don't love him
And he hates me too.

C.K. Ceanette, Grade 11
Waterloo High School, NY

Fairytales Are No More

At some point,
everyone believed the stories.
They hoped,
and dreamed,
and yearned
for their own little fairytale.
With kings and queens
princes and princesses,
talking woodland creatures
and fairy godmothers.
Then, the tales were
whisked away.
The dreams faded,
and the young princes and princesses
grew up and out
of their little kingdoms.
Their dreams became goals,
and the fantasy evolved
into the cruel,
unforgiving and whirlwind journey
that is Reality.

Nicole Garzon, Grade 11
Bayonne High School, NJ

Burned

Like the warm sun on my cold skin, it started out pleasantly.
I had been shivering for so long that I was hungry for warmth.
For the first time, I was sure that I had something that was all mine,
something that I could hold on to, I could love, I could trust.
You were the one who destroyed the wall I had built around me,
the one who opened the door to my caged heart.
I was consumed by your radiating light,
engulfed by the heat you gave off.
Now, warmer than ever before, I was on top of the world,
as if everything were molding around in my fingers
as if I were the creator.
I had built myself up and placed myself on a golden pedestal,
in a trance from how everything I knew had suddenly become new.
In a quick, devastating motion, you swung your leg and tore my tower down,
destroyed me until I was eye to eye with you,
brought me crumbling down and used the rubble to rebuild that wall,
and close the caged heart once more.
Like the warm sun on my cold skin, it started out pleasantly.
When it was over, the summer sun had burned me,
leaving red, bubbled flesh across skin that once craved a warm touch.

Michelle Klejmont, Grade 11
Bayonne High School, NJ

Make a Sidekick

Preheat oven for 400 degrees
2 cups of troubled childhood
1/2 cup of super hero knowledge
1 stick of powers
Just a pinch of rebelliousness
2 tablespoons of mistakes that the hero has to bail his sidekick out of
A dab of parental issues concerning sidekick life

Start out with the 2 cups of troubled childhood in a bowl
Add the 1/2 cup of knowledge and 1 stick of powers
Mix well to get that justice smell
Pour 2 tablespoons of mistakes for the youthful flavor
Sprinkle the rebelliousness and parental issues
for that texture you're always worried about
Put in oven for 18 years
While you wait, feel free to make an evil assistant for dessert

Robert Creenan, Grade 12
Clarence High School, NY

11:11

Every time that clock hits 11:11,
She sits there and wishes.
Wishes for a better tomorrow,
A better place to be.
A place with better people,
Where she can finally feel at home,
Where she doesn't have to worry,
Where she can finally be herself.
Maybe one day on 11:11 her wish will come true,
Then maybe she can start wishing for something she wants instead of something she needs.

Brandi Santiago, Grade 12
Holy Cross High School, NJ

Word for Word

Everything has already been done

Every song has been sung, every word has been spoken
Every memory thought, and every promise broken
Every smell has already been smelt
The deepest feeling, already felt

And in understanding this, you see what you are
Look up at the sky, try to count all the stars
Just a tiny speck, floating among the rest
Feeling the same highs, failing the same tests

But being a speck can be a comfort at times
Someone's always outdone even your most wicked crimes
And somebody out there feels just like you do
And somebody somewhere wants to be someone new

So contemplate this when you're feeling dramatic
Your life isn't the only one that seems tragic
And all that complaining, guess what? It's been heard
The same sentence, word for word

Jessica MacGregor, Grade 10
South Hunterdon Regional High School, NJ

What Melts the Snow

Summer is a time when the sun awakens,
Where the birds are resurrected,
And the clouds create a sense of peace,
Rather than block light from touching the Earth.

Summer is a place where you are free to
Have your head in the sky,
And have your feet dangling below.

Summer is a time when you can cry in between the raindrops,
For the drums of thunder overpower your weeping.

Summer is a place you don't have to dream,
Because dreams, they are as real as reality.
Images of love, of life, of hope, of adventure,
Fluttering under the zealous sun.

Summer is where I grabbed at the sun,
And brought its warmth into my heart,
To heal and to cherish
All of the scars of the snow.

Kristen Wainwright, Grade 10
Ridge High School, NJ

Found My Self

I was given something
I could never get anywhere else, my Self.
I had been to plenty of places
In the seventeen years of my life.
But none ever gave me myself, except for one.
People there gave me a chance
To find my Self before being some One.
Thankfully I found my Self,
So I finally had the chance to be me.
It took a lot of time
But the people there are patient,
And they'll wait for you to be you.
People everywhere else aren't patient,
They probably don't know the word;
They never gave me a chance.
I learned who kind people really are,
The ones who are patient and will wait for you.
'Cause no matter what, they'll be there for you,
That's what people there do.
They are waiting for me to find my Self,
And because I found her they found me too.

Amy Isler, Grade 12
Purnell School, NJ

The Flame We Both Needed

I try to figure out what went wrong
Some say things are best said in the form of a song
There just aren't enough songs to sing

I cry when think of your pain,
Of how horrible I could be
I poured the water on the flame
The flame I knew we both needed

I just didn't know I'd need it too
Now I'm nothing without you
It's happiness I can't find

I hope your days are filled with glee
I don't deserve the light
You're better off without me

I can never stop loving you
This much I know is true
I can only ignore the pain
I hate to think I won't have you.

Jesenia Ginyard, Grade 10
Progress High School, NY

If I Was a Lovely Rose

If I was a lovely rose I would like to be in a lovely garden of my keeper
My keeper would always love me and care for me like the one who made the earth
If I was a lovely rose I would like to stand in the big market where I can be admired by people
If I was a lovely rose I would like to make people happy with my sweetening nectar and my bright color
If I was a lovely rose I would like to teach the little roses about life on earth,
so they would grow up and make people happy like the lovely rose I imagined to be.

Nickie, Grade 12
Francis Lewis High School, NY

Seconds

On shadows yonder, that is what you fear against, that rain he is wondering, spilling over like dreams. To cry when the words have begun, to turn to my desires, just seven wondrous seconds. A trapdoor you were falling through drifts across the sea. How to shake my nerves when he must dance for them, how to paint after the ending? He burns the sky with his blood. Soft endearments surround the ideal. Even if you can't speak the rhythm, we are just a part of time. I keep this treasure to build my dreams. I fly this soul to carry you.

Mia Farinelli, Grade 11
Horace Mann Upper School, NY

Life

What is life?
Is it something to fear or cherish?
What is the point of life?
What is to happen if we were to perish?

What is life?
Are we play things,
for someone pulling strings?
Or do we have a say in what we do,
with all of our experiences,
being exciting and new.

Why do we fight so hard for life?
When everything ends the same.
Seriously, why do we fight hard for life?
This odd, never ending game.

If it were to all end,
would there be any point to be alive?
Just to struggle,
in an attempt to survive.

What is life?
It's repetitive, it's mundane
When you think about it,
it's enough to drive one, insane

Life,
is like this poem.
It can end sooo abru-

Dawud Abdur-Rashid, Grade 10
Bishop Ford Central Catholic High School, NY

What I Have, I'll Give You

I have food and you're hungry, I'll give you it.
I have drinks and you're thirsty, I'll give them to you.

I have cool air at home, you don't
I'll invite you over to stay

I have warmth, you don't
We'll cuddle until dawn

I'll share my all with you
I'll share my smiles, my laughter,
My tears and my sadness

I'll share my heart, my soul,
And I'll share my love
With you and you only

Because I love you, and I swear,
I never want to let you go
And I can't let go and I won't…

Because I've shared too much with you
And I swore to the heavens and the Lord,

What I have, I'll share it
Love it and give it to you

You and only you
Forever.

Yvette Castro-Gonzalez, Grade 10
Bishop Ford Central Catholic High School, NY

To End

I wake up —
Drowning in my own tears —
Who am I? What has the world become?
The tears sting,
My heart beats ring —
Faster and faster —
When I think about it —
Faster and faster —
When I think about them —
Faster and faster —
'til I hit the ground.
Laughter
      Singing
            Cheering —
What is that sound?
It's me — Before I began to see —
That life has to end —
Life isn't always.
You do the do and then you die.
Saying you have your whole life —
Is just a doltish lie.

Frantzline Tingue, Grade 11
Liverpool High School, NY

Untitled

Not caring.
Because I know nothing lasts forever.
Mad at you one day.
Friends the next.
It doesn't faze me.
I have a heart.
I know what's real, that's all.
Trying not to dream so much
Because you can only get so much.
Not wanting to get my hopes up.
Dreaming is easier than living in reality.
You can't get hurt in your dreams.
But when you come back to reality.
Everything hurts.
Car crash.
Falling onto concrete.
Everything is ten times worse.
Yearning to go back to the dream.
Images only vivid to you.
Trying not to get my hopes up.
I stopped dreaming.

Jennifer Okorie, Grade 12
Columbia High School, NJ

Civil War

The cannon cracks splitting people,
Countries tear apart.
We want to be free so we fight
Our brothers and sisters.

The North wants to stay together
The South wants to be free.
We take it to the battlefield
We forget that we fight our friends.

We scream for peace and then beg for it
When the words don't work the guns do.
The first bullet pierces through the General's chest,
You look satisfied until you think of the Thanksgiving you shared.

Lincoln screams "free the slaves," Davis will not yield.
General Robert E. Lee defends his country
Ulysses S. Grant burns through the union.
The North Prevails and we reunite.

A civil war leaves scars that never heal, we can't forget those we killed.

Shawon Ahmed, Grade 10
Townsend Harris High School, NY

Who Said Anything About Giving Thanks?

Let's give thanks, shall we?
Yes, let's give thanks.
Thanks for what?
Thanks for this delicious meal even though Aunt Jennie messed up the stuffing.
Yes, let's give thanks.
Thanks for what?
Thanks for these halves of melted white candles.
Hey! You still have plenty of wicks left!
Ok grandma, whatever you say.
Back to giving thanks, shall we?
Yes, let's give thanks.
Thanks for what?
Thanks for the people we have around us today.
I say, that is a grand thanks.
Yes, I agree.
Let's eat.
Don't mind if I do.

Gabrielle Spencer, Grade 11
Clarence High School, NY

Nature and the Girl

Her eyes blue like the sky,
Bright and full of light and twinkling among the stars.
Her long golden hair blows in the wind like the field of golden grass, smooth and natural.
Sunrise to sunset, her beauty is announced through the whispering wind.
Her face illuminates, no need to cover it up.
Emotions swaying, changing course as if a new season had begun.
If only she knew what nature has given her,
Natural beauty.

Brett Lelie, Grade 10
South Hunterdon Regional High School, NJ

Basketball
I dribble the ball I see the floor
I look up and nobody is there
So I take him on
I get by him then
I see my teammates I pass the ball
I cut through I get the ball back
Seven seconds left I pass the ball
Again I get out in range of a three
I call for the ball
I'm like John Wall
I get the ball
1 second left I shoot and swish I won the game
I feel great and like a champion I feel like a saint
Isiah Merced, Grade 11
DeSales High School, NY

The Angel
Her blue eyes
Her blonde hair

Her soft skin
So fair

The Angel

Her heart so kind
Her hands so gentle

Her soul so pure
She is so special

The Angel

She is so cute
She is so beautiful

She is herself
She is so thoughtful

The Angel

She keeps me warm, and safe
She holds me close when I am scared
She keeps me company when I am alone
She lights the way when it is dark
She is The Angel
She is My Angel
Phillip Bennett, Grade 12
DeSales High School, NY

the Abandoned.
the looming full moon showers its light
to the silent sonata
of the misconstrued

boats of reminiscence
teeter through the tumultuous rivers
in search of

…an island of serenity.

the crescendo of the spontaneous waves
picks up

most boats capsized
only a few still upright

the lost and forgotten
lay lifeless in the bottom of the
barren sea

clouds part
the midnight sun
nestles the survivors

as the moonlight
breaks through
the hardened hearts

…of the Abandoned.
Christine Wong, Grade 10
Great Neck South High School, NY

Who We Are?
We come from near,
We come from far,
We are equal,
We are alike,
Sometimes the closer we are,
The farther we are from understanding
What makes us different?
Ignorance taking over us!
No!
There is no race,
No shape,
No age,
No inequality,
So, why do we see each other as aliens?
The way we look,
Or how we speak
No!
Nothing can break this beautiful bond.
We are unique, we are intelligent,
We are…
The Human Race
Ridwana Islam, Grade 11
Norman Thomas High School, NY

As I Watched the Flowers Die

As I watched the flowers die,
You can tell where man had been.
You could hear the sad wolf's cry.

The little rabbit who had once been so shy,
Fights for its babies with its teeth as sharp as pins.
As I watched the flowers die.

To these horrible deeds I will not comply.
As man peels the bear's skin.
You could hear the sad wolf's cry.

The birds scream as they fly,
And the bobcat no longer grins.
As I watched the flowers die.

And for the innocent dead I sigh,
And for those who have become too thin,
You could hear the sad wolf's cry.

All the creatures say goodbye,
And for my uselessness I feel chagrin.
As I watched the flowers die,
You could hear the sad wolf's cry.

Julie Burgos, Grade 10
Long Branch High School, NJ

A Chaotic Psychosis

Soft blue skies
falling upon you.
Golden rays of light
scald your skin.
A soft smile
mutates into a grimace of torture.
Song birds pleasantly chirping their song
chased away by the black crows of your thoughts.
Angels become
the darkest demons.

Sanity vanishes.
A small room.
Screams of those in mental affliction,
giggles of those enduring even more.

Rocking,
back and forth,

back
and
forth.

In the asylum of your mind.

Alyssa Peryea, Grade 11
Northeastern Clinton Sr High School, NY

One in Earth

My breaths are heavy, my sight is blurred
Pulses slowed in the passing seconds
But I do not feel this
For the Earth is my cure.

There is not much time left
For I can see a blackening in the horizon
But I do not care for this
As the Earth is my light.

For the poppies, lilies, and daises speak to me
And caress me with the passing of the wind
For the dirt is my bed sheet
To let me know I will be safe.

And when the oaks and evergreens grow
To protect me from my doubt
I can, at last, rest easy
To hear the song of the house sparrow.

And even when I feel myself escaping
I know very well that when my eyes shut
I will become the poppies, dirt, oaks, and songbirds
I will become one with the Earth.

Steven Joseph, Grade 12
Francis Lewis High School, NY

The Gifts I Can't Neglect

Small and shivery, tapered ends.
Stretch, crack, and pop.
Gyrating at their curious joints.
Squared off at the top.

Blue circuits running under,
The sensitive olive tone,
Blistered, bruised, and hung to dry.
Unrewarded and alone.

Uprooted from the ground one day.
Enriching lives like the soil it was in.
Everyone has to start somewhere so,
The endeavored reach is wide, though the reacher himself is thin.

Calloused grooves, sandpapered pads,
Never allowed a break.
Nervous, slippery, deprived of care.
Dirt embedded, mud has caked.

Though once untouched and princess soft,
Never can go back.
Beautiful in an ugly way.
Generosity, they do not lack.

Fiona Capil, Grade 11
Union High School, NJ

Gray Skies

I'm tired of these gray skies
Only showing only tears and lies
Breaking all of my desperate tries
I'm tired of these gray skies

Where's the sun
Where's the light
This world is falling
For evil's plight

There's darkness everywhere
Tears even children share
This game of life just is not fair
There's darkness everywhere

What does the future hold
I can't see it with my eyes
There's something clouding my vision…
Oh now I know why
I'm tired of these gray skies

Deshawn Chery, Grade 10
Medgar Evers College Preparatory School, NY

Insomniac

Eyes open, my heart pounds
I sit awake and listen to the sounds.
Yes, the world is a noisy place.
But, I feel like I am in dead space.
I cannot fall asleep tonight
I try and try to win the fight.
When morning comes and I see the dew
All I do is think of you.
The day goes on, my patience is thin
I think of you and I start to grin.
You make it easy, you make it fun
When I'm with you I'll never be done.
You're the reason I do not go
You're the reason I do not know,
When to stop or when to leave.
When we part I use my sleeve
To wipe my eyes and make them dry
I feel like a wuss when I cry.
But I'll see you tomorrow and we'll be silly.
I hope I'm not tired because I have reached insomniac-ability.

Dan Levine, Grade 11
Briarcliff High School, NY

Triumph

A dark rainy day, the wind blowing the trees
All nervous,
10 minutes left to give our all,
Only one sound we need to hear

The ball was slippery, the grass was wet
For 80 minutes, the sound of heavy breathing,
The ball being kicked, cheering from the crowd
Only one sound we need to hear

The score was tied, the sky grew darker
Everyone's hope was strong and bright
Bright as a star in the late night sky
Time running out,
Still haven't heard the sound we need to hear

All ran to each other, screaming, happy
We were on top of the world
We heard the sound we've been waiting for,
The swoosh of the ball hitting the back of their net

Jillian Johannes, Grade 12
Holy Cross High School, NJ

So Fake It's Real

We live in a world full of fake.
Fake hair, fake nails, fake face.
But what's the meaning of this fake-driven world,
Or the cause of this new, unreal race?
Bodies or people are no longer unique.
They're changed and bred just to please.
Needles, injections and harsh surgeries,
Fill the gap in their hearts with such ease.
But what is the point of this temporary you,
The changed and evolved human being?
How long will it take for the scars to heal,
And the real you become just a dream?
What is the secret the makeup tries to hide,
Why do we attempt to cover up real?
The world pushes a similar, uniform mold,
And we follow, believing it's no big deal.
Who are these people who make up the world,
Who create and feed us these lies?
Surely if we can figure that out,
Not one more real soul should die…

Jennifer Holley, Grade 10
Cassadaga Valley School, NY

Ready, Set, Gone

I'm only 14
Mom said she'll always help me
But I have to do this on my own

Pushing me to my limits
Just leave me alone
I know what to do
I'm a big girl now

"hey ma' look no hands!"
I'm not that innocent little girl anymore
Truth is, I never was

I know what's what
I understand big words
I can read between the lines too.

Ready, Set, Don't Go
Sorry Ma it's time to let go
You didn't push me away
I just grew out of my car seat
Keana Rodriquez, Grade 10
Progress High School, NY

Basketball

Shooting threes all day long
One on one
Down the basketball court
Tenser than football
Never giving up
Snow is falling
Still dribbling down the court
Nothing will stop the DVB team
We practice hard
Until we get the plays down
Blue and gold forever and always
Running to get in shape
Scrimmaging all day long
Quitting will not be tolerated
When it comes to girl's basketball
Number one
Ronisha Rooks, Grade 10
DeSales High School, NY

My Heart

My heart is like fireworks
Explosives and full of amusement
Sparkly like the 4th of July.
My heart is like a joy ride
Manifesting for a ride
Gregarious and auspicious to ride on.
My heart is like love,
Deep, passionate and affectionate
Like a hero who inspires devotion.
Celestina Asabor, Grade 12
Technology High School, NJ

Here Comes the White Man

The land my father and I once used to know
the land of the great growing trees, one where nature ruled our existence
has been changed forever since the white men came over

They came along with ships in large numbers, with great beasts,
and guns ablaze they began to storm my father's land
they took and enslaved my tribesmen
the green land my father once knew now painted red

They seemed harmless at first, fascinating perhaps
but since the white man came the world we once knew was beginning to fade
many tribesmen forced into labor soon fell to new diseases
and as our numbers dwindled a new group emerged
here comes the black man: so new, unique and still forced to submit to the white man

The white men brought us tribesmen to our knees
they brought disease,
they destroyed our green land to form one of mass production
they dared to challenge our traditions, and forced us to a new religion
we once praised the sacred land, the trees and animals all
but they bowed before a sacred tree, and we were obliged to follow as so

as the tribesmen died, as did their traditions
the land we knew under thumb of nature, now ruled by a crown
green as far as we could see now red with the blood of the dead
Alexa Rizzuto, Grade 10
Townsend Harris High School, NY

Scars

Awkward, small, and shy, too naive to notice why.
She heard the snickers, but couldn't see,
what they found so funny.

Two round glass cutouts hide emerald eyes, like a mask covering what's inside.
To complete the costume, she needed the wardrobe.
All long clothes to conceal the beast people saw behind.

The words didn't cut like knives,
no.
The words morphed into creatures.
Eels shocked her heart.
Bees stung her arms.
Wild dogs scratched at her legs.

But they enjoyed it.
They watched the scars set in, with sinister smiles drawn upon their faces.
Her pain is something they will never feel.
But those laughs.
Those laughs.
Those words.
Those faces.
Their devious moods.

Are with her forever.
Selena Hart, Grade 11
Paramus Catholic High School, NJ

College Football

Football is my favorite sport to play and watch
Huge games being won and lost
Games just slipping out of grasp
But then being pulled back
Rival games remind me of
The face paint
The fans
The big hits
The team
The game
Championship games on the line
The tension is rising
Career ending hits
One crowd cheering
While the other is booing
Freshman learning the ropes
Seniors final farewell game
Those last second games
I can't wait for college

Matthew Hall, Grade 11
DeSales High School, NY

Closed for Winter

Waves crash down on this fine, grainy sand,
But, still, all is calm in this cool, barren land.
The soft calls of seagulls, high up above.
Two hand-holders pass, so deeply in love.

I myself am alone, hands deep in my pockets.
A lighthouse spins, bulbs flash in their sockets.
This place is forgotten, emptied for winter.
The sky vaguely darkened like a bold window tinter.

Maybe a storm is coming this way,
But, instead of departing, on the ground, I lay.
The cool, ocean air breathes deep on my face.
Miles and miles lasts this wide, open space.

I could move from here, back up to shore,
But compared to this spot, it would be quite a bore.
So, I just lay there, wrapped up in thought.
From this empty beach, there is much to be taught.

Samantha Ball, Grade 10
Hillsborough High School, NJ

Flag at Half-Mast

I sit and watch as the flag gracefully
Flows in the wind.
As I watch, I can't help but wonder
What the cause of the flag at half-mast is.
What happened, how did it happen?
All questions I ask myself
As I sit and watch the flag
Flow in the wind at half-mast.

Joshua Suiter, Grade 10
West Morris Central High School, NJ

Stare

I wanted to see her look
Even though I'd have nothing to say when our eyes met
I wanted her to look.

Would I be able to see the pain in her eyes?
The sorrow in her heart?
All these that were hidden to fool those naive.

She flipped her head to look and faced the clock,
My body froze in hope that our eyes might meet,
But they never did.

She turned her head back around and glared out the window,
Brown curls slapping her face.
Her hands trembled and were placed between her thighs,
Again, to hide everything she is.

She thinks no one noticed,
But all I can do is stare.

Mackenzie Parker, Grade 11
West Morris Mendham High School, NJ

Details

Endless green extends beyond
Yet only to some its value has dawned
This land is a view, as we all know
But to some it is home, a place to flourish and grow

I see trees; plain and bare
But to some this is their beloved lair
I see grass; mundane and plain
But to some this is their dear domain

I see clouds; fluffy, yet deep
And notice the birds that chirp and peep
The sun, the moon, the gleams so bright
Reflect on harmony, day and night

We're helpless to ignore accessories, details
While we read our texts, our messages, e-mails
But some, I hope, even just a few
Appreciate life as more than a view

Gabrielle Oppenheim, Grade 10
Hackley School, NY

What You Live For

Some say old age is a curse, and that adolescence holds the golden years of life,
But, how can one really know until they are old and gray and looking at their shoes?
When you are old with many wrinkles coating your brow,
You will surely have tales to tell a young, handsome business man next to you at the bus stop.
You may have the honor of sitting by the kitchen window, making up stories about the birds that scatter your garden.
Glancing at the yellowed bubbles in your cup of cooling coffee, you contemplate years hence.
With several or many regrets and uncountable victories, you see a beautiful reflection in the coffee this time around; one of boldness and reverence of what he used to be.
Sometime, when you are old and gray, you will worry about taking your blood pressure pills.
You will reflect and think of how your sons could have been better men to their wives,
And worry how their children might think of their fathers, your sons.
But, then, your attention will be redirected to your aching knees and failing muscles.
You will hear them whisper behind your back as if to sneak in a, "He's losing it."
And your beloved wife will lie there sick in bed, not recognizing your face.
To you, her face will still gleam the same way it did on your wedding day,
Her lipstick still untouched.
In this case, you will probably forget all the little things that you thought mattered in life.
Nowadays you focus on the hooligan squirrels chewing at your tomatoes or wooden picket fence.
However, the one thing that will forever brighten your day is a visit from your smart, beautiful grandchildren who you will try and advise to not make the same mistakes you did.

Julie Petulla, Grade 11
Bayonne High School, NJ

Sunglasses or Umbrella

Sky usually has glorious days where its best friend
Sun will come out and make Sky's day a little brighter.
Other days they will disagree and battle foolishly about the weather predictions.
Sky starts to weep and turns a dark blue and Sun goes down.
At night Sky goes to sleep on a cloud pillow and thinks about Sun.
Sky is melancholy and smashes the pillow and the feathers dash out like mini raindrops.
Later, Sky's friend Storm screams like roaring thunder at Sky's bond with Sun.
Storm settles an idea to throw a party at night at Moon's house; Storm invites Sky, Sun and Star.
Moon strives to help Sky and Sun turn their half-friendly relationship into a full one.
At the party Moon wishes on a shooting star.
Star magically grants Moon's wish.
Finally, at the party Sun and Sky apologize to each other for fighting.
Sky transforms into light blue and Sun comes up and they illuminate the world in unison.

Sabrina Perlleshi, Grade 10
Pleasantville High School, NY

I'm Ready

Everything I've done has been for me, and because I don't want to let the people I honor and care about down,
I told myself over and over I can do it, I can be successful, but today being successful is hard, but I won't give in, I won't give up.
I'm working 24 hours of the day accepting nothing but life lessons and new experiences.
I'm ready
I'm ready; I'm growing up seeing things different and making good decisions.
I'm ready
I'm ready to explore the world and enjoy life and catch every positive life has to throw me.
I'm ready
Taking good with the bad and sacrificing old ways turning them into solid gold
You may not believe me now but you will see me soon and when you do you'll know
I'm ready.

Shanessa Jones, Grade 12
Rahway High School, NJ

Revenge

Confused and unknowing, lost of all control,
Seeing and unseeing in life,
Without a role;
To play a part of life with your heart blind,
Only to find what lines enemies hide behind;
To trust, to distrust is a game all the same,
With trickery and blame,
Insane and sane, corrupting the mind,
Leaving a heart with its own way to find;
They tremble, they cower, they are afraid;
To play the small trickery of a game,
Inside they feel it's right to hide;
When emptiness and fear are left inside.

Express your words! Express them to me!
Stop shooting glares it's foolery!
To act so childish, to play these games;
They fathom me not but you; all the same,
I've heard it before, I've seen it all,
Your anger is shown, your weakness,
Causes you to fall, off your high throne you lounge upon;
For your city despises you; breaks down your wall.
Jocelyn Serrano, Grade 10
Island Trees High School, NY

Can I Live?

Can I go outside one day and not be in fear
I'm tired of seeing my mom in tears.
She worries bout me every day
and it saddens me that there's nothing I can say.
Can I not have to worry 'bout getting robbed,
I wonder to myself why these people can't just get a job.
You say one wrong word
and you get shot and what does that prove?
One person dead and you get locked up.
I see a fight at least once a week over some stupid stuff
all because that person's trying to prove they're tough
and for what? It disgusts me that it's easy to get guns
and taking a life away is fun.
Life growing up changed — things aren't the same
and I've come to realize this ain't no game.
It's sad out here and I only have one question
CAN I live?
Marcus Eason, Grade 12
Brooklyn Collegiate, NY

Our Tune

When you make each day a song you relish every moment.
Every laughter a beautiful tune, that heals a broken heart.
Each person a different note a magical sound of their own. And
with every voice an exciting pitch. So when we make each day a
song, an unexplainable tune, we make each moment last.
Sabrina Pierre, Grade 11
Paramus Catholic High School, NJ

A Brother

When you look up brother in the dictionary,
Its definition does not do its part.
It states that you are related in some way,
However there is much more to that.

Even though some siblings may fight,
And want to kill each other at times.
It is those moments when you smile together,
That will always be in your hearts.

Whether he is teaching you a new sport,
Or trying to help you with your homework.
A brother is always there for you,
Like all good brothers should be.

Nothing can separate a sister and brother,
Not distance nor a storm.
Since the memories are always there,
And all of the funny stories that can be shared.

Not everyone can say,
That they can relate to what was said.
However I am one of the few,
Who can say that is all very true.
Courtney DiGia, Grade 10
Manhasset High School, NY

The Eagle*

How do you soar above the clouds?
Your body is tattered as if you have fought a great war,
Your glorious wings are damaged yet still you fly,
The wings that shield the forest down below.

Your eyes have the sun's radiance,
Undying, unwilling to be put out,
They see through the illusive fog,
And show the way to your kingdom.

No soul,
Has ever flown so high,
You inspire change,
See through the scorn of others,
Illuminate the sorrowful,
Black and white landscape,
That has tarnished life below.

Wind, why do you love him so?
Trapped inside an invisible barrier,
You still hold him up,
Whisper in his ear,
And carry him across the world.
Aidan Murray, Grade 11
North Shore Sr High School, NY
**Dedicated to Nelson Mandela*

The Movement of His Soul

There he was going
Side to side
There he was so
Shy!

There he was smiling through town
Skin so soft
And smooth

Making every day worth
Being around

Never changing always
Rearranging!

From the smiles
To the laughs
To HAPPINESS
To hugs, to cries
To sad goodbyes

There he was
Going
Side to side!

Brooklyn Young, Grade 11
Newfield Sr High School, NY

What He Is to Me

He is the gold in the cave.
The faith in my soul.
He is the sapphire in the dragon's stomach.
He is the eye that makes the owl whole.

He is the song in my head,
The smell of dirt after rain.
He is the light of the moon,
And he is the blood in my veins.

He is the dance of the wild.
He is the sin in our hearts,
The shadows of men,
The dream society ripped apart.

He is my greatest fear,
He is my greatest hope.
He is the light of the stars,
And the sky's kaleidoscope.

He is the love we all cherish,
The moment of clarity and confusion,
He is what he is to me,
Both reality and illusion.

Elisa Barguil, Grade 11
Townsend Harris High School, NY

Feelings of the River

Down by the river,
Too cold to go swimming,
Too hot not to,
Feet in the water, hands in the sand,
The perfect contrast of touch, the perfect contrast of feelings.
Down by the river,
Water in a rush,
Racing against the fish,
Both whirling around me,
I begin to wade in, knee-high now,
The perfect contrast of movement, the perfect contrast of feelings.
Down by the river,
The sky shades of purple, the trees turning orange, the water crystal blue,
The perfect contrast of color, the perfect contrast of feelings.
Down by the river,
Moon in the sky, stars sparkling,
Rushing water,
Chirping crickets,
Mother calling,
The perfect contrast of sound, the perfect contrast of feelings.

Justin Dornisch, Grade 12
Holy Cross High School, NJ

Porcelain Dolls

They sit on the book shelf,
never moving,
but always looking like they're watching me.
Some consider them creepy,
but to me they are comforting,
Through their eyes I see my grandparents,
sightseeing in Switzerland,
traveling all over Italy,
discovering the beauty of Alaska.
My porcelain dolls make me feel closer to my grandparents,
looking at them, I can see each place they visited,
I can hear the stories my grandpop told of where each doll came from.
They may never leave that shelf,
but knowing they are part of a memory,
makes them a treasure in my eyes.

Jennifer Baiada, Grade 12
Holy Cross High School, NJ

Trapped

Trapped. Afraid. Scared. But still, hopeful, optimistic, loving.
All these emotions go rushing through me; like water over a
waterfall. Highs and lows, one scary roller coaster ride.
Gray then blue. Trapped then set free. Trapped by your hopes,
your expectations of the future. Set free by how much you care;
you believe that all my dreams will come true. Gray brings back
the past, the part we all try to shut out. The door we wish would
stay closed forever. Forever and a day, perhaps. Blue sheds light on the future,
reminding me that nothing lasts forever. If
we stick in this together, we can help make each other
better, and keep floating on the blue.

Angelica Kwiatkowski, Grade 11
Clarence High School, NY

Choose Me

She smiles at me
I just stare
She tries to hold my hand
I pull away
She wants to tell me she loves me
But I walk away

I smile at her
She just stares
I try to hold her hand
She pulls away
I want to tell her I love her
But she just walks away

I wonder where everything went wrong
She wanted to be there now she is gone
She walks away without a word
I feel the tension in my home
Wishing everything was not gone
She has choices to make
I hope she makes the right decision
Mom I have advice

Choose me!
Caitlynn Hamm, Grade 11
Ketchum-Grande Memorial School, NY

Remember

Smile when you're happy;
Cry when you're sad;
Speak your mind;
Scream when you're mad.

Laugh really loud;
Dream really big;
Share all your thoughts;
Eat like a pig.

Kiss a lot;
Hug really tight;
Dance all the time;
Forget the fights.

Watch the stars;
Take your time;
Fall hard;
Know the lies.

Understand change;
Follow your heart;
Find love;
Never part.
Ashley Russell, Grade 11
Madison Central School, NY

Filled Emptiness

The darkness of light is blinding. The loudness of sound is deafening
The loss of taste overwhelms my senses. The lack of smell overpowers my nose

Eternal regret soon to end

The cold burns my soul. The shadows expose me
I trip over the sky. I slip on concrete

I found the bottom of the hollow abyss

The water dehydrates me. The fire cools me
The anger is calming. The pain is soothing

I beheld the Universe's end

The angels rest in hell. The devils roam in heaven
The right is always wrong. The wrong is always right

I answered every and no questions

I remembered to forget. I woke to fall asleep
I laughed to cry. The silence filled my speech

I am the one who wrote a book on water

I swam on land. Walked on water
Flew underground. And ran the skies

I am the one who created the sound of silence

Holly Morcos, Grade 12
Bayonne High School, NJ

Elizabeth Cady Stanton

Elizabeth Cady Stanton. A hero.
A truly significant person who
Risked her life and duties and chores
Since her life was an unjustified bore
Because she was a woman.
Told by her father she would've been better off as a boy,
Treated in a male-dominated society as some silly old toy,
She seemed that nobody else could understand
The difference between women and men. And the truth is, there isn't one.
So Cady set off to the undying and remarkable quest
And worked and toiled to show at her best
What women were really made of.
She organized the 1848 Seneca Falls Convention
Which was the first U.S. convention on women's rights.
She fought for the rights of education, owning property, voting and more
Until the very end…
…Even if it did not depend
Whether she was to live to cast a ballot herself.
All that had mattered was that inequality and sexism was shattered
Thanks to one incredible amazing hero called
Elizabeth Cady Stanton.

Catherine Vozikis, Grade 10
Townsend Harris High School, NY

Taken for Granted

Nothing like the brisk spring air,
Or the startling summer sun,
And the cool ocean breeze is appreciated

Only when the frigid winter is gnawing at our fingers
Biting off our toes
And freezing our faces,
Do we realize the beauty of summer,
And the distaste of winter

Even the flowers and animals too realize,
The opportunity to cherish such a beautiful time,
And awaken to prosper as we humans do

A time like this is in our hearts
And in the hearts of all
Hopefully staying there forever,
And bringing that same change,
That we all look forward to

Sean Grimm, Grade 11
Manhasset High School, NY

Are You Really Gone?

I look around the house and
I see you nowhere
I see flowers, and cards
I think it's a dream
I want to wake from this nightmare
Are you really gone?
Is this one of your pranks
Will you walk through the door?
I will hear your bike come through the driveway right?
I will walk into your bedroom and see you in the bed
But I won't, and I will never see you again
Laying in your bed
Driving up the driveway
You will never play one of your pranks on me again
This nightmare will never end

Laurie Pedro, Grade 12
Purnell School, NJ

Under This Shower

Some girls are like princesses trapped in a tower
I'm the girl alone outside under a rain shower
The boys notice those damsels in distress
The beautiful hair, slim body and long dress
This is the time where I receive a test
Do I change who I am to be like them?
Do I trade in my jeans for a hem?
No, I refuse to be fake just like the rest!
I refuse to suck the life like a pest
I am strong, I can create my own power
Even if I'll be alone under this shower

Morgan Cox, Grade 12
Middle Township High School, NJ

Fall

Homemade apple pies,
Excellent football teams,
The sun is slow to rise,
A orangish-yellow color scheme.

Leaves litter the ground,
Crunch, crunch, crunch beneath your feet,
The colder air all around,
Such a break from the summer's sweltering heat.

School is back,
Fresh supplies and fresh brains,
All ready to carry around their nap sacks,
Anticipating all the knowledge they'll gain.

This is why I love the fall,
Winter, spring and summer cannot compare,
They don't bring the same things at all,
I just love that crisp autumn air.

Gabrielle Schwind, Grade 11
Douglas MacArthur High School, NY

Pure Hearts

Pure hearts are hard to find
I've lost a pre heart that was close to mine
In time I wonder will it heal
If you lost a pure heart you will know how I feel
A pain that can't be explained
As if everything you thought was important changed
Lost in all your emotions
At times in positions when you don't know how to act
Wondering will my lost loved ones come back
This pain came from my dear pure heart that's no longer attached
I never thought my dreams could get snatched
Leaving me vulnerable no way to react
A pure heart can be such an impact
So hold on tight and don't lose grasp
Enjoy your pure heart and remember your laughs

Jarvis Knight, Grade 12
DeSales High School, NY

Down an Empty Highway

My truck flew down the empty highway
Never slowing for even a second
Into the dry landscape
Down an empty highway
I could feel the gears turn
And feel the pistons pump
And hear the roar of the engine
And the sound of the wind whipping at my truck
The dust rose behind me as I drove
Rising higher and higher throughout the dry landscape
Down an empty highway

Michael Nardozzi, Grade 12
DeSales High School, NY

Independent

It starts with you
Follow your heart
Your choice
Your control

No one will stand in your way
Don't be scared of being alone
Fear is only holding you back
Isolation can evolve a person

Look deep within yourself
Embrace what you can't touch
And get a good grasp on the world

Some hide under the mask of others
Those who can't stand on their own
The voices that never spoke

The truth that is buried
Darkness that fogs our vision
The unanswered questions

A dangerous adventure that a waits
All the opportunity to try
The freewill to choose

Being independent
Woravan Tangtrakul, Grade 10
South Hunterdon Regional High School, NJ

Dark Guardian Angel

A monitory eye
observed from a distant tree
as those words assimilated.

My excessive fear
would erode away my rationality
as you had anticipated.

You nurtured
with little sympathy,
winnowed out all of what I was attracted.

Your affection was exclusive
for you knew our impending destiny.
Together we would never be distracted.

Your voice is motive inducing.
I'm grateful of your abnormality.
My negatives you have supplanted.

Dark guardian, you know now
I am boundlessly free
with these wings you have granted.
Elizabeth Wood, Grade 11
Newfield Sr High School, NY

A Milky Way Love Affair

Like the galaxy, our lives are constantly moving
You are the moon and I am the Earth
And we are slowly drifting apart
Your exquisiteness haunts my dreams
At times your impeccable love can seem boundless
Like the radiant heat that travels from the blazing sun to the earth
But at other times your soul can appear to be as frigid and piercing as a fierce comet
Journeying though space desolate and narcissistic
But I can't depart from you
Like a globular cluster of stars bound by gravity
You're like nothing I've ever seen
Your voice is riveting
Your features are stunning
But the love we once held is now fading away
Like the immense, white celestial body that disappears when morning arrives
You're like a constellation of stars that I can't take my eyes off of,
But you refuse to remain with me perpetually
You shattered my heart like two meteors colliding
But kept a fragment of it to show that you somewhat care
And wistfully, that is fulfilling enough to me
Because this is a Milky Way love affair
Eric Coffey Jr., Grade 10
Southampton High School, NY

Comprehending the Incomprehensible

Can such a mind be grasped?
Having created the green leaves, a bestseller.
One, two, three, ninety-nine, oh I lost count!
The trees, the flowers, the plants, all 'round us an influx of customers,
Copyrighted nineteen eighty-six. No, that can't be right,
Copyrighted nineteen thirty-two. Grandpa must have seen him!
Wrong again. Copyrighted in the beginning.
Ah then he must have been here before that.
But what can come before the beginning?
Can we find the start of a circle?
I have studied geometry, though I'm slow with area.
We have landed on the moon, though not Mars.
Medicine cures diseases, though not all.
Oh how much we struggle to no avail!
No, dust will never understand.
Mina Henaen, Grade 11
Bayonne High School, NJ

Music Is Life

Music is an escape from my real life
It's my best friend when mine aren't around
Music speaks the words my heart is afraid to say
There's all different kinds of music for different types of people
It speaks to people all over the world, in many different languages
Music is a little piece of paradise where people wish they could find
It's a little piece of heaven but under the clouds
Music has a way of changing someone's entire mood or day
It speaks to stubborn souls and finds its way in their heart
To me, music is a way of life and without it my world wouldn't be the same
Hailea Higgins, Grade 11
DeSales High School, NY

Tomorrow Comes Soon
While my body sleeps
My mind finds relief
And where it used to walk
My mind now is free

The wind stole my words
Swept them from this world

Any melody to be heard
Fell the voice my body partnered
And from the stony soil
A love it seemed had flowered

Perfect plants are superfluous
If not buried in cement
For memories as useless
As money already spent
Brian Matlaga, Grade 11
Christian Brothers Academy, NJ

Pink
Dear God,
I know you said
you wouldn't forsake me.
my fight has just begun
the days ahead seem weary
I'm not sure if I'm up for the fight
so many have died
so where does my faith lie.
I have no hair
and I have no strength
and the treatments have
exhausted me.
my hope is for
today
and my faith is for
tomorrow
Alliya Butts, Grade 10
Holy Cross High School, NJ

Think
Open up your eyes,
take time to realize.
What you need,
in contrast to what you want.
Don't just look beyond,
see what's right in front of you.
See life as more than a picture,
but from another point of view.
No matter what it is,
what happens,
what you do.
Do things wisely,
for your decisions are part of you.
Victoria O'Selmo, Grade 11
Liverpool High School, NY

Reiterate
Waking up in the morning,
Looking at my blank ceiling
My eyes a glassy stare, my mind empty,
Fearing the world
I forcefully drag myself out of the bed,
Into the shower, the lights off, I close my eyes,
Playing out today's events,
Out of the shower my clothes on
With my mind full my stomach empty
Starring at my untouched breakfast,
I get up leave the house
Headphones on and loud, trying Trying to ignore this world around me,
Entering the school headphones off
Putting on a false smile
I greet my friends
At home on the bed, pen in hand, eyes on the book,
My mind elsewhere,
Homework unwritten, I turn off the lights,
Playing out the next morning
In my mind
My mind
Sean Shaeen, Grade 11
Bayonne High School, NJ

War
A little boy was playing in the yard with his toy gun.
His mom shook her head and said, "War is not a game, my son."

"But Mommy, I need practice so I can be a soldier.
I'm going to join the army. Well, once I become older."

He grew up, his dream the same. Soon it was his senior year.
"I'm joining the army now." "War will change your life, my dear."

"I know. If my life is changed, I hope it is for the best.
I'll try hard and give my all; I know God will do the rest."

Years later he found out that he was going to be deployed.
He informed his mom, who said, "War can scar your mind, my boy."

"Yes, that's right. I'll take the risk. I'll do what I need to do."
Her eyes filled with tears as she hugged him and said, "I'll miss you."
Heather Van Voorhis, Grade 12
New Jersey United Christian Academy, NJ

Death Becomes Her
Humble; death is, to wear a painted veil
with a facade of beauty held to her lips.
Where her rigor mortised grip shall prevail,
to sullen blue splatter upon her hips.
Her crooked grin holds secrets so untold.
With lips parted close, ready for a lie,
to reclaim honor is her only goal,
before she breathes her last goodbye.
Sherad Maneeram, Grade 11
Brooklyn Preparatory High School - Harry Van Arsdale Campus, NY

The Dog

Running through prairies,
Skipping through fields,
Wind flying,
Moving through fur.
Ignorance,
True bliss,
Carefree,
Nothing matters.
True freedom,
No problems,
Howling at the wind.
All the rights you can imagine,
Everything you need with you,
No one to stop you,
Nothing in your way.
Do what you want.
What if men had this freedom?
Would this be good?
Or would this be abused?
I think we would.
I'll leave it to the dog.

Reinaldo Gentile-Rondon, Grade 11
DeSales High School, NY

Emotional Condensation

Rain falling from the sky
She sits and watches the days go by.
No longer alone, although
Not with anyone by her side.

The rain washes the images away,
Clear thoughts for a new life.
Why does no one understand?
Left alone to rot,
For fruit flies to attack.

Sunlight appears,
The tears brushed away.
Joyful rainbows expose her mind.
The pain revisits before long,
Unfortunately the water cycle starts again.

Katarzyna Bezrudczyk, Grade 11
Bayonne High School, NJ

Wings

Their names scrawled in sin
Their souls have broken skin
Those in the book of the Fallen.
Their names are tainted
Their lives are faded
Those in the book of the Fallen.
Their wings are black
They cannot come back
Those in the book of the Fallen.

Marna Moore, Grade 10
Camden Catholic High School, NJ

Walls to Mend

I have come back home,
The place I have despised ever since I was a little lass,
I have come back home,
To the people who I loathe and them me.
Then why do I go back?
Well, that answer is, at least, simple.
I go back,
To look at the place I despised and to remember why I left.
I go back,
To watch the people that I loathe and to be proud of my success.
You may ask why I hate this forsaken place.
No, not for the quiet that seemed eerie and ghostly to me now,
That used to be so familiar. (Maybe because I was so used to the gloom.)
But to look upon the place where I was reared,
To look upon all the drunks and drug addicts that tried so hard to make me a part of them,
That now roam the place of my childhood,
And thank the gods that never happened to me,
That I rose above the wall that kept me in.
I tore the walls around me down,
But now I go back,
Because of my promise…to mend walls.

Toni-Nicolle Bretz, Grade 11
Vernon Township High School, NJ

All Against Her

They call her out when she's wounded.
Any pain that they can inflict they take as a prize.
They hate her; she walks with her head down trying to be invisible.
She wishes they weren't against her.
They hit her with their books when he's not looking, they get away with it.
What right do they have to be against her? none.
She has a perfectly good heart, if they would just give her a chance…
They think her teardrops of pain are fun and games for them.
Their words are like swords that make her bleed.
They all think it is funny to knock her down when she's in the hall.
She feels like nothing around them.
She doesn't talk at all when they're in the room.
She's pushed around by them so much that it makes her cry at night when she's alone in her bedroom.
She is always taken down with just a single word.
She's tied together with a smile, but her smile is coming unraveled
from them always being against her — what reason do they have…

Sherry Jo Sheehy, Grade 11
Friendship Central School, NY

Untitled

I believe that you can make your own happiness
I believe that being you makes happiness
I believe that people can only hurt you as much as you let them
I believe that, if you have dreams, you need to go for them
I believe that you shouldn't have people in your life if they bring you down
I believe that you don't need a relationship to be happy
I believe in independent women
I believe in *you*

Lucy Mantell, Grade 11
DeSales High School, NY

Dreams

Dreams, such curious things.
They can show you what you want most, what you love.
They can transport you to a fantasy.
They can take you back, to a time of castles and fortresses.
Or perhaps they will take you to the future
Big cities, bright lights, fast cars.
Yet without warning
They can show you what you fear most
They can revel real pain
Show you scenes of sadness and fears.
They never take a side
Yet without provocation they can cripple you
Cause you to wake with shakes and tears
Or they can show you great bliss and joy
Making you smile in your sleep.
Yet even the best of dreams bring sadness
Because when you wake up they are gone, only a memory
And even the worst nightmare can bring joy
Because this time when you wake
They are gone, all is right no more tears.
Dreams, such curiously cruel things.

Brian Suchowierski, Grade 11
Holy Cross High School, NJ

Dear Swift

I don't really like you
I don't like where you come from
I don't appreciate you as much as other people say I should
I know I shouldn't judge but
Many people have you
And I'm one of many that don't want you
But you just keep clinging on
You come from this world of a family
And it's not something I know
You're a constant reminder of what a failure he was
Yet you couldn't walk out the door with him
You have a meaning
And I don't like the pace that you're running
It's a bit too slow for my race
And when the time comes for you to be replaced
I won't look back
I won't say goodbye
And there won't be any notices
Your owner never provided any.
Sincerely,
someone who doesn't want you.

Sade Swift, Grade 11
Beacon High School, NY

He Was Already Gone

I love you
I miss you.
I wish I could hug you
But I can't
you are too far away.
A place I cannot drive to
a place that is not on the map
it has no road signs
no speed limits.
No cars or building.
But people.
More importantly you.
People say I can visit you where they wrote
your name on a polish stone.
But there I can't hug you,
I can't see you.
You're too far away to see you smile.
But not too far that I can't feel you around me.
not too far that I can't
hear your voice in the wind.
And not far enough that I can't say I love you.

Anna Caldwell, Grade 12
Purnell School, NJ

Consequence

The foulest of the fowls is the one,
Which pecks the soul—
And neither does it fly nor swim,
But nests upon the wearied heart,
And perches their on top the burdened limbs—
Go— shoo!— the heart's been pained,
By wicked talons through the blue-blood veins!
What prey must it be cruelly made,
Of an ancient man who has already
Withered 'til the chilling air bit the marrow bone,
A man whose ghost there sleeps alone,
By the coffin of his buried corpse?
How merciless that ugly avis,
With blackened beak and pale,
Light eyes which shine down on the frail,
And crooked claws— the large dark wings—
It neither sounds a melody nor sings,
Quiet there with taunts it stays,
Until the life within a man begins to fade,
And long, long are centuries whilst it remains,
Oh, Consequence! The wintry bird that plagues—

Yinan (Nancy) Wang, Grade 11
East Brunswick High School, NJ

Balance

A body discarded for gold
A heart left undead
A family went wrong
A life ruled by gods
A queen waiting to shine
Gold to Dust
Bone to Skin

A humble servant awaiting orders
A soul guided by angels
A tear burning in flames
A child left scarred
A mother in tears
A father sent to hell
Black to White
Life to Death

A princess praying for life
A prince ready for death
A picture of life cracked and smudged
Mother to Father
Princess to Prince
Queen to Servant
Cristina Mastropasqua, Grade 10
North Bergen High School, NJ

The Future

The future, the future
How great it must be
To imagine the wonders
Of new technology

The advantages are endless
Opportunities await
Peace is relentless
As we try to create
The building blocks of generations
Great accomplishments indeed
None that are bad or mislead
But instead maintain nations

Although we may argue
About the many problems of the world
The power of moral values
Will constantly be hurled
Toward the evil and malicious
To those who disagree
About how speechless
The future must be
Jordan Rassmann, Grade 10
Brick Township High School, NJ

Unexpected Friendship

When I first met you,
I thought you were another person,
I would grow to hate.

I was wrong. You were different.

Our friendship grew fast,
I never thought I would be telling you my secrets.
We have only been friends for two months.

I normally don't trust people,
But I had a different feeling about you.

We would and still talk every day
I felt I could go to you over everyone else.
You understood.

The bond that was created between us was indescribable
People even thought we were in love.

We do love each other,
But our love is different.
We love the fact that someone finally understands.

I honestly thought we would never be friends,
But the word friends doesn't even begin to describe what we are.

I never had any intention of this friendship happening, but if it didn't, I would be lost.
Joseph Falco, Grade 10
Island Trees High School, NY

Road to Nowhere

I walk beside you and your tone on a road to nowhere,
You follow along with your rhythm and take me there…
This road has no lines, no curbs, no signs and no flow,
It has no sounds or cars or people to know…
It's a one-way street that remains silent the whole way,
During the night it's no different, it's the same as the day…
To walk the safety of this street takes no skill at all,
But to survive the treachery of your thoughts may cause you to fall…
Without you here I'd have nothing but a battle with my mind,
I wouldn't have your songs that allow me to escape most the time…
I sing along with you, although you aren't singing back,
Quickly I turn my head, realizing my mind was somehow cracked…
All this time you've kept me company so I trusted not to look,
But from the sight I saw when I turned my head I think that I'll stay shook…
Almost certain I could hear you there as your voice had come through mine,
I didn't realize I could stop my pain from aching all the time…
I supplied the energy, the words and song to show me that you care,
I walked beside my secret friend, but nobody was actually there…
Shocked at this certain thought, I continued on my own,
walking on this deserted road, I found myself alone…
Strolling down this path of nothing when soon I started to ask,
How long till this road to nowhere makes me forget about my past?…
Matthew Verini, Grade 12
Douglas MacArthur High School, NY

My Favorite Thing

Of all the wondrous things in life, it seems
So difficult to pick a single one.
Creation holds the grandeur of all dreams
Though nothing new exists under the sun

There are so many joys throughout the earth
And countless features make our lives here grand
So tell me how to name a sunset's worth
Or pick a favorite single grain of sand

The miracles, too many here to name
Like love, and joy, and music, even sight
"The greatest" is a title naught can claim
Of all the things that bring our lives delight

With all these wonders found under the sun
Do tell me how to pick a single one

Victoria DuVall, Grade 12
Finger Lakes Christian School, NY

Sisters

Being a sister is the best job around
The connection between us is the greatest to be found
Whether it be many miles away or even worlds apart
We will always remain together at heart
No matter what we do or where we go
We both always know that we have each other
My sister is like no other
My sister is the best of the best
She will always pass the sisterly test
She defines the word sister well
Everyone can tell
No ifs ands' or buts about it
I love my sister and I'm going to shout it!

Maggie McDonald, Grade 11
DeSales High School, NY

The Way It Is

She walks past you
No smile on her face
You know she sees you
So you keep up with her pace
She turns around and stares you down
You're wondering what's with her frown
She starts walking faster
Yet you know she wants you to come after
She starts to run
Her speed like a gun
If this were the Olympics she would have won
Tired of chasing after her, you accept that she's done
But you can't understand this sudden shun

Markella Tranquillus, Grade 10
Bishop Ford Central Catholic High School, NY

Green

Yet another sky I've never seen
I find one, fly, then crash to the ground
Wings melted from the heat
I feel like I could slip over the edge of the earth —
Off the green and into the black night
Like I didn't see it coming.

Exhilaration turns to self hatred.
Something new becomes something old.

Plastic, metal, insecurity:
All the same and all surrounding me
The comforting pain of home, is home.

Looking down at her screaming up at me
(A template for too many memories)

A small part of me is laughing
It knew the joke all along
And knew the punchline would hurt
A demon on my shoulder
Or maybe in my heart
Bright green and hurting.

Emma Percy, Grade 11
Clarence High School, NY

Happiness

What is happiness?
In my opinion,
Going to a key university,
Getting good grades to pay back my parents,
Every day studying with fun,
Having a positive mental attitude,
It is happiness.

What is happiness?
In my opinion,
Living with my parents,
Enjoying their company,
All of us living together,
I don't need to bear everything by myself,
It is happiness.

What is happiness?
In my opinion,
Living in a wood house which faces the sea,
Every day breathing fresh air,
Listening to classical music,
The sunshine is warm,
It is happiness.

Yan Shen, Grade 12
Purnell School, NJ

My Mother

My mother
The best person in the world.
She is beautiful;
She is smart;
And she will always succeed.

My mother never prefers anyone
She is sensible
She loves my sister and me
But she does not spoil us

Because of her,
My sister is becoming a well-organized girl.
Because of her,
I am becoming an independent girl.

We are so honored
That she is our mother.
We love her.

Yiting Zhao, Grade 10
Bishop Ford Central Catholic High School, NY

Endless

The night draws out,
No one is about.
All of the walls lay bare,
With nothing but a gashing tear.
All secrets creep out through the shadows,
Following are the desperate bellows.
Empty picture frames yell and scream,
Needing to be fulfilled with a hopeful scene.
The horizon does not shine through,
Until the day is new.
Peaks of bright,
Give the shadows fright.
Waiting for the light to dim,
Leaves massive emptiness and an abundance of grim.
The night draws out.

Ashley Luster, Grade 10
South Hunterdon Regional High School, NJ

Working Carpentry

When I am working I am free
Sometimes I make my self bleed
When I am the boss no one will ever get lost
When I work alone I will always get home
When I work on a roof my boss sees all the proof
When I work on sheetrock I work a lot
When I paint I make the owners faint
When I work on wood floors I make the owners poor
If I work on a frame it should be in the hall of fame
When I get paid their wallets begin to fade
When I use there will always be a fight
When I hire I will always fire

Nicolas Bermudez, Grade 12
DeSales High School, NY

Do You Remember Any Longer?

The wind whispers your name,
The cold is biting at my cheeks,
Almost like the kisses you gave me,
Do you remember?

The wind whips my hair around my neck,
Brushing it gently.
As gentle as the words you once whispered in my ear,
Do you remember?

It begins to grow colder,
I wrap my arms around myself now.
You once did that,
You remember don't you?

It grows colder still,
And believing these are your arms around me warms me none.
So I unwrap my own arms,
Letting the bitter cold remind me you are no longer here.

Rachel Borasky, Grade 12
Paul V Moore High School, NY

Noah

God said to Noah "I am going to put an end to all people
The Earth is filled with violence because of them"
Noah had a wife and three sons
Japtheth, Ham and Shem
God said to Noah "Make yourself an ark of wood"
Noah was a man of God
God said to Noah "I am going to bring the flood waters
Everything on Earth will perish"
Noah walked with God
God said to Noah "Bring two of all living creatures into the ark"
Noah did as God commanded
The waters flooded the Earth for one hundred fifty days
God remembered Noah and the Earth was dry
Noah, his family, and the creatures walk on the Earth
God set a rainbow in the sky

Mary McCole, Grade 11
Bishop Ford Central Catholic High School, NY

A Better World

The world is uncertain
Full of the unexpected
Disasters and terror always lurk
Waiting to strike at anytime
It is a cold and heartless world out there
So how can this be a better world?
Well, I shall start by creating peace
By ending all war and corruption
And uniting all people
Under a place I call Harmony
Where tranquility is eternal
And life is a beauty.

Kathryn Guzman, Grade 12
New York Institute for Special Education, NY

Thunder

Hold on
To your memories of youth
Don't forget all those times
Where the earth felt alive

Hold on
To your dreams of happiness
Where love was formed
And all your sense roared

Hold on
To the chances you are given
For they may not last
Opportunity is on your track

Don't let go
While the wind is on your side
Accomplish the unrealistic
And hold on
Rianna Jobanputra, Grade 11
Clarence High School, NY

Waiting for the One

Once was a girl
Who put everyone first.
Thinking they'd treat her better
Instead it got worse.
Trying to survive,
Breaking down and crying
Was the only thing keeping her alive.
Waiting for the day
For someone to come along
Hold her in their arms
And say, "I won't do you wrong,
Enough is enough,
Time for you to be happy and live.
I'm not here to take,
I'm here to give."
Alisha Figueroa, Grade 10
New Brunswick High School, NJ

Lost Gains

Known as a name,
Once as a kiss,
Inspiration I wish I knew.
Free from judge,
Thought as love,
I swear I missed your smile.
Music.
Music you played,
Slowly fading speed.
Spinning, gaining, ending.
False movement.
Dreams, only dreams.
Hannah Farrow, Grade 11
Clearview Regional High School, NJ

Color

I step outside my door,
To be greeted by a brisk wind in my face.
In front of me,
I find an alien world.
A layer of white covers everything around me,
And color is nearly nonexistent.
Snow is piled on tree limbs that ache from its weight,
It flies through the air like a thousand pieces of confetti,
Covering every inch of the ground in front of me in a blanket of white.
I stare at this strange beauty,
Astonished by this overwhelming winter world.
Just yesterday,
Standing in this exact spot,
I observed leaves dancing in the street with the wind
Creatures scurrying in the sunlight,
Children playing in the streets.
Overnight,
My world has been completely transformed
By this first taste of winter.
Erika Ester, Grade 11
DeSales High School, NY

Thanksgiving

God has put us on the world as we share our love on this wonderful day
To give Him all our thanks and praise on this blessed Thanksgiving Day
With a beautiful and loving family warm special moments are shared
The are the ones who offer so much care and all their love
Everyone comes together as one to hold hands and pray to the above
God is within us and He always shows us the way for He will always stay in our hearts
Ever be at my side to guide me and my precious family who are so close to me
Continue to give me the strength to live the journey of life
I will always be thankful for what I am generously blessed with
For having such a bountiful life here on Earth with such compassionate people
I thank God up above for breathing and all that He has given me
There are so many of God's gifts in the world that I deeply appreciate.
Marc Persaud, Grade 11
Bishop Ford Central Catholic High School, NY

A Poet Wannabe

The blank sheet has erased all of my memories
No matter how deeply I dig into my recollection
the ideas and creativity escape me
I punctiliously seek them to enrich my vacant lines
but the rapidly scurrying thoughts continue to mock me
to mock my incapability to grasp their evanescence
I stare at the empty space that ought to be occupied by wit and ingenuity
while the transparent souls of these qualities playfully dance around me
insisting to bring the honored guest— indecisiveness
so here I am
the poet-wannabe
who diligently tries to express, me
Doris Yuan, Grade 11
Townsend Harris High School, NY

Inspirational Hero

The tender touch of warm hands,
Caring, open arms welcome
At the toughest and simplest times.
A gentle smile forever lasting
Lights up the whole world.
Compassionate advice,
Listening to all you have to say,
Words of wisdom,
Smoothes out the path of decisions.
Most courageous person
Ever to enter my life.
Bravery displayed like no other,
Hard work from day one
Never gave up.
Still standing strong
By my side,
Never leaving.
Described by a word
So complex, yet so simple.
Only a love known by a child.

Gabrielle Nalewajek, Grade 11
Bayonne High School, NJ

Time Heals All Wounds

It is said
Time heals all wounds
Time shows how to forgive
How to forget
How to become stronger
And even how to love
Love takes time
Time is not something that waits
We all have a short time on this planet
During that time we must learn
We must love
We must be one One without division
During our short time we need to heal
End wars End pain End division
That is our job
To take the time to heal all wounds
We must do the healing
It is the only way for all the wounds to heal
True time is needed
But the responsibility is ours

Theresa Dewa, Grade 12
DeSales High School, NY

Diversity

Diversity, diversity — An unassuming word
So humble, in fact, you'd never guess what it meant unless you'd heard
The idea that it embodies is just such a powerful one
That it's always occurring 'round you — can you see it being done?
The untainted mind of a child can see what we really are
We're all the same, more or less — and won't we all go far?
So then why is it that there are some people who can see
The world as a place designed for them but not for you or me?
Is it because he's different? Doesn't fit your narrow view
Of the way you think the world should be? A place for only you?
Well, I've got news for you, my friend — You think you're right? How come?
What's normality for one man might not be the same for some
You can't decide, all by yourself the way someone should be
You aren't God; Accept them all! We're all people, that's key
I hope that one day everybody learns to get along
So many different thoughts and no one's right but no one's wrong
A monumental task it is for all to see each other
As equals, fellow humans, like your sister or your brother
When people start to think like this then just maybe we'll see
What it means to live within in a world of true diversity

Liam Lang, Grade 11
Douglas MacArthur High School, NY

Light Up the Dark

It was pouring on a Tuesday afternoon, the day you walked into my life.
You were sunny with your careless attitude, you were just my type.
I could sing with you, I could climb to all my dreams.
I could be with you, but could you be with me?
When I see your smiling face I can't manage what to say.
You take my breath away, take my breath away.

You are perfect in your imperfection.
You are an angel, sent for my intention.
Words can't describe all these butterflies
When I see you standing there,
I can't breathe
When I see you my heart skips a beat,
When I see you my life lights up,
You light up the dark.

Emily Hulse, Grade 10
Delaware Valley Regional High School, NJ

Since I Couldn't Say Goodbye

Since I couldn't say goodbye, I hope to see you again.

Hoping to hear your voice.
Hoping to hug you.
Hoping to see you.
Since I couldn't say goodbye, I wished we could play one more time.
We would catch up on lost time and talk about how much fun we had playing together.
When I'm playing a video game, I think of you.
I think about how much fun it was to play games with you.

So I'm hoping that you will think about me until we meet again, my friend.

Kia Lloyd, Grade 11
New York Institute for Special Education, NY

Sleeping Beauty

Can I wake
to your angelic face
during midday?

I'd gaze upon the shy goddess that you are
        trapped in sleep, keeping quiet
because I'd know disturbing your benign heart
        would be a great sin.

And sleep for you is often
'cause even Hypnos desires a taste
of your breathtaking affection.

So when you'd wake
        and vision frisks your cordial eyes
            colored from painite, each movement
        would shock my nerves, strapping me down tightly
on the border of cardiac arrest
with your kiss.

I see the millenniums of vehemence;
        I see every sole hour
    embedded in your flesh,
embedded in mine,
    — embedded in us.

Tawfiq Alhamedi, Grade 11
Riverdale/Kingsbridge Academy, NY

Labels

"I don't wanna live in the modern world"*
Where society killed the teenager

They want us to be "perfect"
By the way we:
Look,
Dress,
Act
Society wants total control of us
Yet they are the ones to label us…Who are they?

Put us in groups and we are stereotyped
They judge us

They don't know our secrets
Or for that matter who we are
I will be proud of who I am…I am proud of who I am
Let them label me. Let them make faces. Let them call me names
It may hurt
But around them I will stand tall
They can't stop me from being me

Now…who are you?

*Taken from "American Eulogy" by Green Day
Rachel Tabak, Grade 10
Maryvale Sr High School, NY

Beautiful Baby Blue Eyes

Beautiful baby blue eyes,
Staring right up at me,
Beautiful baby blue eyes, looking around all lovingly,
Beautiful baby blue eyes,
It hurts to see you cry,
Beautiful baby blue eyes,
I love to watch you when I sing to you,
Beautiful baby blue eyes,
Dancing all around,
Beautiful baby blue eyes,
You are so funny to watch yelling at the refs,
Beautiful baby blue eyes,
Watching the news like you know what's going on,
Beautiful baby blue eyes,
Thinking of you when we are not together,
Beautiful baby blue eyes,
You are so dear,
Beautiful baby blue eyes, you are loved by all,
Beautiful baby blue eyes,
You are forever loved,
Beautiful baby blue eyes.

Ann Erdle, Grade 11
DeSales High School, NY

It's Your Time to Burn

I'm tired of feeling confined
All I wanted was for you to be mine
All you gave me was someone fake
Sorry honey, mannequins cannot bake

You destroyed my heart
Now we'll always be apart
I'm no longer invading
I'm just slowly fading

In your eyes I glow
In my eyes there's something I don't desire to show
I want your heart to burn
When you see me, I want your stomach to churn

When your heart turns into ash
No more tears will splash
When your soul goes to the devil
You'll be reaching a whole new level

And now I finally feel free.

Alayne Mahler, Grade 12
Boonton High School, NJ

Dark Street

Life is nothing but a dark street, minuscule lighting —
you're afraid to trip, you can't see but you still walk…
hoping that somewhere, somehow on that seemingly empty street
you find yourself in light.

Dayalin Suriel, Grade 12
Urban Assembly School for Law & Justice, NY

Sonnet 38

Lost away at sea,
Not a light to guide.
Her waters took me
Out with woeful tide.

Debris is only me
In this wreck all alone.
Trapped in this woeful sea,
Drowning like cold, black stone.

No hands to grasp me.
No hands to save me now.
Lost and gone at sea
Without a hint of how.

Nature seems no cause for trouble.
Normality's pain should double.

Andrew Layden, Grade 11
Shaker High School, NY

Dream Become Reality…

A day of November two thousand and eight
USA lived a great and key moment;
Black community had kept the faith
And he became the new president.

He represents a whole population
Residing in those famous white walls;
He appears as a motivation
Also for the youth who love basketball.

"Yes we can" were his significant words
When he was candidate to the elections;
Forever it will stay engraved on boards
And for memoirs of the next generations.

He is the first black to head America,
Everybody knows Barack Obama.

Bastien Motte, Grade 12
Redemption Christian Academy, NY

Spring

Spring
blooming flowers
warmth is in the air
sunbathing
fruits ripening
my birthday
swimming
camping in the wind
fresh grass
bees making honey
long bike rides
spring time fun

Abbigail Kime, Grade 10
DeSales High School, NY

Young Heartbreak

Your words like a sequel to a once-loved novel.
Strange but familiar.
Enigma fills your eyes, along with the ancient sign of regret that will last a lifetime.
It's too late, took you too long.
Your apology is somewhat meaningless,
For the tear in my heart had already been stitched up.
But, let it be known, the seams will always be loose, never the same as before you.
Memories of you will appear before my eyes,
Before I can think better of it, before I can stop them from flooding my thoughts.
They hurt — these memories.
Though they are a thing of the past, every time they swarm back into the front of my mind,
Like wild bees, I am filled with the same emotions I had at that time,
Only this time, with regret as to that I was so naïve, so foolish to ever believe you were true,
That you were faithful, that you deserved my trust.
Oh, what I wouldn't give to go back in time, to warn myself of your power, your hold on me.
I now see how you held me by a string attached to my heart
Above the deepest abyss of my emotions, and when you made that one final statement,
The string snapped and all there was left was darkness.
I was so lost, so confused, so hurt.
But you were my past,
And now, I'm my future.

Melissa Rorech, Grade 11
Island Trees High School, NY

Torachel

The problem was you forgetting.
I wanted you to remember my name.
I went to that white room every day, in hope.
There was always a slight chance you would wake up.
A slight chance you would never forget.

You did not forget. I did.
Although I can recall the peach lipstick and rose blush that graced your complexion
Even though I can remember your words and choice of fashion
I am unable to replay your voice
Your voice which reprimanded me
Your voice that called me "Fresh" when I said something rude
Your voice that whispered "I love you" or "Give me a kiss"

Not even a decade has passed and I have already forgotten.

Su Cappello, Grade 11
Bayonne High School, NJ

Not Caring

Was it the sound of wet street as cars pass by
Or the smell of rain as the leaves fall to the ground
Or the phone call reenacting an argument the night before

Sorrow and pain were buried behind her huge smile
To all she was happy and everything was fine
But she was in pain hurting like a mother in labor

She hated them for making her weep and not care about her feelings
Back to safety where a smile shields and hide the pain

Natalie Rivera, Grade 10
Progress High School, NY

The Promise of October Wood

Lovely, the October wood dripping honey
As we walk in our rhymes
To forget the green as we go

In the seasons strong
We riddle ourselves
Between the strings of our lighted senses
Rediscovering those cried-out colors
Amongst the falling grace

Here, majesties of language
Make castles overhead
And the words they whistle out
Define what matters most
The greatest facets of the glass

So in this moment, I pledged to him
One day, I'd meet him in a seed
Where we'll hold hands in the soil
While the Earth warms us right
As we wait for the coming of the rain

Isabella Nugent, Grade 10
Watchung Hills Regional High School, NJ

Forgive Me Mother

Blessed is your face
Blessed is your name
My dearest, my mother.

Blessed is your smile
Which makes my soul want to fly
My beloved, my mother.

All the nights
And all the times
That you cared for me.

My wrongs, you corrected
My anger, you accepted
But I never realized it.

And now I ask myself
Who, other than you, will embrace me?
Who, other than you, will cover me?
Who, other than you, will tolerate me?
Your pardon mother, forgive me!

Ahmed SanaUllah, Grade 11
Bayonne High School, NJ

A Glint of Hope

Amidst a desolate mountain range lies a glint of light, a solitary candle against darkness.
Hope.
The darkness engulfs the light, but it can still be seen, pulsing.
A heartbeat.
At the center of the light is a factory.
Life.
A dilapidated roof, a rusting structure.
Promise.
A whistle blows and workers stumble out covered in soot, worked to the bone.
A seed.
The men head to the watering hole to drown their sorrows in liquid relief, all but one.
Growth.
He stops in front of a quaint house nestled under a large oak.
A smile.
The screen door swings open and a little girl runs down the porch steps. Fireflies shimmer.
Warmth.
He drops to his knees and embraces the girl. The soot falls away, he is rejuvenated.
Triumph.
In this moment time stops. His problems fade into the darkness and the light grows stronger.
The light breaks through the darkness.
Hope.

Jake Shelton, Grade 11
Manhasset High School, NY

What He Chooses Not to See

He says he is afraid of the dark,
He explains the feeling of blindness overwhelming his soul'
The feeling of not knowing what is around him.
He runs for a candle to illuminate his way;
Back to his genuine life, because he is content of his own walk on life.
But as he progresses on his journey, the dark disguises himself;
Into his closest Adversaries; failure, isolation, humility.
No where to run, he runs to the dark;
Where his life is hidden from him;
He embraces the blindness, who shrouds him from his enemies;
Who "shields" him from the troubles on his walk;
But in reality, is pushing himself deeper into the dark.
Further into the dark, he regains his vision;
In which he becomes his adversaries;
In which he becomes failure, isolation, humility.
He runs for a candle to illuminate his way;
Back to his genuine life, because he is content of his own walk of life.

Joshua Octaviano, Grade 11
Bayonne High School, NJ

All in One Minute...

I looked at the time it was 1:20,
thinking does he like me,
or picture me as an ordinary girl,
who is there just to be comforted,
or just thinks of me as the girl of his dreams,
all this runs through my mind,
I looked at the time,
all in one minute, 1:21

Oneida Anglade, Grade 11
Brooklyn Preparatory High School - Harry Van Arsdale Campus, NY

The Man Who Changed the Presidential Game

It was the year 2008 which could never be late
There was a man who believed the country needs change
He knew many people would dislike and hate
But that did not stop him from making his bang

He showed he was a unique orator
He told the country, change would come
He said, follow me I will be your navigator
It did not matter where he was from

This man could be the first black president
Yet he acted so calm and cool
He made us feel like he was our next door resident
He had our stomachs twisted like a whirlpool

Barack Obama is his name
He changed the presidential game

Christian Kessee, Grade 12
Redemption Christian Academy, NY

The Cry of Thunder

Thunder BOOMS!
Men cringe, women shriek, curtains close
Animals scurry into their cozy homes
As the sky begins to hurl down fresh, hot tears

Thunder ROARS!
In anger, its clouds deafeningly collide
Lightning flashes with greater outrage
Will no one listen?

Thunder WARNS!
A loud heartbeat of the clouds
As if reminding preoccupied mankind down on land
Of the power of Nature

Rozana Rahman, Grade 11
Noor-Ul-Iman School, NJ

My Jacket

A year ago I left you my jacket
just in case you got cold.
Yet it isn't till now you return it
ah! The worn leather has gotten old!

It's wrinkled and covered in dust
the pockets and hood are dun
the copper zipper is starting to rust
and the red strings on the hood are gone

The fake fox fur inside is stained
the once onyx sleeves have now turned gray
my jacket! A waste! What a shame!
Why couldn't you have just asked me to stay?

Carmen Urruttia-Orme, Grade 11
Tappan Zee High School, NY

Cry of the Blue Tigress

Far too brazen
With such bombastic swagger
How meaningless
Modesty, shame, respect:
Have you not any?

This privilege, choice, freedom bestowed upon you
And you've abused it
Corruption and profanity ever so ubiquitous
Those who gave you life
Are the ones who are pained the most
Has filial piety become obsolete?

What confidence you exude
Such panache you display
You strut about with not a care in the world
Are you not concerned, even the slightest bit?

Oh, but the consequences have not yet risen
Every seemingly trivial matter
Is recorded by Gabriel's brothers
Basked in ideology, etched in destiny
Lasts for an eternity; what is eternity?

Forever, until the sun's last kiss

Hurmat Hashmi, Grade 10
Clara Barton High School, NY

Ocean Daze

We drove all night aimlessly in the dark
No path on our minds just following our hearts
Just a couple of kids on a summer night
Smiles were illuminated by street lamp lights

Shouting loud for the world to hear
Laughing with the wind, we had no fears
Unplanned and unexpected from the very beginning
From that night on, I couldn't stop grinning

Waves crashed and fireworks lit the sky
With the sand between our toes days flew by
Lifeguarding, fairs, and watching the stars
September, well, that seemed far

Not everything was perfect between the frames
At times we came to realize, life wasn't a game
Lessons were learned and memories made
Some things will never be looked at the same

I was taught to live and learn
And that sometimes life takes unforeseen turns
It was a summer that was unimagined, no doubt
Filled with the people, I could now, never live without

Ashleigh Shay, Grade 11
Ranney School, NJ

Left in the Dark

When light turns to Dark
Worries and fears come out.
There's less time to see
And more time to doubt.

Feeling low, feeling sad
Seeing the day end.
Losing hope just watching
The sun descend.

Be wise and you know
There's no other date,
Like the one that just passed
That we can duplicate.

The day be splendid
The day be dire.
Smile one last time
Before the lights retire.

Whether tears come
Or my hope rekindle.
The fact remains
The lights always dwindle.

And things are left unexplained.
Amy Dupuis, Grade 10
South Hunterdon Regional High School, NJ

There's Someone at the Door

There's someone at the door
Winter is knocking
Should I let it in?
It's almost that time of year

Winter is knocking
The low, freezing temperatures signal me
It's almost that time of year
A smile makes its way onto my face

The low, freezing temperatures signal me
I see Christmas light in the distance
A smile makes its way onto my face
I wonder how much it will snow this year

I see Christmas lights in the distance
The snow covering the soft, prickly leaves
I wonder how much it will snow this year
Winter is getting impatient

The snow covering the soft, prickly leaves
Should I let it in?
Winter is getting impatient
There's someone at the door
Tom Chatalbash, Grade 12
Massapequa High School, NY

June 6, 1944

I can hear the waves hit the shore,
today is June 6, 1944.
I feel my heart pulsate inside my chest,
I check my ammunition,
tighten the straps on my vest.

Eisenhower's words
wash over me like the sea,
"The destruction of the war machine
the elimination of Nazi tyranny."

The screams of people fill
the sense of emptiness, like that in a den.
I can feel the courage and fear
of 160,000 other men.

I remember once you said
that this will make your father proud.
I hope Dad feels that way,
but tell him I'm one of many in a crowd

The ink is almost finished
in my oil-smudged pen.
The doors to my boat have opened,
victory is close, but so is an end.
Syon Das, Grade 10
Townsend Harris High School, NY

Seasons

Slow down in the air,
candid, soft snow
all is white,
children playing snows,
families making snowmen,
retiring to the house for hot cocoa
this is winter.

Outside we can hear
the chirping of birds,
the happiness of the children,
we can smell the perfume of flowers
this is spring.

Blue sky, green garden
eating watermelon,
sunbathing on the beach,
going picnic,
this is summer.

All is orange, yellow, red
small winds, cool breeze
birds flying south, red sky at sunsets
this is autumn.
Ying Zhang, Grade 11
DeSales High School, NY

Shame on the War

Shame on you,
For causing the fear
And sparking the tears
That flood them every night.

Shame on you,
For tearing apart
Lovers from the arms
Of the ones who wanted to fight.

What kind of monsters are we,
To lead an army
Towards certain death in the night?

Shame on you,
For ruining the lives
Crushing the hearts and minds
Of those who don't believe in it.

Shame on you,
Who used your power to choose
Which side is to lose
And who shall live or die.

Live, laugh, and love no more.
Shame on the war.
Caitlyn Patullo, Grade 11
Delaware Valley Regional High School, NJ

Final Attachment

There's this attachment —
It's not so easy to explain.
I feel like I have been with you all my life,
But no you had to leave.

I feel my pulse rising —
As my heart takes each beat.
There are no tears left for crying
Making me so sick I can't even eat.

It's a longing for your return —
Or just the smell of your skin.
It's ripping through my body
Pulling at the tip of every limb.

I can't say I just miss you —
Because that would be a lie.
I know you're always in my heart
But I feel empty inside.

So send me an angel —
Or give me a magical wish —
Because the one thing you still owe me
Is a final goodbye kiss.
Nicole Creedon, Grade 11
Warren Hills Regional High School, NJ

Sympathies with Me

White man came to this foreign land,
Red man helped them understand,
How to grow and till this land,
Little did the red man know,
Whitey had a master plan.

We enjoy simplicity and using what we need,
They were set on conquest,
Over concerned with greed.

There was no racism,
No such thing as segregation,
Just told GET OUT,
Hence the mass migration.

It didn't even take weapons,
There was no need for war,
Biological pollutants,
The red man was no more.

We had it all,
Land as far as the eye could see,
Now we have nothing,
Sympathies with Me.

Anthony Annony, Grade 12
DeSales High School, NY

Bliss

The sweet breeze fanning the hair off of my face,
The chime of the ice cream truck,
The tweet of a hummingbird high in the plum tree,
Pages frantically turning as I thirst to solve the mystery.

The clanking of heat in the pipes,
The sensation of tea warming my body,
Curled up in my favorite blanket,
Smiling as young love unfolds.

Guided by the faint glimmer of a flashlight,
Hiding under the covers,
Too afraid to come out,
Because of the suspenseful tale.

In the living room,
As my dad is watching football,
And my sister is practicing piano,
And my mom is chatting on the phone,
Barely able to concentrate on the words before me.

It is not the place that matters,
Rather it is the simple act of indulging in the words of a book.

Amanda Sarria, Grade 11
Bayonne High School, NJ

Onto the Open Plain

Onto the open plain ran the creatures
For they are now creatures
Twisted by violent scenes
They ran for freedom away from harm's way
Onto the open plain
They couldn't escape they knew their time had come
And so they fought for freedom
It was all they could do to escape certain destruction
The world consumed itself
Onto the open plain
Chaos had twisted it into its current form
Fire burned and ground gave way
Onto the open plain
Man against Man
Gun against Gun
And so they ran
Onto the open plain

Joshua Chapin, Grade 12
DeSales High School, NY

Make the World a Better Place

Make the world a better place
Take everyone's pain away
speak what's on my mind cause
I have a lot to say
I tell the little kids don't worry ok
cause my one and only wish is
to make this world a better place
Filled with a lot but don't speak of much
Life will eventually end
There is no rush
To my close friends and family
I will always keep in touch
Just let's get rid of the hate and focus on the love

Derrick Anderson, Grade 11
New York Institute for Special Education, NY

Retribution

You brand me a liar, a cheat, and a thief
You, who does not even know me, determines who I am
You manipulate a few to conform to your will
And the rest follow suit and believe
You think You have won
You think I have been defeated
But like the phoenix I will rise up from my ashes aflame
The world will know of Your treachery
I will expose the truth
For it is you who is the liar
You who is the cheat
You who is the thief
And You who will fall in defeat

James Teresco, Grade 11
Paramus Catholic High School, NJ

Bells

All the bells let loose tiny rings
In high pure notes of hope they sing
Carrying their Christmas cheer
That they've held inside all year

In a jingle, on a hat
They carry something that few have
Optimism, hope, and song
Rolled into a ball, three for the price of one

Of all the Yuletide deals
This one feels the most real
What you see is what you get
Take what it is, and don't get upset

Seasons need no mistletoe
Or giant trees that sway to and fro
All that you really need
Is a bell or two, to keep things cheery
Kim Peterman, Grade 10
Raritan High School, NJ

Cherish Thy Presence

Watch me
As I fade away into
The eternal Darkness of a lonely
Night
Nevermore to be seen again.

Watch
As I fade into eternity
As the sun does
without cause.

Hear me
As my voice carries through
Time
Lacking the intention to ever be
Forgotten
Dylan Trovato, Grade 10
South Hunterdon Regional High School, NJ

The Written Word

If I spoke only when spoken to
I wouldn't say much at all.
My words could only exist on paper,
Soon crumpled into a ball.
The lovely thing about paper
Is its fragile timelessness.
We preserve it for years into centuries
Or destroy it with one fatal rip.

I write with the strokes of an artist,
And type with the fervor of a pianist.
Gina Lione-Napoli, Grade 12
Paramus Catholic High School, NJ

Me Change? Never!

I asked my friend once to describe me in one word.
She said I was a mess and I thought I had misheard.

I was really shocked by what she'd told me.
But the more I thought about it, her point of view, I began to see.

Maybe she was right; I may have made some mistakes before.
But when I tried to fix them, I somehow messed things up even more.

I said things I didn't mean and I meant things I didn't say.
I didn't think before I spoke and there were consequences I had to pay.

Isn't it funny how one word could make me
Think of changing myself to what others expected me to be?

But of course I would never change anything in me.
I like who I am and I don't care what others see.

So I still mess up in almost everything I do.
But I like myself just like this; being different is good too.
Barbara Hanna, Grade 11
Bayonne High School, NJ

To Flame Work the Sun

The sun is a hot glass bead,
Slithering its way onto a warm mandrel
Above an azure lance.
Red hot.
Slumping unless you keep turning the mandrel,
Rotating and shaping it.
Sunspots are only visible where you held the bead too low in the torch,
Where you let the glass burn,
Where the blue of the flame nearly ingested the bead whole.
And yet some are content with such beauty.
They are the ones that dip their sun in vermiculite to keep warm.
Others aren't as happy with the result.
They are the ones who turn off their torches and extinguish the sun in cold water.
Unable to withstand the immediate temperature change,
The sun cracks and sizzles.
Sends sparkling remnants flying.
And disappears.
And with the absence of the bright sun welcomes darkness,
The faint glow of a now cratered and assassinated sun,
And the jewels that sparkle and twinkle within the proximity of its shadows.
Jasmine Garnett, Grade 10
Christ the King Preparatory High School, NJ

No H8

A child of God,
but accused of being different.
They teased and taunted and discriminated,
that's how cruel this world is.
Darling, baby boy, sweetie,
there can be no one like you,
because we're all different.
"It Gets Better"
That's what you believed, and for a second,
we believed it too.
You're a hero,
for all the wrong reasons,
but we still believe you were put on this earth to open our eyes,
to learn to accept everyone,
because we're all human,
and children of God.
"Don't forget me when I come crying to heaven's door."
You are at heaven's door,
and accepted the way you are.
Goodbye, Jamey.

Suzanne Miranda, Grade 10
Paramus Catholic High School, NJ

Define Truth

Lies confide within every soul
Consuming everyone within a black hole
Trapped inside a never-ending mirror
People just can't see what's clearer
Corporate organizations shrouded in mystery
Our leaders should have learned from history
One truth cannot make up for numerous lies
Congress always needs to improvise
It doesn't matter how many concerns
Because we cannot heal all the burns
That get lit from rich fiends controlling
Senile cronies keep patrolling
Politicians never keep their word alive
It would be better for some to take a dive
Mindless puppets giving illusions
That disrupts our thought, giving delusions
Why can't our answers be met
Instead we are their mindless pets
So please rip out your rotten tooth
And define what is the forsaken truth

Christopher Krysztofowicz, Grade 10
West Seneca West Senior High School, NY

Alive

When all the world stops, I keep going.
When all the world forgets, I continue knowing.

When all the world sleeps, I lie awake.
When all the world quits, I take no break.

When all the world is lost, I am found.
When all the world is quiet, I hear each sound.

When all the world backs down, I try harder.
When all the world is intelligent, I want to be smarter.

When all the world is numb, I can truly feel.
When all the world is fake, I know that I am real.

When all the world is blind, I can use my sight.
When all the world is hopeless, I can see the light.

When all the world gives up, I continue to strive.
When all the world is dead, I know that I'm alive.

Jessica Flynn, Grade 11
Ward Melville High School, NY

Christmas Time

Christmas time is the best for me
Getting presents from under the tree
Sharing smiles and laughter with one
The true festival has just begun!

Family time has never been better
Under the tree, I find a new sweater!
Knitted to perfection by my grandmother
I couldn't bare to ask for another

Enjoying the holiday, yes indeed
Giving food to those in need
Loving and caring for the ones you know
Sharing kisses under the mistletoe

Decorating lights all around
Highlighting the entire town!
I wouldn't want to be anywhere but here
And it's definitely the best time of the year!

Cameron Davidson, Grade 10
Bishop Ford Central Catholic High School, NY

Daylight

Wish me into daylight,
into the breeze I blow away
and my bones are left standing.

Have the daylight melt me
away so anything disappears
and I'm free.

Ashlyn Lackey, Grade 10
The Lawrenceville School, NJ

I'm Sorry I'm Not Sorry

As you look at me with those dark, desperate eyes
Warm after you've expelled all your lies
Really I should apologize—I'm sorry for leading you on

The drink is thick and orangey sweet, in taste all others it defies
I ask with a laugh "Is something in this?"
As you look at me with those dark, desperate eyes

In the cold late night—sweater blanketing thighs
I tuck my knees closer and lean into you—you're
Warm after you've expelled all your lies

When you find out about him your sweetness is gone
I relish the new you, though really I should apologize
I'm sorry for leading you on

I laugh out my false promises
And in the leaves we lie
As you look at me with those dark, desperate eyes

I chug the poisoned attention
And hold back the dawn
For you love me unconditionally—
Like a shaky fawn—
And I'm sorry
I'm not sorry for leading you on

Jessica Dorsky, Grade 11
Hastings High School, NY

A Snowflake Among Flowers

You are truly a snowflake of flowers.
You radiate like the sun's morning glow.
Your beauty unwithered throughout day's hours.

It's not just how your kindness towers,
But how you lift others out of woe.
You are truly a snowflake of flowers.

You are not one to make people cower.
With your personality pure as snow.
Your beauty unwithered throughout day's hours.

It's you who keeps me going though this shower.
The rain that freezes us as we row.
You are truly a snowflake of flowers.

It is you who gives me my superpower.
With your grace and eloquence like a doe.
Your beauty unwithered throughout day's hours.

If you were to leave I would not be sour.
I know you would make happy a new Joe.
Because you are a snowflake of flowers
Your beauty, unwithered throughout all hours.

Maximillian Johnson, Grade 12
Manhasset High School, NY

Lighthouse Lead Me Home

At times I feel I've lost my way,
I evanesce like dreams at wake.
The memories resonate with tears,
as I clash myself with all my fears.

Lost and gone; drifting away,
troubled waves crashing down on me.
The time, the pain, still I can't breathe.
Lost and gone; now lost at sea.

My anchor now, where have you gone?
You held me tight, you felt so strong.
The steadiness that I need now,
I see you're gone, nowhere found.

So I drift about, and I float my own,
trying my hardest to find my way home.
But the ocean gets so cold at night,
I need you here, I need your light.

Just as my hope began to fall,
I see it in the distance now, standing bright and tall.

The light is overbearing, but I finally found my shore.
You were always here to guide me by, I was never on my own.
Lighthouse lead me home.

Alyssa Naimoli, Grade 11
St John Villa Academy High School, NY

All But Torn

If you say something
Enough times
You will surely believe it.
Repeating, repeating, repeating

The undulating waves of the ocean
Call to my body

The hazy clouds of the sky
Call to my heart

The unwavering earth
Call to my mind

Look up. Stay. Move Forward.
My soul is all but torn.
And the loneliness caresses — like the faintest of pins and needles
And the loneliness cuts like the harshest of knives.
Until it shatters, like crystal in a world of glass.
Beautiful,
But shattered.
Dreaming, wishing, hoping
"What if?"
But life is best imagined.

Tiffany Moran, Grade 10
South Hunterdon Regional High School, NJ

You!

When you're gone, I remorse.
I want the truth from the right source.
I keep falling, deeper and deeper.
The world keeps getting rougher.
Love keeps getting imperceptible.
Families are becoming disconnected.
I don't want to feel deceptive.
I don't want to be left out.
But I don't know what you're about.
When you're near I get pensive.
And you sense it.
You dominate my thoughts with your absence of words.
To my heart, it's like swords.
Each and every stab you complete.
Makes it obsolete.
Your goal is vague.
It drives me insane.

Yelisa Espinal, Grade 12
John Dewey High School, NY

Carlsbad Beer

Oil greased hands
Smack open an outdated fridge
Postered with black and gray fingerprints.
One last Carlsbad beer bottle rolls inside that sticky plastic cage,
An oasis in a garage of dry stale heat.
Yellow teeth, dull and cracked
Tap the smooth metal ridges with one satisfying crack.
From the deep mud glass
Erupts a fountain of pillowy froth.
One last beer, thick, wheaty, and freezing.
One last reason
To forget why he hadn't called on
His birthday or
Sent them any letters or
Walked her down that aisle.
He finishes the last drops in a satisfying gulp
And heads back to work.

Emmalina Glinskis, Grade 11
Stuyvesant High School, NY

Halloween

Chilling October air
Like a scene out of an nightmare
Candy crazed kids fill the streets tonight
Filled with laughter and with fright

On an adventure for the sweets
The sounds laughter and screams fill the streets
Filling their bags with sugary delight
All the way up to midnight

To me the holiday is different now
Time to hang out with friends and chow
To hang inside and enjoy the heat
And give out candy to those who trick or treat

Steve Noworyta, Grade 12
Holy Cross High School, NJ

Try

Try as hard as possible
Do your best at everything
Try as best as you can
When you try, you succeed
Success is the best
Getting it right
Success is not gained by defeat,
It's gained by hard work
Determination
And trying as hard as possible
Success takes time, it's not achieved overnight
But rather over time
Trying hard will get you closer to success
Success is an achievement all by itself, nothing is better than success

Brandon Lowrey, Grade 11
DeSales High School, NY

Life's Decisions

When on the beach
One can consider their choices
Sitting and pondering the good and bad
Weighing the options
Agonizing over the pros and cons
Every little possibility has meaning
No detail can be left out
While the options and possibilities are endless
One must choose the option that best suits him or her
But one cannot sit for too long and over analyze
Because precision is necessity
The ultimate culmination comes about
The decision must be made
To jump into the ocean or stay out of the water

Daniel Brown, Grade 11
Bayonne High School, NJ

My Dear John

I knew that eventually you would go,
But some things remained that I didn't know.
Why is it so hard to say good-bye?
And when will these tears begin to dry?
I miss your blue eyes glancing at me,
When I look around now, that's what I yearn to see.
But you left and now you're far away,
And I ponder over the words I never got to say.
Your life includes being in the reserves for a year.
Never seeing you again is my biggest fear.
Some day you'll be fighting across the sea,
All I ask is that you remember me.
Be brave for me and promise to hang on,
Maybe someday you'll be my Dear John.

Brittany Bursa, Grade 11
Hunterdon Central High School, NJ

The Voice to Her Melody

The first notes are all she needs
Her heart drums within rapidly
She raises her arms and begins to sway
Hoping this dance will carry her away

Away from the sea of thundering bodies
Who don't understand the lyrics to her song
They shout and drown out the rhythm
Yet she fights to listen on

On and on she moves in the midst
Desperately holding on to the pulse
She's lost herself but she's found something else
Something that keeps her going 'round

Around the twists and turns she finds
A new voice singing to her melody
She dries her eyes, stands up straight and tall
Because the music was inside her all along

Kalyani Parwatkar, Grade 10
Hillsborough High School, NJ

Shopping

Shopping is my hobby,
Bright colors as in lime and green,
Go perfectly together in a seasonal schemes.

Hard work until I save,
Can't get any bright colors today,
I was really looking forward to that fleece sweater.

Shopping is not free,
You have to buy everything,
It takes money and lots of green.

I plead and I bet,
And I still get no money,
So I have to work instead.

Ebone Griffin, Grade 11
DeSales High School, NY

Teenagers

The older you get the more difficult life seems to be
Growing worries about things you never did see
Peer pressure gets heavy
And knowing when to say no can make you feel unsteady
High school can be a blast
But it's over just that fast
Watching the friends you keep
Potentially turning you into someone you don't want to be
The stress of heartbreak and relationships rise
And efforts to fix everything takes up all your time
With college approaching sooner than ever
We can't forget that being a teenager doesn't last forever.

Nia Pierre, Grade 10
Bishop Ford Central Catholic High School, NY

Humbug and Dry Leaves

Crackling permanence no longer exists
Futures are held by the feet and paws who walk across
Life cripples into auburn and amber dust
Crisp golden disappointment
Sacrificial lambs of parents' widespread arms
Fallen memories from arbors
Plans crafted but remain in calendar pages as time folds over
Offspring of lingering thoughts

Smallest creatures await to push them closer to the end
Jewels seeking attention
Opinions reflected on armor
Begin their treasure hunt across Nature's welcome mat
Cause a child's shriek, a baby's whimper
Before delicate legs snap
Splintering to form ash
Laid to rest with the purple promises strung across skies
Forgotten within seconds
Covered with crimson velvet

Emily Yankowitz, Grade 11
Scarsdale High School, NY

'Til Judgment Day

My soul bares so much
I give in but I try so hard
I give and I do not wait to be asked
What will be of me
I don't know
We'll live forever and never die
This life long war will go on
I'll keep on fighting
And I'll keep on trying
He'll weigh our hearts
Look into our souls
See what we have done right and wrong
We can choose but he decides in the end
Where we'll spend eternity is unknown
But we get what we deserve

Christian Rendon, Grade 10
Bishop Ford Central Catholic High School, NY

The Human Anthem

It's completely unacceptable to not find time
that's preferable for good and true and just authentic work.
But we as humans are susceptible to influence's
preferable to live life on the beach no shoes no shirt.
We see the end and beginning, the start and the winning,
and all the girls that we never meant to hurt.
And for its merciless spinning, the world must be grinning,
that equator on the globe looks like a smirk.
Yes we don't have our careers, yes we lack ambitious thrust,
call us peons call us peons if you absolutely must.
But if we peons had all eons to decide for what we lust,
then I promise you I'd climb a corporate ladder lacking trust.

Joseph Chiavaro, Grade 12
Washingtonville Sr High School, NY

The Prayer

Piercing rays of light, but I
Swore I'd keep my eyes towards the heavens
Though they meant nothing to me
I, I was strong enough
Shadowless, but I
Swore I'd take care of myself
Though I was so damaged
I, I needed no one
A dirtied pearl, but I
Swore I'd beat everyone else
Though I was fighting to live
I, I was worth the best
Hypocritical, soiled, empty, but I
Swore I'd never lose breath
Though my knees were weaker than my dreams
I fell, I knelt, I prayed
I, I survived

Marina Makram, Grade 11
Bayonne High School, NJ

Noumenon on Paper

Everyone has a story to tell
Therefore, what makes my poetic
Expression more or less different from
The person next to me or in front of me?
This is a rhetorical question
For I have no answer to, for the simple
Thoughts and facts that I do not believe my
Writings are any better or less than anyone else's.
The page is the canvas for many artists
Whether writing with a pen, or that paint brush—
Even crayons, they're the conductors', Yes
And my audience, you who partake in
The poetic readings are my orchestra.
Leaving my heart and soul within every word
Your eyes and minds bring them back to life
Yes, that is why I have many stories to tell
And the outsider can decipher, what I am articulating.

Tynedia Brooks, Grade 12
Irvington High School, NJ

Procession

Death never comes nicely
It's not wrapped up in a nice bow
There's no notice
No holiday
No one hiding in the shadows
To say I got ya
These are dark times
That lie ahead of us
Haunting our every memory
Even before they're made
And the final act of the last scene
Leaves the life of the brown eyes

Laura Rode, Grade 10
Argyle Central School, NY

For the Wordless

I'll never author or great poet be,
A truth I feel quite melancholy of,
I fear that I oft speak uncertainly
When searching for the words to show my love

While others pen their ballads I must sit
And hope that you will somehow love me still,
I'll never sing a song to praise your wit,
Or wax poetic at your stubborn will.

I know not how to weave a clever phrase
I cannot tell you what you mean to me,
My mind is but a twisted, tangled maze,
Which, though I love you, I can barely see.

So love, to you I promise to do this,
Where words do fail, I'll give to thee a kiss.

Rebecca Shaw, Grade 10
Horace Mann School, NY

Morning Beauty

Lovely morning sun rises in the east
Awakening the endless sleeping beast
Illuminating the salty sea waves
Bringing light to the dark undersea caves

Warm sand surrounded by immense palm trees
Frolicking in the morning ocean breeze
Relaxing the ears of all who are near
What an amazing thing to see and hear

Early risers setting out to explore
The soothing sounds of waves washing ashore
The vast endless sea right before their eyes
Free and running beneath the clear blue skies

Narrow sandy path leads to paradise
It always seems to attract and entice

Jessica Breen, Grade 10
Paramus Catholic High School, NJ

Solitude

Sitting outside
Getting some fresh air
All of the beautiful scenery
You can only stare
Forever
You wish you could stay
Because you know your annoying children
Are far far away
Though it may not be for that long
You will truly see
That being in nature's solitude
Is what you rightfully need

Chelsea O'Neal, Grade 10
South Hunterdon Regional High School, NJ

Often a Welcomed Friend

Often a welcomed friend,
Although to some he comes too soon.
The symbol of the end;
Too many people he will tend,
And bring their lives to ruin.
Often a welcomed friend.
For no one the rules will bend,
Soon you'll hear his tune.
The symbol of the end.
All of his victims to eternity he will send,
You will be swept away like a monsoon.
Often a welcomed friend.
Your spirit shall live on, the world it will transcend,
It will pierce your heart like a harpoon.
The symbol of the end.
The hearts of your loved ones will soon mend,
One day you will all again commune.
Often a welcomed friend,
The symbol of the end.

Stephanie Alia, Grade 11
Pompton Lakes High School, NJ

Me

I'm not perfect.
I may not have lots of friends
But that's okay
I'm loud, and maybe annoying
I talk to much
And often get in trouble
I'm different and don't always fit in
I'm often called weird
I'm not the fastest or the smartest
I may be made fun of for the stuff I like
And sometimes it hurts
And I might not live up to the
Expectations of others
But at the end of the day,
I realize I'm perfectly happy being
Me.

Julianna LeBron-Rivera, Grade 10
Bishop Ford Central Catholic High School, NY

A Brother's Hero*

August 23rd, 1991
A hero was born
Bravery, generosity, serving
Recruited to the Army
Private First Class
Powerful, strong, never quitting
He is my brother
PFC Roberto Hernandez
Army strong
HOOAH!!!

David Hernandez, Grade 10
Bishop Ford Central Catholic High School, NY
*Dedicated to my brother, PFC Roberto Hernandez.

Pictures of the Floating World

Awaken in the sea of luminescence.
Spark the infinite current.
The ecstasy begins.

Spray the sky with sunlight;
the golden shadows expose the horizon.
The savage fauna and brutes ascertain the melodic wisdom
planted in tapestries of green at the bottom of the sky.
The answer to why,
now and then,
continues to elude them.

The incarnation of time serves as no guru.

But forth goes each epoch
into the shards of ardor.
As every opus passes, the wonder is awakened.
Radiant eyes see the world,
and sacred minds feel the heart.
Silence told the globe to start,
and life took the world by storm…

Michael Gerver, Grade 12
Smithtown High School West, NY

How I Wish You Were Here

Six years later and the feelings are still the same.
I'm left with emptiness and many sleepless nights.
I know that you're in a better place.
But, I miss you like crazy.
Oh how I wish you were here.

I feel like giving up on everything and everyone.
But, I know that you wouldn't be happy.
I miss your hugs and seeing you every day.
I miss hearing your voice.
Oh how I wish you were here.

Nobody really understands me,
It's like they never really knew me at all.
I'm in this world but yet I feel trapped.
I feel broken and lost.
Oh how I wish you were here.

Kayla Hernandez, Grade 11
Green Dot New York Charter School, NY

Falling

Falling, falling I thought I could fly
As I fall, I see my life pass me by
I can't believe how big the ground is starting…to look
I am wondering how long this fall took
Little by little, I start to cry
How did I get here, I, I don't know why
I am going to die or so it seems
Then I woke up to find out it was a dream

Keron Pierre-Louis, Grade 10
Bishop Ford Central Catholic High School, NY

You

Tonight the stars shine for you
a misspoken place where love waits
and your beauty looms
guiding us through a maze
where our stories coincide
alluded by your touch and
the impeccable spark in your eyes
brought down from the clouds by gravity
fighting against us
oh how we could be our own enemies
two halves guiding each other
yet avoiding the hole that would
render a single entity
as I fall for you
the innocuous but intimidating beauty
lay in my arms, as our hearts converge
into a single beat
and your smile takes the best of me

Danny McCauley, Grade 11
Riverdale/Kingsbridge Academy, NY

Autumn

The sun sets earlier now,
those long, sunny days of summer
are now gone.
Leaves turn radiant colors,
replacing the summer flowers,
matching the sky at sunset.
Cooler air comes,
with icy breezes here and there,
foreshadowing the winter months.
No more barbecues and picnics,
instead we have bonfires and hay rides.
Tank tops and flip flops
replaced by hoodies and boots
Warm apple cider replaces cold lemonade,
and all this tells us that autumn is here.

Steph Shockley, Grade 10
Holy Cross High School, NJ

Life Is a Feast

Sometimes life is ice-cream
melted before you realize
sometimes life is cheesecake
giving you the soft and gentle feeling
and lasting in your mind
Sometimes life is coffee
bitter but with a persistent aroma
Sometimes life is lemon
never know it's sour or sweet
until you taste it
I define my life in different delicacies
to prove my passion for them
and also my passion for life

Jiaming Liu, Grade 12
Purnell School, NJ

Friend

Just like my teardrops falling I'll remember every sweet sound you made,
every little touch and movement that clings to me, never disappearing

And friend, I'm not sure what happened but I'm sure we'll be okay,
they say the grass is greener on the other side in this everlasting world of gray

Please just come home soon so I can see your bright smiling face
because I just can't go on without it, never knew something great could end this way

I pray for your returning, every moment passing makes me need you more,
all I hope is that one day you'll realize you need me and you'll end up at my door

And if that doesn't happen you should know that I miss you too much,
and I will be desperately waiting for you to come save the day
counting all our sweet memories along the way

Friend. I miss you, I need you, I want you by my side
I thought we were inseparable but I guess it was only a lie.

Amanda Gross, Grade 12
Douglas MacArthur High School, NY

A Better Day

Why is it so dark and cold? I asked myself.
The wind blows; the clouds are black; the sky is gray,
feeling down hoping for a sunny day.

But when that sunny day starts to *fully shine*;
the sky turns blue; the clouds turn white and a visualization of a beautiful sight.

As the grass turns green;
the trees and flowers will glow and the curtains will start to open like a Broadway show!
"Standing ovation"

Hector Bryant, Grade 12
Progress High School, NY

Freedom

A man leads his sheep
Down a wasted old path
One Monday afternoon

They're led to a land
They see every day
Without sun
Stars or moon

The day came when one
Of these many sheep strayed
From that wasted
Old path

That lonely white sheep
Led a radical's life
While the rest of them
Were black.

Tyler Barrett, Grade 10
South Hunterdon Regional High School, NJ

Emergency

Tick tock goes the clock
Voices are running in and out
Holding my mother's hand, you walk
Towards the end, as she screams and shouts

No one can save me,
All I can do is take the pain in
Yet those lies, those stupid lies
The human mind always sins

I'm so bare and weak
So on the road, I'll just sit there
Waiting for my soul to arrive
You kiss me goodbye on the cheek
Yet I still sit, unhappy and bare
For my body is not awake nor alive.

I'm...not...okay.

Natalie Cioffari, Grade 11
Paramus Catholic High School, NJ

Education

Education is important
And you should make it a priority

Having an education can take you far.
Educate yourself and learn as much as possible.

Having knowledge, understanding, and common sense,
Will help your future and open doors.

Education is to be taken seriously,
It's not a joke it's not boring but interesting.

Educate yourself because it's only the interest you put in.
Teachers educate you so take advantage.
Don't waste it!

You are what you make of yourself and future.
Why waste the opportunity while it is there
Rise to the opportunities given.

Michael Colon, Grade 10
Bishop Ford Central Catholic High School, NY

Nature's Violent Angel

Adored by the young,
Despised by the old,
You're as pure as the sky that delivered you.
From you, we create angels and wars.
You're as deadly as you are gentle,
For your army can overpower a nation.
With one icy fall,
You halt the birds of the skies,
And cause collisions of the tigers in the streets.
Your army comes together to form an almighty barrier against Man.
Even though Man tries to destroy you before you attack.
Although the origins are the same, each individual is different.
Nonetheless you fill me with ecstatic pleasure.
Each solstice you're released from the gates of heaven
And you gently fall to Earth
To tap on my windowsill without a sound.

Miriam Rammal, Grade 11
A Philip Randolph High School, NY

Alone

She reaches out but his hand is gone.
Her heart is like a night club's song,
The sound pounding in her ears
Drowning the feeling of her warm tears
That are erased by the water engulfing her head
As she sinks in the water to darkness and dread,
Wishing the bottom would come but there seems to be no end
To how long she'll have to continue to pretend
And be someone who she isn't at all.
Although she tries to stand up tall,
She's tired.

Abby Powell, Grade 10
Manhasset High School, NY

Flight of the 3 Year Old

Weightless
Free
How it felt to fly around my ceiling fan
I'm 3 years old
Have been for years
All it took was a jump from my bunk
And I could fly in circles all night long
Can't stop
Don't know how
Don't want to
People are talking beneath me
Making only empty sounds
To not wake up is all I want
Awake I'm too scared to jump from my bunk
Dreams might not catch me
I'd much rather be
Free
And weightless

David Barnes, Grade 12
Holy Cross High School, NJ

For My Best Friend

"Best friends forever," we thought we'd remain
Sisters instead, of course we became
Through the good and the bad
Whether we were happy or sad

From barely talking, being very shy
To laughing until we cry
We became so close in a matter of days
And eventually we shall go our separate ways

We will call to one another when times get rough
And we will never have had enough
Enough of the gossip and late night phone calls
Planning the next day's trip to the mall

Alina Sardana, Grade 11
Clarkstown South High School, NY

Evils of Society

Ignorance will get you nowhere
We must be civil to one another
We were put on this earth for a reason
And it is not to discriminate
On the contrary to appreciate
To give thanks for everything that life has to offer
Many are less fortunate than others
That does not give us the right to look down on them
Instead of approaching them with a frown
Give them a hand and greet them with a smile
Life is too short and we must not waste time
By judging others
As a matter of fact
We should treat each other as we would our brothers.

Janelys Hernandez, Grade 12
New York Institute for Special Education, NY

My New Car
I'm getting a car today
I'm so excited
I don't want any delay

My car is shiny and new
It just came off the lot, I'm very lucky
There were only a few

My car is red
It has chrome wheels, leather seats
It is comfortable like a bed

My car is fast
It makes my heart race like a stallion
With this car, I will never finish last

With this car I will go far
Together we will never fail
For a long time it will be my star

We will treat each other well
Already we are so attached
We are perfectly matched

I will never regret or forget
Buying my Corvette
Damani Campbell, Grade 10
Bishop Ford Central Catholic High School, NY

Change
Change to me is like an everlasting curse,
Is it for the better or is it really for the worse?
Change can happen anywhere, and at any given time,
Yet some things never change, like the value of a dime.

While others may work to make their change come true,
Others' change may appear to them right out of the blue!
Change will happen whether you want it or not,
It is quite unlikely it will occur straight on the dot.

Change is viewed differently in everyone's eyes,
But for me, I view change as a wonderful prize!
You never know what will come out of it,
Whether you will be hindered or receive a benefit.

My feelings towards change is straightforward,
I will feel locked up like a prisoner or as free as a bird.
Change is necessary in one's life to fully live,
And those who try and control it will not have much to give.

Change may not always be for the best,
But you begin to realize it is just another test.
You learn to cope with the difficulties of life,
And in the end come out on top of the strife.
Darren Chen, Grade 10
Townsend Harris High School, NY

Our New Age
I am hopelessly perplexed
In a world with no answers
And people with no heart.

Where the sky is fed with toxins
And the floor is accessorized with waste.

Where love is a word you say for fun
And trust is given out to everyone.

Betrayal is commonly expected,
Preachers often neglected,
And drugs casually accepted.

In belief that money makes happiness,
Women sell their bodies,
Men sell narcotics
To boys younger than me.

Our recent generation is turning into the old
And the new doesn't learn from the mistakes that we told.

People come to America for a better life, apparently.
But little do they know
Here, it's illegal to be free.
Veramarie Jimenez, Grade 11
Bayonne High School, NJ

Run Away, My Love
My love, you feel so far away.
It's almost like you're drifting away,
into a sea of loneliness,
into a sea of emptiness.
In a cardboard box, that you call "safe."

If you fear love, I could leave,
so I don't feel that you're fleeing from me.
We, then, could live so happily,
apart from each other, so lonely.
But you flee into a cardboard box, that you call "safe."

You flee with fright of what this could be,
you have no interest in knowing me.
I'm just a person who brought you love,
only loving what you could be.
I don't understand why you flee from me,
but I now know a fear that you should flee.

So now you flee from the sharks of the sea.
That cardboard box wasn't the protection you need,
it was me.

So now your life is at an end
in a cardboard box on which you thought you could depend.
Dara Dendekker, Grade 12
South Jefferson Jr/Sr High School, NY

Boy

Alone in life
No one there by his side
Tormented soul
Who wants to die

Just because he is different
Makes him the target
For the school enemies
Who treat him like a carpet

But behind this poor tortured soul
Lies a being most unique
He's funny, smart, and beautiful
So much so that I can't speak

He doesn't see what he means to me
Because he is in despair
For he is my world, my life, my love
I wish he could see that I care
Alexandra Marto, Grade 10
Staten Island Technical High School, NY

Maps

The traveler's curtains
are carefully drawn maps
devoid of latitude and longitude,
of a compass rose from
the seedlings of direction,
of an equator line
separating fire and ice,
of what makes
the world concrete;

As the voyager traces his
fingers among the creases,
he rubs the spine of the
bony frontiers that serve
as his own fascination
Jocelyn Hassel, Grade 12
Townsend Harris High School, NY

Picture

Pose for a picture,
Lend me a smile.
I wanna keep a memory,
One that is mine.
I'll make sure you like it,
So it'll be one we can frame.
A cool black-and-white,
That looks like it's from those good ol' days.
Pose for a picture,
I know you really hate it,
But I'd hate more to see you go,
And me be without your loving face.
Laura Eng, Grade 11
Manhasset High School, NY

Life with Autism

So many different kinds of what I have.
I have Autism.
But I like to see how other people act around each other.
I hate crowds, but I want to be part of the group.
Alone, I try to understand the world.
Scared, I find I just don't understand people.
I find that I do not quite fit in.
So I create a world where I belong.
Rejecting physical contact, I hide away.
Remaining silent, I watch the world.
I listen to conversations.
I learn who is nice and who is not.
I find friends, but don't always understand what they say to me.
I don't play sports.
I'd rather read instead.
I sing too.
I want to be treated just like every other kid.
I can be social, but I never feel safe on my own with people I just met.
Maybe someday everyone will understand.
Life with Autism is not easy.
It is difficult and it is part of my life.
Mary Rose Costello, Grade 12
DeSales High School, NY

All Those Years

She is sixteen years old, asking her dad for the keys.
She crosses her fingers, and he slowly agrees.
her father is there waiting at the front door, his arms raised.
She pushes past him, and moves to the car.
His arms slowly go to his sides, his warm smile fading.
He goes into his room but leaves the door open
Just in case she changes her mind and needs a strong shoulder to cry on,
Someone to squeeze her tight, and tell her everything will be all right.
She is on her way home, her phone ringing in her pocket.
She soon will learn her father died the night past,
And only the nurse was there to hear his last words.
Tell her I love her with all of my heart, and if it was her desire,
I'd tear the world apart.
Tell her that I'll always be there waiting by the door for her to come home.
I'll leave the light on so she can find the way.
Tell her that we'll be together again someday.
She drops the phone, her heart, it clenches.
It twists and turns inside her chest.
All those years he'd given her his best.
While the whole time, she'd taken whatever she wanted,
And given him the rest.
Naomi Rowe, Grade 12
DeSales High School, NY

I Am This

This is what it feels like.
It hurts to realize.
Scorching so painfully.
It's so hot, it burns.
Don't leave me.
It breaks me.
You can see me, can't you?
It doesn't matter how hard I try.
How can you not feel it too?
I felt you stir inside.
What is it you don't like?
I can only change and do so much.
It doesn't matter does it?
I can't make you care.
Please don't hate me.
I am this.
You made me crazy.
I am this.
You changed the way I felt.
I am this.
I love you.

Candi Keifrider, Grade 11
Pleasantville High School, NY

Homeless Thoughts

Food?
Clothes?
Shelter?
When will they come?
Basic necessities I am not able to fulfill
Being homeless is no fun
Stealing is wrong
But what choice do I have?
Begging is embarrassing
But it helps fill what I lack
The war goes on
They pay no attention to their own
I am out of a job
Nowhere to call my own
The summers are not so bad
Though the winters get awfully cold
Now that I have nothing
I long for what I once had
Poverty is no joke
It's not just in Africa
It's just as real, right here in America

Shontae Salmon, Grade 10
Townsend Harris High School, NY

Icicle Shots

She held out the chalice to me,
the gilded glass dark and empty against her ghostly fingers.
Her beautiful cruel eyes examined my soul, trapped on the stage that was my body.
She beckoned me again, those glassy icicle fingers caressing my throat.

I sighed resignedly, my cynicism and feeling too far gone.
I reached inside my chest and pulled out my heart.
I examined it; what a pretty little thing, still uninfected by the poison that surrounds it,
feeling its feeble, innocent beat in my hands, soul, and mind.

I squeezed it, watching those innocent red beads
plink and splatter into that inky cup, a black widow banner against her flawless snow.
"Go ahead," I said, "Drink it.
It should taste all the sweeter."

Even as I watched my heart crumble to snowflakes, I
tossed it aside, listening to her guzzle me, relishing
those plinks and splatters, nothing but another icicle shot to her.
I staggered on, watching my stained hands turning to white, turning to ice,
all moving towards that spot where my heart used to be.

Dan Light, Grade 11
Bethlehem Central High School, NY

Make the World a Better Place

As I wake up in the morning, I feel different
I don't feel human.
I want to be a hero.
I want to protect my home, stop crime,
save civilians of my town, and make this earth peaceful no matter what happens.
I want to be a fighter for justice,
even if I have to die for my purpose in life.
I will survive to protect the one I love the most.
I am a warrior out to save the world, a soldier of heaven and hell.
I will and I shall make the world a better place
to live in and keep safe from harm and danger.
If I can't save the world, I will avenge our conquerors!
I will demolish the evil around the world and
I will not stop fighting until the last breath of my soul is taken.

Khalique Lewis, Grade 11
New York Institute for Special Education, NY

His Song

Do you hear that…
Listen…isn't it wonderful?

He draws me in by playing his music, so gentle and soft.
When he plays he makes people gasp, in amazement.

As he plays, he keeps drawing me in
pulling me closer to that something that's so, magnificent it's breathtaking.
I wish for him to play his music again and again
until I have fallen back into my eternal slumber.

He is dearest to me, and I shall always enjoy him: The Piano!

Khali Howe, Grade 12
St Raymond High School for Boys, NY

On That Chilly Day

On a chilly day,
I am sitting on a classroom chair.

Suddenly, cold air surrounds me.
My nose starts to tingle,
and then a small drop drips down my nose.

My inner nerves start working.
I quickly put my hand
under my nose and do not let go.

I desire a tissue,
but my teacher won't stop speaking.
My patience is tested,
But I wait.

I'm getting more impatient.
Every minute is like walking
through a heap of fire.

There's only five minutes until the first bell.
I can do this.

Two minutes: I still can do this.
Then one minute: I am dying.
Thirty seconds: My patience is done.
"Teacher?"

Diane Choi, Grade 11
New Hyde Park Memorial Jr/Sr High School, NY

Bread

I've scoured all the local supermarkets and specialty stores for weeks
searching, perhaps, for a lost relic, for a kind of holy grail.
Substitutions I've tried were just that: substitutions
for a golden obsolete tradition, one long hidden
from the scorn of technology.

Long loaves of pre-made garlic bread, four day old clubs
of baguettes, even that despised Wonderbread,
that soft and tasteless imitator:
these would have been offensive to my mother.

I long for one loaf of her ciabatta,
for the flour dusted on her hands
and the ribbons of oil up to her elbows.
I long for the crisp crust and grooves
for memory-holding
and the smell that perfumed the house—
the smile in her eyes
as she slaved away before the oven,
the smile in her eyes
when she sliced into a loaf—
the cloud of hot air that escaped
like a dying woman's last breath.

Ashley Zhou, Grade 11
The Pingry School, NJ

Life Is a Panting

Life,
I am of both your directions
Existing more with the cold frost
Strong as a cobweb in the wind
Hanging downward the most
Somehow remaining
Those beaded rays have the colors
I've seen in paintings — ah life
They have cheated you
Thinner than a cobweb's thread
Sheerer than any —
But it did attach itself
And held fast in strong winds
And singed by the leaping hot fires
Life — of which at singular times
I am both of your directions —
Somehow I remain hanging downward the most
As both of your directions pull me.

Ciara Wright, Grade 12
Holy Cross High School, NJ

It's Been So Long Brothers

I met them when I was a small boy
I was told they were my brothers
We soon became close
And I loved them like no others

Their names were Michael and Gabriel
I admired such common names
When I heard they weren't living with me any longer
I suddenly felt my heart go up in flames.

I hadn't seen my brothers in 10 years
But when I finally saw them again, there were no tears.
I could feel our bond rebuilding
And I was very thankful this past Thanksgiving for my brothers.

Ayodele Adeyanju, Grade 10
Bishop Ford Central Catholic High School, NY

Slither, Ribbit, Hiss!

In jungles, swamps, and every plain
Little critters play their games
How their blood runs cold the secrets will remain
People aren't humane

Without them
Life be void
Some are colors of the gems
People tend to avoid

Turning colors to defend
Snakes, frogs, and turtles
Reptiles can be a friend
They're in your thoughts, and your stomach curdles

Derryk Davidson, Grade 10
Monmouth Regional High School, NJ

No More Goodbyes
Let's not have any more goodbyes, I've had enough already.
And, I'm not sure if I can make it through another climb because I'm starting to feel unsteady.

This is happening way too often, numerous goodbyes.
But I want it to stop so I can finally dry these eyes.
These tears keep coming down, all caused from every one of you.
You may not realize it, but it's from the awful things you tend to do.

I don't ask for these goodbyes, they just seem to happen way too fast.
I should know because I have had so much experience with them in my past.
I don't want anymore, let's put this to an end,
Before it's too late and all our lives start to descend.

You never see it coming, it hits you quick and hard,
And all you're left with is a heart that's scarred.

So why does this keep happening? Let's just say hello.
And let the world take us wherever we are meant to go.

No more goodbyes is what this world needs,
There should be more hellos in order to succeed.

Melissa Carle, Grade 12
Roselle Park High School, NJ

The Enchantress
It is midnight.
The sky is a midsummer's eve of ocean blue,
And the wind has ceased its robustness, resulting in the trees' paralysis
Even the deceased, below the cornucopia of emaciated, white lilies, ceased wrestling in their graves.
The refine wine has never been more divine.
I am infatuated with the ethereal.
Every night at this lake, at this hour, we besot our naively hopeful minds; maybe she'll choose a lover,
One she'll eternally enchant.
It is 12:01 and her audience of wealthy men floods her arena of glory.
The ephemeral beauty exudes precise purpose—to enchant.
The reflection of the moon upon the lake is magnificent.
Like a spirit ascending into heaven she rises from the depths of the lake.
The pools of blue that take refuge in my eyes seem to effortlessly reside within hers.
She has all of us completely under her spell, her spell of imperial charm that…enchants.
I feel her power.
I feel her essence.
I feel…the ENCHANTRESS

Kimberly Clay, Grade 12
Benjamin Cardozo High School, NY

Motion Picture
When you get something you've worked so profoundly and hard for and sustained it for a distant amount of time, everything that captivated you at the first glimpse, the first intended stare that caught their eye and put the picture in motion almost gives you the unbearable feeling that what you desired for the utmost of your days, that felt limitless almost timeless regardless of what anyone said now puts you in a vulnerable position; should you sustain a different approach? Or find individual freedom and wait for the picture that was in motion to become a motion picture, sequels will come only to find different origins, separate ways to willingly live your life.

Jazmine Herbert, Grade 12
Burlington County Special Services School, NJ

Family

Family.
You need family
What can you do without them?
Their love.
Their support.
No matter what.
Family always has your back.
Family provides.
Family helps.
You may fight.
You may argue.
Family is always there.
When you need them the least.
When you need them the most.
Family can bring joy.
They can cheer you up.
Family knows how to press your buttons.
Their opinion matters.
You may agree.
You may disagree.
Family is important.

Devon Walton, Grade 12
DeSales High School, NY

Serenity

The beautiful landscape a lush dark green.
The sky as clear as glass.
Horses galloped, cows grazed
Birds flew everywhere
As if they owned the world.
Beautiful serenity.
Peace a privilege.
Out in the mountains
Surrounded by Mother Nature's gift.
Standing alone,
Looking down on the valley
Made me feel powerful and unstoppable.
The crickets chirped
The sunflowers swayed with the wind
Dancing to the wonderful sounds of nature.
My heart was filled the minute I fell in
Love with beauty.
Enraptured, fulfilled I turn to find
That same hidden beauty in people
And make my life a constant
Scavenger hunt.

Stephanie Blair, Grade 10
West Morris Mendham High School, NJ

Transcendentalism

When you look outside, she is there,
We take advantage, but is it fair?
We grow and devour, While she runs away to cower.
She gives us signs to leave her be,
Yet we destroy with much glee.
Her future we do not consider,
However, with no voice she cannot be bitter.
She watches us in despair,
While we give her heart nothing but a tear.
She sheds a tear as another innocent animal goes down,
But on our face you will never see a frown.
This is not what life intended.
It had hopes to be very splendid.
The humans appreciating nature,
Grateful for every last feature.
We were meant to grow side-by-side,
Not progress while the other one died.
We have disrespected what we were destined to love.
Nature was there when all we had was the man above.
Stop worshiping the materials we have and think of what we are losing.
Can we again love nature instead of the technology that is so confusing?

Imani Reed, Grade 12
Absegami High School, NJ

The Essay

Her eyebrows furrowed,
Concentration was painted across her forehead,
Adrenaline pulsed through her veins,
Her heartbeats pounded harder against her chest,
Small beads of sweat formed at the nape of her neck
with the sudden rise in temperature,
Scratching her pencil aggressively against
the stage like smooth lined surface,
The soles of her shoes tapped furiously against the cool tiled floor,
Her eyes darted rapidly back toward the clock,
Each second ticked away like loud explosions,
Her agile right hand danced across the page with tremendous grace,
Making loops and dips when necessary,
RING! RING! RING!
Letting out an enormous breath of relief,
She sashayed out the classroom,
Content with her performance.

Helena Yang, Grade 10
Watchung Hills Regional High School, NJ

Silent Beauty

Lightning lights up the sky to a bright shade of purple,
silent and beautiful to the human eye a thing so rare and ravishing you let out a sigh,
no roaring thunder no footsteps of rain just pure utter silence
without the loud sounds that remind you of violence.
You sit on your porch on an old rocking chair slowly taking in the cool summer air,
knitting a sweater but of course not meant for this sort of weather.
The sky lights up again what a sight
time stands still as slowly fade off into the night.

Karissa, Grade 11
Henry Hudson Regional High School, NJ

The Winter Blues

Winter is almost here
It makes me want to shed a tear
The summer months were so kind
If there were a few more I wouldn't mind

The temperatures can go below zero
If someone would cancel winter they would be a hero
The fog on the windows, the ice on the car
In this awful weather you cannot go very far

Winter is a scary sight
If you like winter you must like night
The sun goes down much too soon
The worst part is we have to see the moon

Hopefully winter will not last long
Maybe we should sing a summer song
If the groundhog sees his shadow more winter will come
Even though I hate it, it is great for some

Jonathan Sclar, Grade 12
Douglas MacArthur High School, NY

Guitar

Playing guitar is one of the best things to do
Being able to play songs out of the blue
I get to play all kinds of music
It's so good it sounds like magic
Strumming all the strings
Hearing a note as it rings
Getting rid of all my stress
Playing the hardest songs with success
The types I can play are numerous
And the opportunities are limitless
Playing an instrument gives me a lot of joy
One of the best things to enjoy
Playing the same songs
Famous bands have played all along
You should try it too
I'd teach you, but now I have to bid adieu

Atik Ahmad, Grade 12
DeSales High School, NY

Dreams

A thought is thought of, never forgotten
but is it fresh? No. But never rotten.
I will share a thought, a thought that pertains
to a sentiment, to me, that truly remains
Of what you might ask? I'll be sure to tell
Sky is not the limit. Neither heaven nor hell
The limit is far, no one can see
Beyond the horizon, you cannot perceive
If I tell you my own, yours won't be unique
Rest your head and count to three
They're yours to keep.

Steven Hou, Grade 10
Hillsborough High School, NJ

The Game

everyone is just a game piece
in the game of the world called life
every aunt, uncle, nephew, and niece
every son, daughter, husband, and wife
we need to learn how to play
know the directions and the rules
and even if you don't want to we play every day
whether you'll go to work or go to schools
as sad as it sounds it's a competitive game
some people try hard some people don't
some people are poor some rich in fame
while some people pay some people won't
people can lie or stick to the truth
they can fight or stand back in fear
you can choose tables you can choose booths
you can hide like a shadow or make yourself clear
it's all about your strategy
you can play for today, tomorrow, or next week
do you have time to play with me
you can always win if you're always strong and never weak.

Zachary Milack, Grade 10
Island Trees High School, NY

Let Them Hear You

My voice has not been heard.
I stay quiet.
Your voice has not been acknowledged.
You stay quiet.
Our voice has not been proclaimed.
We stay quiet.
Our voices get lost in the crowd.
Lost in their journey to acceptance, so
the world closes its door to us.
It isolates our differences,
exposes what others may call faults.
I call them people.
It takes only one to change many;
raise your voice and tell them,
"This is the real me. I will be quiet no longer!"
We have been heard.

Taeonna Pope, Grade 11
DeSales High School, NY

Guidelines to Existence

Life is all but chance—an utter romance
So take your time, and don't forget to laugh, love, dance
You only get one shot
People tend to disregard that a lot
You get times of cheers, times of tears,
But, you survive the pain and manage to stay sane,
While you endeavor for no reason, going through the seasons,
Do not conform, rather create your own norm
You need to take a break for goodness' sake,
And look back to ensure you're leaving your own track.

Sara Boutrs, Grade 11
Bayonne High School, NJ

Depression of a Teenage Girl

She feels like she's alone, but she's really not.
She feels like no one understands her.
Even though, everyone tells her they do.
They tell her to believe, and everything will be okay.
But will it ever be?
She still feels alone.
She cries and cries, day and night.
Night to day.
Once a beautiful child, now a zero.
Her dream is to write.
Write her story life.
So why not continue,
the only thing she believes in?
Every day gets harder, and harder
But she refuses to give up her dream
She never sleeps, because she's to busy chasing her dreams.
Will she ever escape this nightmare of depression?
Who knows...

Jalissa Cruz, Grade 11
Raritan High School, NJ

Lost Hope

They say be careful what you wish for
Because you might just receive it all
But who was he not to catch her as she began to fall
Those days that seemed to last forever
Only lasted until the middle of November
It's difficult to say her heart is drifting in the sea
She often reminisces of what used to be
A kiss on the cheek and a soft smile to begin their day
It was times that these when she'd never thought he'd say
Goodbye my lover, this can no longer be
For both times and people change and so she needed to see,
Their memories together, they remain in a drift
It was said that he made her the happiest she could get,
But oh how quickly she'd be the one he'd forget
Her hopes are to one day see him once more,
Promising to not allow her heart to get sore
And so now it is her time to move on,
Take a deep breath, sigh, and be thankful he is gone

Jessica Ramsin, Grade 10
South Hunterdon Regional High School, NJ

Loneliness

We, human beings, living in the world.
Everyone has a lonely soul.
We came to this world,
Lonely.
We will leave this world,
Lonely.
No exceptions,
Solitary soul in us,
Lonely shadow behind us,
Forever and ever.

Bonnie Zhang, Grade 12
Purnell School, NJ

Chocolate

Chocolate is good, chocolate is fine.
I would eat chocolate anytime.
Chocolate is a simple sweet treat.
It is what I love to eat!
I ate so much I gained a pound.
Now my belly is very round.
My mom yelled at me because I gained so much weight.
All because of what I ate.

Now because I went on a diet,
I feel like starting a riot.
Because I did not get my food,
I might have to be rude.
Someone may get nixed,
All because the sleeping giant in me did not get his fix.
All I want is one bite.
Otherwise I may get into a fight.

Kristina Azevedo, Grade 10
Paramus Catholic High School, NJ

The Blessed Country

The melancholy pebbles cried out in joyance and ecstasy,
As they were flung into the rupturing waters heedlessly,
The ravishing blue sky looked down enthralled in delight,
As little bewitching eyes blessed it with their mere sight,

The frivolous brown sands slithered out of the little naked hands,
As they were magically transformed into castles of the fairylands,
The vociferous winds soothingly played a harmonious song,
As they lightly brushed against the tender cheekbones playing along,

The sparkling stars earnestly listened to grandma's old tale,
As they tried to shower their radiance upon the curled-up snail,
The merry lambs jumped about gaily in the heavenly twilight,
As the euphoric children of God turned into sunflowers overnight,

Ohh...Blessed, blessed! How blessed is this country?
That is gifted with children all humpty-dumpty.

Anokhi Kastia, Grade 10
West Windsor Plainsboro High School-South, NJ

Autumn Leaves and Raindrops

The words like autumn leaves
With the wind, they fly.
Or raindrops in April spring,
Falling from the sky.
Make it bold to stand off the page,
Clear in black and white.
But when everyone is saying left,
I am going right.
"Where are you going?" they shout.
"That's the wrong way!"
"Chasing the leaves and
Catching the rain."

Dania Olivo, Grade 10
Henninger High School, NY

Into the Woods

Puff of dust. Particles settle. Shuffle feet.
ZZZ…CRASH…TWIRL…
No green. No blades of grass. Just dust.
ZZZ…CRASH…TWIRL…
Just rock. Just granite. Just cement.
ZZZ…CRASH…TWIRL…
Design. Shape shifting. Unnatural.
ZZZ…CRASH…TWIRL…
Cement becomes pavement. Lawn replaced. Bare ground.
zzz…crash…twirl…
Wander deeper. Wildflowers. Tall trees.
zzz…crash…twirl…
Just bark. Just shade. Just leaves.
zzz…crash…twirl…
Observation. Wonder. Awe.
zzz…crash…twirl…
Check for dampness. Sigh. Sit and stare.
zz…cra…tw…
Nature. Environment. Bliss.
Silence…silence…silence.

Olivia Novick, Grade 11
Jericho High School, NY

Night

When the sun sets,
The moon shines bright in the sky.

The light is gone and
Darkness covers everything.

The children sleep
While the adults still work.

The sky has many stars
That shine very brightly.

A couple could stare into the night and
Realize how much they love each other.

So many things happen during the night
That cannot happen during the day.

There may be darkness but
The night is good.

Ryan Arteaga, Grade 10
Bishop Ford Central Catholic High School, NY

Thanks Dad

You were the first one to teach me how to tie my shoe
I tried to do everything you told me to.

You taught me my wrong from right
You told me to never give up a fight.

You were always there when I fell.
You promised not to tell.

How you put up with everything, I'll never know
You always wanted to be my friend, never a foe.

You never forgot a 'goodnight'
I was scared of the dark, so you turned on my light.

I don't always know how to say 'I love you'
I realize sometimes you struggle too.

I know some days I get you so mad
Regardless, I wanted to say thanks Dad.

Stephanie D'Amico, Grade 12
DeSales High School, NY

Lies of a Once Had Been Friend

We meet in the hall and we talk,
Oh the guilt I can see in your eyes.
It was then that I knew,
That it truly was you,
Who had told those despicable lies.

The lies told only in secret,
To buy you your glitter and fame.
To me you were gold,
But now I feel cold,
And I bring to you but only shame.

And so I just wanted to tell you,
I'll hate you till after the end,
You'll look to the skies,
And remember the lies,
You'd told of your once had been friend.

Hate: that which shrivels the heart, burns the soul,
And clouds the mind in darkness.

Sean Murphy, Grade 10
Island Trees High School, NY

Inner Demon

"He who fights with monsters should be careful lest he thereby become a monster. And if thou
gaze long into an abyss, the abyss will also gaze into thee."
— Friedrich Nietzsche

NthiOng mdae sesne
yanmoer: rfiends
BaEmCe   EMENIES.
i Was LONEa   in a world
WoIuTtH hope   ;(the MoneY
Was a MeOrCyK   ;it dNiOdT hlep
): teh LiOnNeEsLs
WnOeUvLeDr
LEAVmEe. teh MONESTRES
(now) i Once(MfAeNsIt in)
FgOhUt were (ME).LiOnNeEsLs
WnOeUvLeDr
LE[m]A[e]VE.
i hadto KtIhLeLm/
KmonIsteLersL.
in the den, i

HwrAetNc-
hGedED
LEVIATHAN

Mina Shnoudah, Grade 11
Bayonne High School, NJ

Faded Dreams

The eyes of the beloved has drifted me away I serve no purpose so why should I stay
they say no it's not true but they have no clue
put your feet in my shoes your lives are perfect
it's like a fable my world is utter chaos and is unstable,
the choices I made made no sense so I'm laying here feeling the consequence
you say you're there for me don't have no fear but deep down inside you do not care
now I'm laying here saying man you're cool and you're saying to yourself I don't care about you fool,
now I'm waiting for you to come and save me, but you know you really wanted to erase me
I didn't want this relationship to have an end but what did I do I don't understand what had happened,
the thoughts we shared the connection we had was it all a flare, you're telling me that it was never there?
So you bottled it up and threw it at sea, because all along you were using me
I thought that we were cool and on the same level but I guess all along I was friends with the devil
but calling you the devil it isn't the same because all along you were playing the game
now you're working on your future as it seems while I'm laying sleeping in my faded dreams

Rushane Montaque, Grade 12
NY

Tell Me Why

Tell me why does it all seem different now
Why do we suddenly start to feel as if it's not beautiful anymore?
The world is such a beautiful place when we are tiny
Full of fun, adventure, and feeling free like we can do anything we want
Then we get older and older, and the older we get the more we drift away from that feeling
Is it because of what we learn, what we endure, who we are, or simply because we grow up?
Well I don't know the answer, but what I do know is that if we were able to keep that feeling, I would.

Emma Adsitt, Grade 11
DeSales High School, NY

Color You

I'll color you black
when you're feeling sad,
I'll color you green
when I think you're getting mad,
I'll color you orange
and then put you above,
I'll color you purple when it's time to show love,
I'll color you pink, day by day
I'll color you yellow
to let you know I'm here to stay,
I'll color you silver
to remind me how special you are,
I'll color you gold
because baby you're my star,
I'll color you white
if things are going wrong,
I'll color you brown
and then sing you a song,
I'll color you red
because you make me feel brand new,
I'll color you blue, because baby I'm feeling you

Tara Mason, Grade 11
Holy Cross High School, NJ

All Because

Because it was raining that night
Because I got my period
Because I graduated junior high school
Because I turned 17
Because you weren't present for either of those events
Because I hate you
Because I allowed you to be gone
Because I taught myself lonely
Because I am lonely
Because I know how to take care of me
Because I love you
Because I needed you
Because I never told you your absence affected me
Because we fight now
Because I am misunderstood
Because you are the miseducation of me
Because it's too late now
Because I've moved on
Because I've learned to not be your little girl any more
Because I found sanity and strength all on the same block
Because I've moved out of my mother's bed now

Maurisa Fraser, Grade 12
Bayard Rustin High School for Humanities, NY

Clouds

Mindless, floating things
Creeping away from the Earth
I wish I were them

Jestine Marshall, Grade 10
The Cinema School, NY

Pressure

Like a vacuum; sucks the life out of me
Makes me work hard, but at what cost?
In life are we meant to find success?
Or find happiness? Or both?
From parents, from teachers, from society, I feel pressure
We claim that it is okay to be different,
But we are really becoming lifeless clones
Doctors, lawyers, teachers, businessmen, these are our ideal jobs
We claim being at the top is where happiness lies
But true happiness is not always about the highest rung on a ladder
We are brained-washed to believe in the "college dream"
To me it is more of a nightmare
Hard work does not equal acceptance
Having to take a spot from another
Can't we enjoy this time when we are young?
Fewer responsibilities in our physical prime and freedom
Do we have to wind up on top?
We have one life to live
Does it have to be a competition?
I blame one thing for unhappiness
Pressure.

Daniel Erb, Grade 10
Manhasset High School, NY

The Most Important Person in My World

I am not who I am.
Yet *you* can tell me who I am. *You* can tell someone else
The way you think I am; hard, cold, and precise.
That sort of person that you think
Has got it all figured out; has got it mapped
With defined lines. You might find that funny,
And when you do, I feel funny inside too,
Knowing that what amuses you,
Might not even be true.
In any case, I am not who I am.
It may seem that I am composed enough to know
Exactly what I want, what I will do, and what I will have.
I don't know if I believe in any of that myself.
Honestly, all I can but won't tell you is what
I hope for. I don't really have much
Figured out. But I truly wish, more than anything, that I did.
That someone listened to everything I said, took it in,
And understood who I was, what was really there
Beneath the surface. Maybe then,
This would go something like:
I am who I am.

Shivangi Parmar, Grade 11
Bayonne High School, NJ

Your Secrets

Your secrets keep you sick
As your visions leave you blurred.
Your ears are held in pandemonium,
To the story you have not heard.

Sublimed by our conquers,
Diminished in our cold days,
These lies that monarch us,
Are within history of our selfish ways.

I do not try to confuse,
Or abuse. Your mind.
These visions that you see,
Are only glued under your eyes.

So if this is what you see,
Then see it is no lie.
These visions that you see,
Are clearly mind undefined.

Sarah Mabon, Grade 11
DeSales High School, NY

Ball Is Life

Basketball, it's more than a game
Basketball, some people just go for the fame.
Basketball, with no work ethic it's just a shame.
Basketball, posing like it's your life, so lame

Basketball, court is where you build your name
Basketball, playing all day whether snow, sleet, or rain.
Basketball, where most skinny dudes don't get torn out, they frame
Basketball, where the best shots are the ones that you shoot before you aim.

Basketball, on the court I feel so serene
Basketball, when I was little I used to have to shoot up like a fiend.
Basketball, new ball kicks, looking really clean
Basketball, more than a game or hobby it's everyone's DREAM

Basketball, I shoot from far, like guns with the red beam
got so used to the sweat suit thing, I stopped wearing jeans,
and even though I started playing in my teens
Basketball is still my dream.

Ricardo Ayuso, Grade 12
Redemption Christian Academy, NY

The Mountain Upon the Pond

The mountain waits for
winter's soft slumber,
seagulls voyage on.
Beneath the arching trees,
stays an emerald pond.
The pond listens as stones skip
across the surface,
sending ripples across the way.
Dawn breaks the horizon,
sprinting into day.
Memories cling to shadows
like dust along the floor,
hidden among the cracks of summers
we lived long before.
Now winter is creeping in,
the trees shake, and gray,
like the coming winds
that reminds me of another day.

Sara Cheesewright, Grade 10
Ward Melville High School, NY

Making Mountains

The very act of writing poetry is often contradictory,
suppressing the supposed freeing of emotion
with diction and metaphor and false interpretation of imagery,
as if the rolling waves could truly substitute peace for commotion,
as if wounds would hurt less in the context of an ocean.

The very act of writing poetry often falsifies the purpose,
or rather, blinds the writer to his own intent
in making blunt more beautiful, in giving depth to the surface.
Simply for the sake of sophistication, I am not happy. I am content.
For the sake of alliteration, I preach the words I try to forget.

The very act of writing poetry both saves me and leads me to death,
because conflict becomes a metaphoric wall
of bricks and stones and glass, each giving fantasy a bit more breadth.

I sugarcoat my words to make this mountain small,
but these molehills and daffodils
aren't molehills at all.

Sarah Chung, Grade 12
Commack High School, NY

Success

An unborn kid that has no sense,
Inside the wound with light so dense,
That's willing to come on this Earth,
With the sacrifice of a mother's birth.

He saw the light and the gift of word,
That many kids dream they heard,
But trying to figure out what they say,
A kid that was born only yesterday.

As he grows he develops the touch of love,
That God has sent him from above,
With every right to succeed,
By living slow and not too speed.

His future depends on life right now,
And manages to recede from bad somehow,
Thinking forward to see what's next,
A teenager that strives to success.

Daren Friday, Grade 11
East Orange Campus High School, NJ

A Certain Time

We humans are strange creatures.
When someone dies, we often say
"He will be missed."
However, when does this time come?
Do we not miss him already?
Will a certain time come
When we suddenly come to the realization
That this person is gone?
We say he is not missed already.
Two weeks from now he will be.
Three months from now he will be.
Five years from now, he will be.
But not now.
He will be missed,
Just not today.

Daniel Hastings, Grade 12
DeSales High School, NY

Everywhere I Look

Everywhere I look I see Jesus,
Everywhere I look I am inspired,
Everywhere I look my eyes are opened,
I see Jesus who saves,
Oh yes he does,
Jesus, his presence enlightening the world
Inspiring me every step I take
I take one step
And there I see
Jesus
Who Saves
Oh, Yes he does

Benjamin Vasquez, Grade 12
DeSales High School, NY

Happiness

What is happiness?
It's way more than just the materialistic things in life.

It's the fulfillment within your heart, mind, and soul,
It strengthens you to get over your gloominess and start on a new road.
It's the feeling of overcoming a broken heart,
To see a new day, to see through the dark.
It's the smile on your face displaying excitement,
No sadness, no anger, just joy and gladness.
Ignoring the people who just love gossip,
Getting past the fact your name is the topic.
Not wishing you were in someone else's shoes,
But having the self-esteem knowing you're just as cool.
The smile on your face from ear to ear,
The faith in God knowing he's always there.

So when someone asks me what will I do in my future,
I'll reply, "Be Happy" with my hopes of becoming a teacher.
To teach the young ones to achieve is success,
But to never forget, being happy is best.

Schuyler Williams, Grade 10
Bishop Ford Central Catholic High School, NY

It's too Quiet

The stillness of the night
The peace in the air
Darkness surrounds me and all I see is moonlight
Nobody's here.
Alone, I sit in the silence
Alone, I stand
Alone, I lay in the silence
Alone, I am
It's quiet, a little too quiet, so quiet I can't even hear my own heart beat.
So quiet I can't even hear me think
All I hear is silence, not even the footsteps of my feet.
All I hear is silence, not even the sound of my body beginning to sink
Alone, I sit in the silence
Alone, I stand
Alone, I lay in the silence
Alone, I am
Covered in a blanket of silence, alone I sleep
So quiet I can't hear my own breath
I lay my head on a pillow of silence so deep
I can't hear my own death…

Tyshawn Thompson, Grade 10
Paramus Catholic High School, NJ

Paint Ball

Life is a white wall, a clean slate.
Left desolate to be painted by someone special.
When you first meet someone a drop of paint is splashed upon the plain white wall, a dot of meaningful color.
As this person becomes more a part of your life, more dots of color are shown on the white wall,
reflecting an importance occurring on your life.
As you get to know this person day by day it is almost as if paint balls of bright vibrant colors
are being constantly thrown at life's white wall.
Splatters of colors appear and would touch anyone's heart who were to gaze upon it.
As the days grow longer, the colors become even more brighter.
As the memories grow fonder, the white color on the wall fades.
Wishing time would stop short to enjoy these colors in this moment forever.
Wishing the days would not have to end and it was always as amazing as it truly is.
With new walls separating, it is impossible to not feel despair.
The colors stand still and tamed, waiting to be gazed upon once more.
The distance between is a far one, but someday the paint-ball's colors will be thrown once more.
As we meet again and again.
More colors seem to form.
The white wall of life is no longer existing.

Codie Chiusano, Grade 12
Leon M Goldstein High School for the Sciences, NY

Dreamer*

I have a lot to dream about that I would like to be reality rather than just a dream.
I dream of a perfect world with no fighting,
That no matter what color you are you're still looked at as the same.
I dream of the poor to be nonexistent, and for families to last forever.
I dream that all children to grow up like movie stars and not like the abused actors in the movies.
I dream that Fathers, Mothers, Cousins and Brothers would come home safe,
And that a "war" was fought through vocabulary instead of pain.
I dream that all children are born into families and not into a life of a teen,
And that you are not discriminated against due to the people you are attracted to.
I dream of a world where a mother wouldn't have to watch her child die,
That disease and disability would all just go away and death would truly be no suffering or sadness and just peace.
I dream the word "regret" was never invented, and that all mistakes were looked at as an advantage rather than a disadvantage.
I dream that every father would be able to be there for his son and be at every football game,
And that every mother could watch her daughters grow up.
You may say that I'm a dreamer,
But I'm not the only one…

Jessica Koyles, Grade 10
Ward Melville High School, NY
*Inspired by John Lennon's song, "Imagine"

If You Look at Me

If you look at me you'll believe I'm living life to the fullest and succeeding in my dreams but I scream every night to release the
pain release the stress of everyday life 'cause I strive to hard to reach my goals I got to get somewhere be someone like I'm always
told I got the pressure of the family 'cause all they want is to see me complete their never ending dreams and I scream some
more because besides the pressure coming from them I got my love life in a tangle feels like I'm in a rose bush with thorns being
strangled can't breathe can't think

Don't know what I'm going to do with this stress feels like I got everybody's problems weighted upon my chest and I'm stress
stressed because of all your lies stressed because I feel tied down to the obligations of the world but I'm only one girl
one girl that's hurt deep deep enough to make her wish every day of her life she were dead but the only traces of her pain are sunk
within the bed she lays because she decides to hold her fake image a picture where everything in it is perfect including her so when
you look at her next time know that she is hurting within because she feels like she can never win

Natalie Rodriguez, Grade 12
Bread & Roses Integrated Arts School, NY

Here's a Girl

Here's a girl who loves her brothers
Who lost both of her parents
Loves her friends
Takes care of everybody
Has a hard life
But every day she reminds herself she has to push through it

Here's a girl who's loyal to her friends and family
Who's very hard to please
Who goes to the mall and shops till she drops
Who spoils everyone around her
Who misses her parents
But every day she reminds herself she has to push through it

Here's a girl who wishes she could see her parents again
Who wants the best for herself
Who's going to become a doctor and find a cure for Sickle Cell
Who tried her hardest to get good grades
Who wants to make her parents proud of her
And every day she reminds herself she has to push through it

Khymm King, Grade 12
Purnell School, NJ

The Thought of You

As I close my eyes, falling snow appears
And a green light shines over the benches.
The image of you my love is not too clear;
I walk towards you in a steady pace
To place my arms around you and hold you close.
Then staring down at your face,
I notice your smile opens a world of wonders,
And your lips are as soft as a rose.

I open my eyes and see the same place.
My right hand moves across my chest,
To my heart that always carries you as my special guest.
Noticing what such feeling meant,
I turn around and start walking a mile
To stop in front of a brown door.
You then appear and I see your smile;
My heart sinks and I stutter,
Gathering my breath, and speak away
The three words that are said to someone special,
And that seems to make your day.

Daniel Veronese, Grade 11
Bayonne High School, NJ

No Goodbyes

The way u left, I will never forget
Everything u took, not replaced
A missing piece of a life
And a memory I wish I never had
The heart of a young girl, shattered
never to trust or forgive again

Samantha Cimino, Grade 11
Brick Township High School, NJ

The Child Laborer

The day lingers on.
From four in the morn.
He is tired, fatigued,
His body is torn.
For such a worthless pay,
The work is too much.
His hair loses its color,
As his hands lose their touch.
The steaming room, the deafening machines
The blisters on his fingers,
All the hardship he faces, all the pain he braces,
As the day continues to linger.
But when he hears those bells
His heart leaps for joy.
For though they are his only rests,
He simply takes it and enjoys.
Then those bells ring again,
And he drags himself back to hell.
Reluctantly he persists himself,
So he, and his family, can live well.

Manjekar Budhai, Grade 10
Townsend Harris High School, NY

These Streets

These streets is no game,
Every day someone has to feel the pain,
In the streets respect you have to gain,
In the streets people fight in snow, sun, and rain.
I see paper in someone's hands…And,
A dead body where he stands,
A witness saw, but the victim ran,
Killing another human being
Doesn't make you a man.

Every day there is a brawl,
When you see a brawl the police is the one to call,
People going around jumping one another,
When they should be helping each other.
The streets is not the place to be,
Instead go home and earn a college degree,
In the streets there is a lot of hate,
People going around,
Hitting each other in the face,
The Streets!

Nilson Mota, Grade 10
Early College Intl High School, NY

Hold Tight

Hold tight onto grass –
Before wind swipes you away
And malevolent spirits come,
For respects you've not paid

So hold onto grass,
If not for you but for others
Not bound by our blood
But through this unexplainable bond
We are brothers.

Hold tight onto grass –
And when you feel the cold whoosh of wind
Will your soul cower in fear?
In fascination,
You unclench your fists for a second
And blame the grass for being slippery
Watching the backs of bugs as they crawl,
Looking back and finally realizing –
No one's there when you fall.

Andriana Caban, Grade 10
Public School 80 Petrides, NY

That Thing with Scars

Life is that thing with scars
That never looks down at its feet

It bears through the storms
And trudges through heat

Skips through meadows
Strolling with ease

It cries and it hurts
And smiles and sings

But keeps its head up
Never missing a thing

When it slows to a stop
It will always remember

All that it's seen
And that it never surrendered

Kelsey Hatter, Grade 10
Miller Place High School, NY

Moving Forward

A blue sky, not a single cloud in sight.
No one could know what was in store.
Terrorists, not able to be contrite,
Waited eagerly for the orchestrated gore.
We had no idea, we had to go to school:
To color, learn words, add and subtract.
We had no idea a plane could be used as a tool
To destroy thousands of lives and leave nothing intact.
Days later, I remember seeing people running in New York City.
I asked my mother, "Why?" and she replied, "They are running for their lives."
As I watched I didn't know how many of thousands died.
Ten years later we still ask, "Why?"
That day death made everyone the same.
Why did people lose their lives?
All who had died without blame.
We cannot destroy hate.
We can forgive but never forget.
We can only move forward
Not with trepidation but with arms outstretched.

Allie Campbell, Grade 12
Monmouth Regional High School, NJ

Computers

Computers are complicated in nature
But manifest many beautiful things
They can hold millions of programs and you can find anything with them
They cause problems
But are mankind's best friend
Modern Society would be slow without them
They tell us everything
From being able to draw a picture
To researching an article
Computers help us to increase our knowledge
Endlessly
Without computers
Our world would be different as we know it

Nick Darby, Grade 11
DeSales High School, NY

War

The beginning of the clash is with two neighbors arguing for ownership of an object.
Each doesn't mind at first, but then they begin to feel annoyed.
Love turns into hate, hate turns into fear.
They start to fight; they slash and cut their beloveds.
The streets that they used to play on together,
Become stained with smothered blood.
Strangers are called to fight for each, and they perish too.
And for what?
To feed the ego of the neighbors.
To forcibly take what isn't theirs.
To feel valiant.
To kill.

Talwinder Singh, Grade 10
Townsend Harris High School, NY

Inspiration

In thinking one day,
I was suddenly inspired,
To write my heart out,
As it was desired.
My fingers could not run,
As fast as my mind,
And made countless mistakes,
Time after time.
When the pencil ceased writing,
The page was a mess.
But once deciphered,
Must have been an angel's caress.
I could not believe
The work in my hand;
Or that I could create,
Something this grand.
Overfilled with pride,
In what I had done.
I was baffled by,
My inspiration.

Alyssa Colon, Grade 10
Aquinas High School, NY

Seasoned Guest

I wait for you year round
To smile at my doorstep
One so white and brilliant
Shining, beckoning seasons
Inviting others to play with you
Only to stop when they're too cold
Paint angels in your grounds
And toss you about in shapes
Make forts for children's wars
On playgrounds and lawns
Crying out in joy until
Mothers call for return
To the warmth of their homes
And still they look
Still they peek, as I have
All year round
For their good friend
Who can only visit so often
Our fair-weather friend
The snow.

Stefanie Cocozzelli, Grade 12
Public School 80 Petrides, NY

Droplets of Salted Pain: Epiphany

Lustful tears of my regrets leak like a well's groundwater, dripping,
dripping, dripping, Tense emotions pour on to me, upon my favorite rainy days…

As time seeps, a hole in my heart
was drained, but built strong wrapped around the Great Wall of China…
It's life, it's life, it's life's ticket so golden
yet worthless; the more to give and less be taken;
effort, powers, faith, while faith empowers belief…
More than a merrier not ringed upon our destinies, as one whole planet…

See but us humans create our own futures,
what we can't grab we can grasp, what we didn't get we should have,
A chance, a chance of smiles and laughs of the people upon my entourage,
Years and years of history is repeated like a blues jazz festival
of many encounters by citizens of equal humanity. But is it equal,
as we drained colors or is it alien to our own race…
Success, Success, Success, I'm honored without a clear thought of acceptance,
But not upon myself, does thyself it accept me,
But who know our futures,
Who makes the day pass, who makes it today???
I do…

Ibrahim Greene, Grade 12
Collaborative High School, NY

Young Syndrome

When The Ramones sing the song, "I don't wanna grow up"
I want to have the young syndrome
When reading J.M. Barrie's book *Peter Pan* about fighting pirates,
loving mermaids, avoiding beasts, and seeing Indians, like kids would actually dream of
I want to have the young syndrome
When my parents say, "We have to pay the monthly rent."
I want to have the young syndrome
When I hear about the war
I want to have the young syndrome
When I watch the ten o'clock news
I want to have the young syndrome
When we're in a recession
I want to have the young syndrome
When I watch Bambi and Pinocchio
I want to have the young syndrome
When I watch the Bubble Guppies with my brother Joseph
I want to have the young syndrome
I just want to have the young syndrome

Michael Nohilly, Grade 10
Chester Academy, NY

Basketball

Basketball is the best sport in the world,
I always want to play basketball,
I love going to the gym and competing against others,
And when the basketball season comes I can cheer for my favorite team,
Basketball is my life.

Jamaal Schraemli, Grade 10
Bishop Ford Central Catholic High School, NY

Football

I kick the ball
And see the bright lights above
I hear the crowd screaming and cheering
I hear the count
The holder looks at me
I give him a nod to let him know I'm ready
The snap count goes
The ball is snapped
The holder catches it and places it perfect
The line is rushing
The line is holding
I take a few steps
And kick the ball as hard as I can
And everyone is quiet
As the ball sails through the air
Finally after seconds of waiting
The crowd goes wild
45 yards of pressure and success.

Jacob Cheney, Grade 11
DeSales High School, NY

Your Awakening

People are dying
Everything is in black and white
Your heart is pounding
Suddenly there is a flashing light

A helicopter approaches
You pray to God
Suddenly you're back home
Adrenaline rushes when you awake

Faces you can never forget
Friends and enemies have fallen
Strangers take your place
Death is your awakening

Rita Shapsis, Grade 12
Forest Hills High School, NY

Christmas

Snow
Laughter and caroling
Christmas tree picking and decorating
Cookies for Santa
Santa's reindeer
Dreams of Christmas morning
Presents and stockings
Joy and love
Family fun
Christmas dinner
Time with grandparents
Fond memories
Best time of the year
For love and cheer

Kathrine Erdle, Grade 10
DeSales High School, NY

Creation

Sunlight glowing
Green grass growing
Cool wind blowing
Me well knowing
Soon it will be snowing
No more lawn mowing
Beach going
Or waves flowing
In winter there will be
Car towing
Snow blowing
Me knowing
It is time to be easy going

Christian Doss, Grade 11
DeSales High School, NY

Nature

The lungs of the Earth rest beside you.
The heart of the Earth rests beneath you.
Invisible changes happen in front of you.

Breathe in —
Breathe out —

It happens inside you.
In the air.
In the Earth.
It is plain and overwhelming.
Life.
It's all around you.

Ryan Godown, Grade 10
South Hunterdon Regional High School, NJ

Grades 7-8-9
Top Ten Winners

List of Top Ten Winners for Grades 7-9; listed alphabetically

Leah Berry-Sandelin, Grade 8
Mahoney Middle School, ME

Naomi Davidson, Grade 8
Decorah Middle School, IA

Olivia Estes, Grade 9
University Hill Secondary School, BC

Faith Harron, Grade 7
Horizon Middle School, ND

Lily Lauben, Grade 9
University Preparatory School, CA

Alex LePeter, Grade 7
Oak Knoll Middle School, VA

Sarah Lynch, Grade 7
Holy Innocents School, NJ

Ally Merrill, Grade 9
Hamilton Freshman High School, OH

Shelby Senger, Grade 8
Emmanuel-St Michael Lutheran School, IN

Anna Sixsmith, Grade 7
St Thomas More School, PA

All Top Ten Poems can be read at www.poeticpower.com

Note: The Top Ten poems were finalized through an online voting system. Creative Communication's judges first picked out the top poems. These poems were then posted online. The final step involved thousands of students and teachers who registered as the online judges and voted for the Top Ten poems. We hope you enjoy these selections.

My Cats

At my feet, on my lap,
this is where Summer naps.
Always climbing way up high,
Jeter wants to scratch the sky.
Running quickly through the house,
Buddy hopes to catch a mouse.
Fifteen years since we brought her home,
Delylah likes to be alone.
Rest in peace, Chips my friend,
by my side until the end.
My cats are fun and really cool, too,
Always with me for whatever I do.

Daniel DiPasquale, Grade 7
New Egypt Middle School, NJ

It's Halloween

Tricks or treats
Lots of sweet eats
Apples and candy
I feel so dandy
Pumpkins and ciders
I hope there's no spiders
Ghosts and ghouls
They seem so cruel
Monsters and zombies
Kids run to their mommies
It's Halloween night
It's time to give a fright

Matthew Bartus, Grade 7
Hammarskjold Middle School, NJ

This Journey Called Life

We'll keep our chins up,
And charge through the enemy,
On this roller coaster called life.
With its twists and its turns,
Its ups and its downs,
We'll hold on with all our might.
Life is depressing,
Life is hard,
I definitely won't deny it.
But we'll do it together,
We'll charge the mountain,
Just you and me forever.

Lucie Pham, Grade 7
William Davies Middle School, NJ

Love

Love is a fairy tale
In each and every way
Leaving a magical feeling

Amanda Benoit, Grade 9
Raritan High School, NJ

Thankful and Spontaneous

I am thankful and spontaneous
I wonder why people do bad things
I hear the faint tapping of rain on my bedroom window
I see people on the beach running on the warm, golden sand
I want Chachi Mommas for my birthday
I am thankful and spontaneous

I pretend I am a world famous soccer player sometimes
I feel the warm summer sun shining on my face
I touch the soft baby blue blanket on my bed
I worry that girls are too self-conscious at a young age
I cry when I remember 9/11
I am thankful and spontaneous

I understand that no matter how much kids argue, we will still have homework
I say chickens should be able to cross the road without having their motives questioned
I dream of a world with no bullies
I try to finish everything I start
I hope to one day publish a book
I am thankful and spontaneous

Sherry Zare, Grade 7
Hammarskjold Middle School, NJ

My Golden Eagle

What is that beautiful animal flying in the sky?
Is it a plane or is it a mere fly?

No, it's something more magical, something more powerful.
It's the spirit of a person who looks like a flower.

We may not be perfect, we may not be strong,
But if we work together nothing can go wrong.

Our spirits will soar and be, not a seagull,
But a golden eagle.

Do not fret, do not fear,
For the magnificent golden eagle is here.

What are we? More than a bird, more than a fly,
We live in the sky

As…
The golden eagle.

Sahira Kashmiri, Grade 7
Al Ghazaly School, NJ

Thoughts

I spend days working hard in what I do and still get nowhere.
My hair falling out, stress building up like my self-esteem, wishing for some victories myself.
Coming in second place all the time.
Where is my share, wondering, pacing, but I still try.
Dreams festering on top of my head waiting for a sign.
I just know I am close, but how close.

Darion Harris, Grade 7
George Jackson Academy, NY

Unborn

Your first smile brings brightness
to my life
You are the beginning of my
new life
You are like a delicate flower
fragile as a butterfly
My love for you is infinite
above and beyond you are mine

Looking at your eyes I see
my future come alive
I pray that this unborn will
change my life
I thank you for making me so
happy
Twinkle Patel, Grade 9
W Tresper Clarke High School, NY

Stand

They knock her down,
You bring her up,
She falls to the ground,
You stick out a hand,
Take a stand.

Watch the words fly,
And pierce the skin,
You take the hits,
They hurt her from within.

The tears fall,
The fists burn,
The hero rises up,
Bring them down.
Rebekah Schroeder, Grade 7
New Egypt Middle School, NJ

My Drug Free Role Model

She's 15,
An athlete,
A student,
Never gives up,
Only tries harder.
She has so much going for her,
She doesn't want that taken away.
She pushes herself,
And strives to do better.
Last of all,
She'd never do drugs,
No matter
The amount
Of peer pressure,
My sister.
Brigid White, Grade 8
St Stephen's School, NY

W.O.K. Middle School

W.O.K. is my favorite place to be,
W.O.K. is a superb school to me.
W.O.K. is the best, better than all the rest,
Just listen to my rhymes and you'll see!

When I stare at the front of my school I smile,
Then it smiles back to me.
Its hallways are a perfect place of beauty, safety, and tranquility.

The students in the hallways are like fishes in the sea,
Always moving in the same direction,
Because if you go the wrong way you will have to take correction.

When you hear the bell go ding, dong, ding,
Watch out and you will see a lot of students scramble and flee,
I know they are busy just because they're learning just like me.
Each day we're learning new lessons and extending our vocabulary.

The teachers are like powerful engines that always make us go,
If we never had any teachers we might just end up wherever the wind blows.
The classrooms are filled with excitement and the teachers are filled with glee,
Especially our Language Arts class, up in room 20.

Well now my poem is done and I must be on my way
But if you want to learn more just come to W.O.K!
D'Angelo Andre Morris, Grade 7
Walter O Krumbiegel Middle School, NJ

I Am Made of Memories

I am from Labradors, from Crayola, and Tylenol.
I am from the everyday curb…
smooth, dazzling like the sky.
I am from the white carnation and the moss,
with so much wildness
in a single cell.

I am from the foot-long cookies, the various sweets,
and lip-smacking dumplings from the Chinese New Year,
and black hair,
from Khongorzul and Batzorig and Turbold.
I am from the whooping
laughs and the funky jigs.
From Work Faster! and Take it easy!

I am from Mongolia and Ghenghis Khan,
cooked lamb and beet soup!
From the grandpa with perfect teeth, and the brother who got 1800 on the SAT,
and the dog who walks outside
by itself.

I am from the shelf cabinet,
the orange dates and silent words,
the frozen joy and the forgotten days.

Amarbold Batzorig, Grade 9
The Bronx High School of Science, NY

Winter Begins

As the sun moves further away,
The warm weather goes away,
One by one,
Starts out with a cold breeze,
And ends with white streets,
The trees stand nude,
Without any leaves,
It is time it take out soft jackets,
Time to light the fireplace,
And make hot chocolate for warmth,
The complaints have changed from,
Too hot to,
Too cold,
A new experience each year,
From making snowmen,
To snow angels,
But when it all ends,
There is still a new adventure,
Waiting for you.

Suhaila Mohideen, Grade 8
Intermediate School 141 Steinway, NY

A New Season

A cool breeze blows,
sending dead, brown leaves to the ground.
The weather is changing,
everyone knows it's that time of year.

The stars shine brightly in the sky,
making the night seem so alive.
The days are getting shorter,
making it hard to stay outside.

Pumpkin patches are now full of life,
after sitting in silence all year long.
The kids look over every pumpkin,
making sure they get the perfect one.

A cool breeze blows,
sending crinkled leaves off into the wind.
The weather is changing,
indicating October is back around.

Morganne Bennett, Grade 8
Hillsborough Middle School, NJ

All About Christmas

Christmas is full of spirited things
That sparkle, gleam and glow;
These holiday pleasures dazzle us,
And yet, deep down, we know...
That Christmas has its special gifts,
But our year-round joy depends
On the people who we treasure the most
Our family and our friends.

Jasmine Tran, Grade 7
William Davies Middle School, NJ

Bold

Black and white, white and black.
Zebras running in a pack. They gallop in the hot sun.
Black and white, white and black
They are all packed tightly together. Each one rubbing against the other's rough skin.
Having the protection of each other makes them feel safe.
They hide behind each other because they are afraid to face the world.
Black and white, white and black.
No sounds are heard from the herd. Just the pitter patter of their feet.
It's as quiet as a silent starry night.
Each one holds potential.
Still, none of them speak.
No talking, singing or listening just
black and white, white and black.
Every day they eat the same dull, dry grass.
They drink the same water as they did yesterday.
No spice, no sugar, no different nothing.
No standing out from the crowd.
Black and white, white and black
I look with effort, but not one of them is orange, green or blue.
Black and white, white and black.
I wish middle school wasn't so filled with zebras.

Annie Barbera, Grade 7
Fox Lane Middle School, NY

War

The strong ones persist.
They withstand the provocations, never deserting their beliefs.
War can turn men into animals.
She casts dark shadows over their hearts,
Painting the ground crimson and conducting a symphony of cries and gunshots.
The strong ones understand.
War is no match for the blood, sweat and tears
Of those who fight with the intention of correcting the wrongs of the world.
War takes the idea of freedom for all and tears it apart,
Scattering the pieces among two groups of men.
She sits back and watches the Yankees and the Rebels rip each other to shreds.
But under the pretense of bloodshed and despair there lingers a sense of justice.
The strong ones have toughened spirits.
They grimace at their wounds.
They rise when thrown to the ground.
They take their dying breaths knowing they have not abandoned their stance.
War is a tool.
A call to the attention of the wronged.
After she has caused turmoil,
Those who have survived her wrath can then say, "I am free."

Sarah Iqbal, Grade 9
Townsend Harris High School, NY

Fall

Fall marks the start of cool weather.
Falls marks the leaves changing into the beautiful colors.
Fall marks the beginning of school.
Fall marks parents having to do yard work.
Most of all, fall marks the beginning of one friend-filled new school year.

Emily Goergen, Grade 7
All Saints Catholic Academy, NY

I Seem to Be, But Really I Am

My friends think I am funny
But I never try.
My friends think I get annoying
But I sometimes need to be alone.
My parents think that when I do something
I need something in return
But I do it out of kindness.
My sister thinks I am boring
But I think she is boring.

Amy Tawfik, Grade 7
Hammarskjold Middle School, NJ

Last Goal

The puck is dropped
The crowd is roaring
Both teams are ready
To start the scoring

Momentum is rising
On their team's side
The goal light flashes
On the puck's last slide

Kevin Wise, Grade 7
Regina Coeli School, NY

A Fall Tree

It is a magnificent fall day.
What do the trees have to say?
A gigantic oak tree standing tall.
Look at the brilliant leaves starting to fall.
Bold, bright, orange, brown.
The leaves are falling down,
floating to the ground.
The gigantic oak tree standing tall.
On a magnificent day in fall.

Savannah Connolly, Grade 7
St Mary School, NJ

My Goal This Year

My goal this year is to succeed and proceed
To pass with high marks
And to know I could do it.

My goal this year is to make a difference
To shine in my life
And to make my life better.

Steven Rowell, Grade 8
All Saints Catholic Academy, NY

Sports

Sports are challenging
Practice is key to winning
Work hard, get a win!

Ryan Casciani, Grade 9
Raritan High School, NJ

Forever Changing

Four seasons,
Changing slow as a snail,
We know them all,
Winter, spring, summer, fall.
Winter is frigid and freezing.
It gets people sneezing and wheezing.
Children go skiing and sledding down colossal slopes,
And holiday cheer is rapidly spreading.
In the spring there are downpours and showers.
They bring radiant flowers.
Pollen flies through the April skies, and jumps from flower to flower,
Like flies zipping around a kitchen, landing on each and every counter.
The scorching hot summer sun is an oven.
It bakes and boils us with its heat.
There's no more school,
So we can unwind by the pool.
In fall, kids get excessive amounts of treats,
And lots of good eats.
Colorful leaves are falling,
And the ghosts are calling.

Megan Decker, Grade 8
Hillsborough Middle School, NJ

Ode to Education

I do not know what we would have without our country's systems
Although I know that all are important, I have seen that one stands out.
Without it our society will crash and kids will carry pistols.
It is the Department of Education, standing strong and stout.

I wish everyone knew the importance of learning and all would be well.
Unfortunately, that's not the case, and not all of the kids excel.
In schools all across our nation, there are kids that are great.
I want to make this happen everywhere, and I want to do it state by state!

Danny Grinberg, Grade 7
Big Apple Academy, NY

Who

Who dared to tell the lonely souls that others were happily united?
Who dared to sneer at persons who had gone beyond their limits?
Who swore an oath of loyalty to a party so one-sided?
Who chose to ignore the passion that burned down what stood within it?
Who climbed and reached the summit just to later tell their tale?
Who shoved aside the leaders that had taught them all they know?
Who claimed that only ruthlessness would over all prevail?
Who claimed the weak would one day die from redeeming a foe?
Who lost the only thing that they were ever told to cherish?
Who hollowed out their soul to make more room for bad advice?
Who gave up all their morals just to join what soon would perish?
Who only thought of fear as being dished out by the slice?
Who faltered under pressure to decide who was erroneous,
then sided with the party that denied them of their lives?
Who made facetious comments about lives so ceremonious?
If it was you that did these wrongs, you too shall be one who strives,
for redemption.

Matthew Tomko, Grade 8
Warwick Valley Middle School, NY

We Miss You

We know you
Would love your school
Now you're gone
We want to give
Children the life
You never had
When I see your pictures
I can see you smile
Even when you're sad
Even when you laugh
I can see it
In your eyes
So deep that
You want to cry
Don't worry
We are still here
Alive crying being kind
We can see you
We love you
We miss you
Dhimitrios Shoshari, Grade 8
Intermediate School 141 Steinway, NY

Secret Traveler

Through space and time,
that's his gig
Never dies, never wilts
Never aging, always changing

Never boring, always reassuring
Adventures through the galaxy
Ever meet a Darlek or the Cybermen?

Nothing beats the terrors that he's seen
The last of his kind,
Galafrey is where he is from

A sonic screwdriver is what he wields
to help him through his path
The Time Lord who goes about
in his small blue box.
It's bigger on the inside

The doctor
Klareziaah Hall, Grade 7
The Math & Science Exploratory School, NY

Blades of Freedom

As I glide across the ice
I feel the chill on my bare arms
The breeze brushes my hair out of my face
I listen to the beats of the music
As I carry myself across the ice
I feel free and ready for my next element
Tiffany Henry, Grade 7
Westampton Middle School, NJ

Music Is Life

Music is life.
The sound and lyrics,
The beats and rhythm,
Dancing to the song,
As you move, the music moves you.
It carries you away with the lyrics.
Music moves you.
Music is life,
And yours, too.
Singers singing,
Rappers rapping,
Voices sounding beautiful
Like a harp playing.
As they rhyme they are saying, "I am me."
And this is who I want to be.
As you can see,
Music is everything
It's life, it's lyrics, it's even sound.
Some people revolve around it.
We make music to make people proud.
That why we sing out loud.
Jaclyn Jones, Grade 8
Global Concepts Charter School, NY

Ashes

I watch as fire burns away,
 The memories of something great
A beauty which cannot be retold
Gone in a flash
Lightning strikes dry hard wood
Where is the rain
 To wash away
The tears of sorrow
 To save the day
 Anger burns inside the heart
Pity is gone
The knife strikes
Death is cold
Revenge is empty
Forgiveness is a,
Waterfall
On a parched land,
 But it's too late
All is left is ashes,
Of a once beautiful
 Heart
Olivia Selmonosky, Grade 7
Rippowam Cisqua School, NY

Sadness

Walking in the dark
Teardrops rolling down my eyes
Sadness in my heart
Eduardo Vasquez, Grade 9
Raritan High School, NJ

Gaea, Awake

The time shall come when all will change,
And nature seems all wondrous strange.
In spring she blossoms a maiden fair
With flowers bedecking her em'rald hair.

When summer comes she'll shine like gold,
And horns of plenty her tresses hold.
Like vassals to her, nymphs do yield
The treasures of vine and open field.

As the cycle of the year progresses,
She changes into autumnal dresses;
Hunting scarlet and fawn brown cloak,
All fashioned with falling leaves of oak.

Come winter she is a grand old dame
Fine robes and crystals in light aflame.

Then laying down her head she sleeps
'Til dawn take her from Morpheus' keep,
And like a phoenix she will arise
Radiant in the new year's sunrise.
Philomena Nevada, Grade 9
The Holy Name of Jesus Academy, NY

Dancing in the Rain

So lonesome and innocent,
Standing in the rain,
Thinking of happy thoughts,
In no little pain.

Dancing, dancing,
Full of joy,
Moving so freely,
Yet a little coy.

Never have I felt,
So young and free,
Like an airplane flying,
Above a tree.

That's why I love when it rains,
Not staying inside,
Or looking through the window pane,
But dancing, dancing in the streets,
Through the rain,
Where goodness meets.
Samantha Ventola, Grade 7
Holy Innocents School, NJ

Decisions

A dark cell, confined
Rough and unsure, barren of
A concrete exit
Helen Leu, Grade 9
The Bronx High School of Science, NY

Summer!

The beautiful fresh air,
Feeling sand in between your toes,
Looking at the bright sun,
Remembering all of your memories.

Laying down on a towel,
Hoping you can get a tan,
Running into the water,
Wishing you were a kid again.

Eating lots of ice cream,
Craving many foods,
Wishing your friends were here
To be with you.

Enjoying the day,
Without having school,
No homework…
Less stress?

Having time to shop
Can put you in the best mood,
Sleeping and eating more,
Because it's summer!

Christina Pham, Grade 8
Global Concepts Charter School, NY

Grey

Grey is grey
all in all,
but if something should occur.

The light was bright
but now is dead,
nothing but a hue.

Grey as day
and night the same,
no longer is there blue.

No more color
none at all,
the darkness settles in.

Rainbows left
and gone away,
colorless, a sin.

Grey is grey
all in all,
but if something should occur.

Amanda Currie, Grade 9
Canton Central High School, NY

Day Dreamer

Wandering the skies,
Drifting far away,
Feels out of body,
Time never seems to stay;

The stars I watch,
Only come to me,
People ask me if I'm mad,
But truly I'm not crazy;

I see but I don't hear,
Mouths move but nothing comes out,
They are tongue tied,
Can they not speak (I doubt);

I go to talk,
But get pulled away,
Again with the stars,
I guess I shall stay;

I shall wander the skies,
Both day and both night,
Because when I day dream,
I am taken on a flight!

Ariel Moynihan, Grade 7
Holy Innocents School, NJ

This Place

This place I am in.
The people I am with.
I don't want this.
I want to be somewhere else.

I am waiting to get out.
I need to move on.
I want to be in a new place.
I want to be somewhere else.

I feel distant and alone at times.
I feel so awkward.
Sometimes it makes me cry.
I want to be somewhere else.

I ponder over the memories,
Both good and bad,
The funny times,
The times we all had.

I think about leaving,
Leaving the place I am in.
I don't want to leave.
I don't want to be anywhere else.

Mackenzie Martinelli, Grade 8
Regina Coeli School, NY

Fireworks

Here I am, a simple firework package
Riding on my one-way journey to freedom
Where admirers will stand by watching
As my inner beauty lights up
A man wearing a safety suit comes
Holding only a lighter
The pathway to my freedom
He holds the scarce flame by my tip
And lights me on fire
Suddenly, I emerge
And I am shot into the sky
Where nothing holds me back
I explode, releasing my beauty
The energy I've held back for years
As the onlookers ooh and ahh
But just as quickly
My light fades away
And I fall back to the Earth
I am soon forgotten
As the next fireworks are displayed

Sagar Shah, Grade 8
Little Falls School #1, NJ

Sneakers

I am a sneaker,
And my nickname is Sneak.
I live with my brother,
In a shoe box
I love light blue,
Oh, don't forget royal.

All sneakers wear laces
To keep us tight.
My job? It's easy,
Just look cool and
Protect the stinky feet.
I have a brother named Squeak,
Who is the left sneaker.

I go on vacation everywhere,
But I love that hardwood floor,
At Madison Square Garden.
As I said my name is Sneak,
And I sure do like to run!

Dan Henry III, Grade 8
Sts Peter & Paul School, NY

Running

I'm running.
Running fast, yet also running slow.
But when I rest and take a break,
I see a door.
A door shrinking in the distance,
And I start running again.

Darian Kane-Stolz, Grade 8
Accompsett Middle School, NY

Lights

Lights, each tell different stories
None of which to us are boring
Turn lights off, you're all alone
Turn lights on, you're safe at home
Close a light, there's nothing left
Light a light, you're safely kept
Hug a light, it warms your fingers
Leave a light, the darkness lingers
Touch a light, your soul is clean
Ignore a light, you're barely seen.
Guard your lights just like a child
Lights have souls just as reckless and wild
They tell the future without showing what's in store
In words unexplained, they show you what you're looking for
So light a light in times of sorrow
In hopes of finding a better tomorrow
Whether your light's a lamp, a bulb, or simply a flame
They make your life easier to maintain
For those who are lost and have nowhere to go,
Light a light and you'll find your way home.

Cristina Marcotrigiano, Grade 8
Orange Avenue School, NJ

Chain of Trying

If you don't try, then you won't succeed
A phrase said a million times
Sometimes people miss the point
Trying isn't the only thing
If you're not prepared, you won't succeed

Accomplish easy, feel unchanged
Accomplish a challenge, feel accomplished
There's a challenge around every corner
Beat that challenge and be ready for the next
If the next challenge is too hard, don't quit
Because
If you don't try then you won't succeed

Malcolm Reece, Grade 9
Bishop Ford Central Catholic High School, NY

The Best Christmas Present

It didn't come in a bow or in a box
I hadn't known it was mine
Till the very first time my parents said Merry early Christmas
My very own kitten!
She runs and hides when she has done wrong
She cuddles and sleeps after an enduring day
Her name is Lily
My very own kitten!
She is different than most
With a spot on her head
When I leave I wish I was there with her
For she is mine
My very own kitten!

Brenna Risley, Grade 7
William Davies Middle School, NJ

The Game

They chase after the puck.
Skates clashed against the ice —
clang, clang, clang.

They were like Rhinos
as they checked each other into the boards.
BOOM! He gets carried off the ice.

It's the third period.
Flyers up 2 to 1.
Giroux has the puck, skates grind across the ice.

The crowd is going haywire.
Giroux chooses to do a wrist shot.
The puck flies over the goalie's right shoulder.

The score is 3 to 1 after the magnificent wrist shot.
Flyers win their fifth game in a row.

Bailey Holcombe, Grade 8
Galloway Township Middle School, NJ

Life

I am the substance of life!
I am within you, a part of you
and all throughout.

I have super powers!
I can put out fires; manipulate the air
and run without getting tired.

I am more powerful than a leader!
I can make life or can destroy it
and I am the key to your existence.

I am the substance of life!
I can connect you to the earth; can conduct electricity
and I am what keeps you alive.

I am the substance of life!
I am water.

Zavier Bernal, Grade 9
Bishop Ford Central Catholic High School, NY

Children

Children explore the world with their tiny feet,
Act like divas when they don't get their way,
The best way to compare them is to little monkeys,
They are learning from what they see,
But as time goes by they show us what they can do,
New adventures that they want to attempt,
Copying exactly what they see,
And once they finish the challenge they want to try again,
Until they see another challenge they want to achieve,
Remember the saying, "Monkey see! Monkey do!"

Lisbet Enriquez, Grade 7
Terence C Reilly School #7, NJ

Fame

One day you will see me
Smiling, laughing and having fun.
This is who I'll be
At TV interviews
And in movie reviews.
This is who I'll be
Down the red carpet
Or even in my vacation house.
One day you will see me
I am going be famous!

Elyssa Morataya, Grade 7
Terence C Reilly School #7, NJ

Playing the Drums

You hear it clearly
The sound of the beat
At the same time
It follows the rhythm
And
The beat of your heart
Every day I think of it
To be the best at what I do
I try harder and harder
To be the best drummer

James Russell, Grade 7
Terence C Reilly School #7, NJ

Drugs

If you are drug free
You will be healthy
No issues with your body
Won't get into trouble
You'll stand taller than the rest
Be an advocate to all
No problem with alcohol
Feel better than them all
I will be drug free
Because that's just me

Jeffrey Goris, Grade 7
St Stephen's School, NY

Shadows

Shadows on the wall
They stare at me all night
I say that they're monsters
Mom says that I'm not right
They are watching me
While I lie in bed
And in the morning they seem to disappear
But yet I dread the moment
In which they return
To taunt me while I dream

Gabrielle Rooke, Grade 8
Keyport High School, NJ

The Mystic Dragon

As I sit down on the emerald green grass,
Staring at the midday sky almost dusk,
I feel relaxed, it is so peaceful outside,
Adoring what Mother Nature has given us.
As I watch all of God's wonderful creations pass me by,
I see a sapphire, emerald, mystic fire breathing dragon,
Hovering above the sky creating a wind current gliding with the wind.
I am amazed at this stunning marvelous magnificent creature,
The dragon descends down dead in front of me,
I am in shock at this astonishing animal.
The dragon moves closer to me and as I move back,
It bursts out an explosion of flames from its wide mouth,
Which captures me and the dragon inside.
I am stunned gazing at the marvelous combustion flames.
They are multiple colors I have never seen before in my life,
The se colors
Are so tasteful and flavoring.
The dragon is staring down at me as if it is proud of me for doing something.
The vortex fades away and so does the dragon along with my spirit.

Edmund Whisnant, Grade 7
Holy Innocents School, NJ

'Tis the Season to Be Jolly

What do I love about winter?
I love the winter snow.
That cold, fluffy, white blanket
fun to make snowmen and snow angels in.
I love the beautiful gray winter skies and the cool, crisp air.
I love the delicious taste of hot chocolate and gingerbread by the warm fireplace.
I love New Years.
Time to party all night.
Kids are playing, everyone is dancing, and the ball is dropping.
"Happy New Years!" So much energy bursts out of everyone.
And my favorite thing about winter?
Watching movies every day, counting down until Christmas.
Everyone is anxiously waiting for the amazing Christmas dinner.
Then everyone gathers around the tree
waiting to furiously rip open all the presents.
Now aside from all the parties
I love winter because it brings families closer together for one season.
That's the real reason winter is
the season to be jolly.

Patricia Ramirez, Grade 7
Schuyler School, NJ

My Destination

Sports
Team work and cooperation is used to succeed.
Practice is a short term goal to achieve.
Focus and dedication is the key.
If you're in it to win, hard work is a continuous strategy.
Doing what you enjoy is most important, so love for sports is my motivation.
Watching legends and see that they fulfilled their dreams is my inspiration.
Success is my destination.

Raven Farley, Grade 7
Terence C Reilly School #7, NJ

Wings

Made of feather
Made of glass
Autumn colors
or bright, bright jewels
Flapping softly
Slicing swiftly
Inner personality
reflected
by external things
Ever changing
and yet the same
In some small way
Always describing
it's 'point of origin'
Magic
or biology?
I will never know
only that
my wings are mine

Stephanie Hauer, Grade 8
St. Anthony School, NJ

Christmas

Fluffy white snow,
Blanketing the countryside.
Christmas lights glowing,
Shining like stars.

Freshly cooked turkey,
Wafting through the air.
Scents of assorted foods,
Drifting everywhere.

Christmas carolers singing,
Going door to door.
Children's laughter,
Yelling as they play.

People exchanging gifts,
Thanking one another,
Celebrating the season,
And our Savior's birth.

James Kealty, Grade 7
Regina Coeli School, NY

Our Potential

I truly believe,
that we all have great potential.
As long as we try,
we will all reach the sky.
We all have sparks inside of us,
that are dying to come out of us.
Once these sparks explode,
you will be left with an everlasting glow.

Kristy Rampersaud, Grade 7
Holy Family School, NY

What Is Life?

Is it unsurpassing beauty
Or great everlasting fame
Is it spending time with family
Or is it just a game

Is life having fame and fortune
Or being a storybook hero
Maybe being really popular
Or is it plummeting to absolute zero

Is life hanging out with friends
Or being really smart
Living your childhood dream
Or is it being a master at art

Life is having fun
Hanging out with family and friends
They expect so much from me
It's on them that my life depends

Ethan Tullis, Grade 7
Little Falls School #1, NJ

Tears from Heaven

Angels, angels way up high,
Your tears of rain fill the sky.
I sit out pondering in the rain,
Wondering if they are tears of joy or pain.

As fog fills the air,
And wind blows my hair,
I sit in despair,
And my heart seems to tear.

You inspire me to be,
More than the eye can see.
You sit way above,
But still you surround me with love.

Your halo is gleaming gold,
And the halo seems to glow,
But still I do not know,
Why your tears continue to grow.

Francesca Purgatorio, Grade 7
Holy Innocents School, NJ

Memories

Your heart is like a camera full of pictures
waiting to be shared,
without it you're empty
like a field that's been cleared,
like a lonesome lost day
and a cold winter's night,
your heart is still beating
with no beat in sight.

Pina Ianniello, Grade 9
W Tresper Clarke High School, NY

The Win

Pretty doesn't make the person
why can't you understand,
Things you say won't knock me down
I have the upper hand.
I remain unbroken
your pride and lies are floor bound,
the brick wall that held me back
has tumbled to the ground.
The high road is full
Of people who overcame,
The trash talk and name calls
That have had them maimed.
Put down your weapon, enemy
the war is over, your time is done,
and to all of those who were hiding
your happiness has begun.
Through the pain and fire,
You've been outspoken,
I stand before you today to say
I will not be broken.

Breana Stringer, Grade 7
William Davies Middle School, NJ

Christmas

Christmas is a holiday of joy
Children are pleased with all of their toys
Family always comes to meet
And fireplaces give off lots of heat
Everyone is full of cheer
There is not a single tear
Most houses are covered with lights
Oh, what wonderful sights
Many children come to believe
Santa comes on Christmas Eve
He will drop off all the toys
But only for the good girls and boys
All the relatives gather together
For a big Christmas dinner
It is a happy occasion
For a large celebration
Although we all have fun and sing
We must remember one thing
Jesus Christ was born today
And it's a religious holiday

Justin Casement, Grade 7
St William the Abbot School, NY

Fishing?

If ever you go out for fishing
And find that the fish are all missing;
Don't sit there and cry,
For the harder you try
You can't bring them back by just wishing.

Marion Young, Grade 9
The Holy Name of Jesus Academy, NY

After the Rain

Smacking against the glass,
the rain hit and then came to a stop.
Slowly the sun came out.
Streaking across the sky,
a rainbow came into view.
The rain clouds finally went away.
Zooming, flashing, and dancing
the rainbow is finally complete.
Wow, what a sight!

Kevin Vass, Grade 8
New Providence Middle School, NJ

Poem

Full of evil,
While sitting there mocking me,
The poem guide rests.
Stumped,
My brain is ready to give up.
Full of confusion, covered in frustration,
Motivated only by the thought of finishing,
I come up with a poem.
A poem that is silently brilliant.

Kaitlyn Chan, Grade 8
New Providence Middle School, NJ

Friendship

A memory lasts forever,
Never will it die.
True friends stay together.
They never say goodbye.

People walk in and out of your life.
True friends leave marks on your heart.
They are hard to find, and give you strife,
But lucky to have right from the start.

Maya Fraser, Grade 7
Regina Coeli School, NY

Weather

Rain
Melodic moist
Dripping plopping sloshing
Fast fierce gentle soft
Falling blanketing flowing
White unique
Snow

Emily Hendrickson, Grade 8
New Egypt Middle School, NJ

Sports

You need to practice
You need determination
Work hard and you'll win!

Nicholas Masia, Grade 9
Raritan High School, NJ

Ode to an Oreo: A Black and Orange Delight

Oh, how I crave those Halloween Oreos.
With their rich orange cream,
Boom! They are instantly in my dream.
Unforgettable is the classic black wafer.
Whenever I munch, I always struggle to conserve and savor.
Devouring four, five, or six never impresses me.
The scrumptious black cookies are gold, you see.
When I observe like the young scientist that is me,
All of my friends eating fruits off of a tree.
I wish they only knew how elated they could be.
I know you are not exceedingly healthy,
But even the wealthy,
Inhale you, oh so stealthily.
I think I know your tiny secret which before ingesting you, I have delved.
I believe the classic Oreos sit months while shelved.
While you and your orange comrades,
Are stocked only during fall.
Thank you tremendously,
For your homemade-like freshness and taste,
Appreciated greatly.

Danny Schantz, Grade 8
Hillsborough Middle School, NJ

Beautiful Darkness

Abandoned and broken,
The enchanting warehouse with shattered windows rests within the desolate valley,
As lightning flashes through the dark, ominous sky.
Splattered moss-green with age,
The rotting oak floorboards threaten to crack through.
Reaching for my soul, grasping for life, craving resurgence,
The warehouse screams for attention.
Out of the stillness,
There comes a crash as glass and wood cascade toward me.

Rachel Turrisi, Grade 8
New Providence Middle School, NJ

Lonely Dog

The lonely dog lies out by the shore,
Having no one to love him and no one to see,
What a great partner he really could be
He longs for a friend to stand by him to the grave,
But no one would do that;
Could he be saved?
He would promise to be a great pet, he would always be good
He wondered if he met the right owner; would they take him if they could?
On one chilly night from around a turn came a van,
And out of this vehicle came a man,
He grabbed the dog by his scruff and dragged him to a pound,
The poor dog had expected love, a hug or two?
But all he got was a cage,
Not even a gentle coo
Will you save this shelter dog?
Before it's too late?
Because that's all this lonely dog wants.

Amanda Perkowski, Grade 7
New Egypt Middle School, NJ

Water

The waves crash against the shore,
My heart races.
My mind speeds back to that day,
The day the waves tried to swallow me whole.
My body quivered like a banana in a blender.

"Splash!" "Gurgle."
I tried to keep my head above the water,
But the water grabbed my legs, and laughed as I struggled.
My mom was a bear trying to protect her child.
She ran in after me and then, we were both stuck.

Together we swam through molasses, barely moving at all.
Our guardian angel was there the whole time.
He saved us, just reached out and grabbed us.
The waves cried out with failure.

That man saved our lives.
I often remember that day,
I think of how fortunate we were.
In the back of my mind,
My fear still overpowers me.
That day in the ocean,
I'll never be the same.

Brooke Delaney, Grade 9
Lancaster High School, NY

Shell

I lay on the ground all alone,
Inside the shell that I call home.
I make a sound just to be heard,
I look up and my vision is blurred.

All I see are a million shells,
Lined up in a row; a barren hell.
All I hear are a million groans,
Longing to be heard just like my own.

And all I want is just one friend,
To change my legacy and make amends.
I stand up from my shell and all are shocked,
This change in order starts to get mocked.

They giggle and laugh at my abnormality,
I stand there and cry at their brutality.
As I look back at the people and see what has become,
As I was thrown away, the masses were all one.

They had joined together and celebrated at my expense,
Just so I couldn't come back, they built a huge fence.
They teamed up and joined in one happy society,
As I hide in my shell against conformity.

Craig Vande Stouwe, Grade 9
Mineola High School, NY

Fall

During fall the leaves start to change.
You can hear the kids cheer.
As children fall into the leaves.
The adults rake the leaves to make a pile.
can you see the trees start to change from good to bad?
As if there's magic in the air.
With fall you can love all its amazing things forever in life.

Sami Alacam, Grade 8
Keyport High School, NJ

The Tall Oak

Moving in the wind
The tall oak sways.
As the breeze blows
Reaching high into the sky
It grows slowly.
Effected by the storm, crashing, down to the ground
Slam the tree is gone!

William Zagorski, Grade 8
New Providence Middle School, NJ

Preparing for Winter

Scattering through the garden
The oak brown squirrel quickly gathered nuts
Stashing them away as winter began
He quickly hopped up the tree
Organizing, cleaning and fixing
The busy and exhausted squirrel was finally at ease
But only until winter arrived

Patrick Brady, Grade 8
New Providence Middle School, NJ

Tears

Though your veins might be blue
And you bleed out red
Your heart is nothing more than dead
I hear the dreaded words that you speak
As I fall back asleep a sickly sweet drop falls from my eye
And carves a path down my painted face
And my world is nothing more than a lie that I make myself believe

Skylar Guica, Grade 8
NJ

Until Winter Goes

Shivering in the cold,
The robin begins to fly south as the winter approaches.
Gliding through the sky,
The robin majestically spreads its wings,
Chirping with joy, ruffling its feathers, splashing in a birdbath,
The robin finds itself a new home.
Sadly, we won't see him again until winter goes.

Sophie Dai, Grade 8
New Providence Middle School, NJ

Fall

Fall is the leaves changing colors
When they float off the trees
Football begins and baseball ends
The weather outside becomes cooler
The days feel shorter
Darkness comes early
Roasting chestnuts, pumpkin pies, wood crackles in the fireplace
Halloween candy is so delicious
Fall smells and tastes so good

Shane Mastro, Grade 7
St Mary School, NJ

First Day of School

On my first day of school I was two days late,
I was really nervous but still in a good state.
My first day of school was not that bad,
But dad picked us up late which made me sad.

I was glad to see all my friends and teachers too,
Especially the new kids, Z and Patrick makes two.
At the end of the day I was happy and glad,
Knowing the first day was good and not really bad.

Joshua Tragico, Grade 7
All Saints Catholic Academy, NY

These Violet Eyes

These violet eyes in a swirling tumult
Heartbroken years and fear's result
For they have not had life, its pain, its pleasure,
Compassion or apathy in equal measure.
Trials and tribulations, without fail,
Long broken hope they will prevail.
For only when these trials and tribulations cease
Will these violet eyes, though closed,
See peace.

Bria Metzger, Grade 8
Warwick Valley Middle School, NY

Thanksgiving

Thanksgiving fills the air
Stuffing, turkey, and mashed potatoes are everywhere
Family, friends, and food all around
While everyone eats, there's not a sound
Our stomachs are bloated
It's almost time for bed
As I sleep, dreams of turkey fill my head
When I woke up, Christmas lights are on
Oh, how I love Thanksgiving!

Sabrina Fittipaldi, Grade 8
Keyport High School, NJ

Friendship

My dearest friend,
I love you.
Forgive me for all the wrong things I do.
If I could erase all the pain,
I would.
Then, we will have a brand new start.
We will never be apart.

Nicholas Acosta, Grade 9
New York Institute for Special Education, NY

Haunted House

I stand before a darkened doorway
The walls are bare and cold
The people who used to live here have long moved and grown old
The floor creeks beneath your feet
Silence kills like a knife
You'll never know what happens next
In this haunted house of darkness

Natalie Sottolano, Grade 7
Hammarskjold Middle School, NJ

Still Doll

Hi Miss Alice
with the glass eyes.
What kind of dream
can you see?

My heart torn
and drifted;
stuck in the patched crevices
were memories that were once
lost in wonderland.

Hi Miss Alice
with that deceitful lips,
how many times had the truthful lies
been cast away and numbed the pain?

Already,
I had spun the truth;
feverish tongue
had turned cold,
and the songs of immortal mourning
can't be sung again.

Still,
you do not answer me.

Victoria Liu, Grade 9
Mount Saint Mary Academy, NJ

Alien

To dive into vast blue depths.
Integrate they say,
As I stare down new webbed feet.

Eliza Williamson, Grade 9
Bronx High School of Science, NY

Full Count

With the sweat beating down my neck
And the arid air all around me
I dig into the box
The dirt at my feet
And the helmet on my head
I hear the ump yell
"Full Count"
There I am
The pitcher's motion is long
I get ready for the ball
"WHOOSH!"
"CRACK!" goes the bat
"BOOM!" goes the ball
"YEAH!" roars the crowd
Over the fence
And I smile back

Ryan Mullaly, Grade 7
St. William the Abbot School, NY

Spring

Spring is a time of year
When there is no snow on the ground
And there are no leaves on the trees
This is a time of rebirth and renewal
The grass comes up
And leaves start to grow
Even the flowers come out of the snow
Animals awaken
From their long winters sleep
And young birds begin to peep
Easter comes and Easter goes
No one seems to miss the snow
Snowmen slowly melt away
As young children come out to play
The sun shines bright to end winter's plight
While people put away Santa's sleigh

Ian Tulloch, Grade 9
DeSales High School, NY

The Past

You would tell me to write,
Well I've been writing,
People say life is too much to give up,
Well I guess I'm crazy enough to say,
Just because you're living doesn't mean,
　Y O U ' R E   A L I V E
Life doesn't keep everyone going,
Your heart maybe pumping,
Your blood might be running,
But that's not all you need,
The time has come for me,
The day I die,
Will be the day I'm finally,
　A L I V E

Nicole Parry, Grade 8
Hommocks Middle School, NY

Drug-Free Poetry

You say drugs are an escape, but It's just Satan's way of bringing souls into his cave
Just listen for a while, I see you rolling your eyes
I'm not here to teach, I'm not here to preach
I'm here to guide you out the darkness and back into the light
When you do drugs and you hear that voice inside your head that's your conscience
And God trying to open your eyes to the horrible things that you're causing inside
So if you want to sit there and get high
Know that you're forcing your family to watch you as you slowly die
Your heart stops and your eyes close
The people around you already know
That the drugs have overcome you and you didn't win that fight
Now we watch you drift as your soul drags along the ground at night
See I can't make you stop doing drugs if you refuse but
I have told you some things that I hope made you want to defuse
Most of you do it because you have problems in your life
That's not a good thing, you need to talk it out or
Find a new way to release your emotions
The more you do them
The closer your life gets to ending
Faster than you can blink your eyes, faster than the speed of light
So do this for me and close your eyes and dream about your life without the high

Yasheema Moore, Grade 9
Middletown High School, NY

Life

I think life is too short to wake up
with regrets. I love the people who treat
me right, and forgive the ones who don't and believe
that everything happens for a reason. If I get an opportunity I'll take it.
If I don't maybe I'll get one the next time.

If I change your life be grateful.
I never know when someday or someone will walk into my life
and make me realize why it never worked with anyone but, me.
So when life gives me brilliant offers, I take them and run away.

Brianna Rodriguez, Grade 7
Schuyler School, NJ

Camp Sunshine

There is a place that I love so,
a place where no one should have to go.
A camp for kids that have endured it all,
Some aren't even three feet tall.
Some are sick.
Some get their wings.
But, they all have been through the most horrible things.
Sticks and pokes and hospital stays, scary nights and lonely days.
Families come to ease their pain, share some laughs and never leave the same.
They make special memories and life long friends,
strength for a journey that never ends.
There is no place.
There is no time.
Quite as special as…
Camp Sunshine.

Kat Conaty, Grade 7
St William the Abbot School, NY

My Roots

Never knew where to go
Never knew where to belong.
I tried fitting in
I tried helping out,
But my life has become one depressing song.
Tears streaming down my cheeks,
No one to say, "It's okay."
I hear their disappointed and upset voices
Whispering each and every day.
The day will come
Where I will leave,
To find my perfect life,
The perfect person,
The perfect house,
To prove them wrong,
To prove that I can strive.
Eighteen is the year
Eighteen is the day
Where I will finally set off.
I will find my roots,
My childhood
And the place where I belong.

Daniella Lillian Badishkanian, Grade 8
St Mary's Prep School, NJ

The Sun

It brightens our day
And rests in the night
It warms our summer
And cools our winters
It sits in space
Spitting balls of fire
And watches all of the other planets
Spin around its gaseous body
It seems frozen in its spot
Pretending to be the king of the galaxy
Ordering all of the smaller planets to orbit around it
It stays still in its spot in space
Waiting until the day
Its life comes to an end

Alexandria Vigliotti, Grade 7
St William the Abbot School, NY

Music

Music always knows just how I feel
Cocky, hyper, whatever it be.
Turn it all the way up and get lost in the beat,
BOOM, BOOM, BOOM it's like a second heartbeat.

My own escape in my fantasy world,
Put on my headphones and pretend it's all real.
My addiction, my drug, just music and me.
The lyrics are like pages of a diary I never wrote,
But I always remember the words.

Kara Larochelle, Grade 8
St Clare School, NY

The Girl on the Other Side

You look in the mirror
And see another person.
A whole other being
That you do not know.
But you do.

The girl in the mirror
Yelling to come out,
Lies between a thick line of glass and doubt.

She hides in your heart
Trapped in a body of lies
Dying for breath
If you stay this way, her soul could no longer survive.

The clothes you put on
And the attitude you wear
Is too heavy for your real soul to bear.

When you finally see her,
You will know.
You are not the same person as the mirror will always show.

Renee Rivard, Grade 7
Holy Innocents School, NJ

Autumn

Your varied vivid colorful hues
Bestowed on Mother Nature's blowing trees
Sadden'd, Demeter reluctantly submits
Meandering in her melancholy state

Hades once again claims Persephone
Preparing for barren Winter's cold-hearted wrath
Crunching leaves bury green lawns
Curvaceous trees stretch out their undress'd arms

Time's never-ending and apathetic way
Rebuffs your temporary stay
Continuously moving forward
Snatching your aesthetic sway

Nicholas Stabile, Grade 9
St Francis Preparatory School, NY

Dreams Reunite

Sweet sounds softly drifting from right to left
Stars twinkling and sparkling above the sky
Water swirling in a tornado with its power
Sea Lion talking to the open sea
Clouds overdrawing the blue sky
Sunrise rising up with its yellow bright flashlight
Palm trees swaying with its big arms
Moon appearing in the sky with amazement
Smiles shine with the big teeth in the reflection
Light bulb twitching due to its radiation

Shahiem Willis, Grade 8
IS 250 Robert F Kennedy Community Middle School, NY

Loneliness

Gone too soon,
Never said goodbye.
Oh, dear God,
How much I cry.
Tried to find answers,
Why did you go?
I was your best buddy,
Now I'm so alone.
I reminisce of what once was,
How happy we were then.
You guided and loved me,
You were my best friend.
What am I to do now, Joe,
I look for you every day.
I ask the dear Lord for answers,
So hard do I pray.
If I had just one wish,
You know what it would be.
My brother, Joe would be in my life,
Sitting here, hugging and holding me.
John Giorgio, Grade 8
Our Lady Queen of Apostles School, NY

My Sister

My sister and I,
We're as thick as thieves.
We love each other,
Hug and squeeze.
Although we have our arguments,
Fight day and night,
I love her so much,
With all my might.
Through the days we scrimp,
And the days we are spending,
My love for her
Is never-ending.
When the days are grim,
She puts on a smile,
Just to cheer me up,
So I can smile for a while.
My sister and I,
We're as thick as thieves.
She's not just my sister,
She's a part of me.
Gina Grunwald, Grade 7
William Davies Middle School, NJ

Leaf Rain

Leaf rain is coming down
Oh, what a beautiful sight
Wind whistles by me
A tornado of colors
The autumn season is here
Ben Errichetti, Grade 7
William R Satz Middle School, NJ

The Chase

She is scaling the stairs, two steps at a time.
Three floors to go to reach the roof.
Bang!
The door shuts on the landing below.
She knows he is fast.
Thud!
Thud!
Thud!
He is not far behind.
The air is unbearably hot.
She can hardly catch her breath.
He is silent but determined.
She can hear his pace quicken.
She bursts through the roof door,
Temporarily blinded
By the bright sun.
Using every muscle in her body.
She sprints straight ahead towards the edge
Of the roof
And then
I turn the page.
Hannah Nagy, Grade 7
Oak Hill Academy, NJ

Do We Notice?

Time goes by, but do we notice
The green leaves on the tree,
Then changing colors in the fall,
The bare branches in the winter,
The new buds in the spring?

Time goes by, but do we notice
The temperatures slowly getting warmer,
Then feeling the heat of summer,
The chill of the first frost,
The beauty of the freshly fallen snow?

Time goes by, but do we notice
The scent of the spring flowers,
The sand between your toes in summer,
The cool breeze in the fall,
The winter snowflakes on our faces?

We should stop to notice
The beauty of the world around you,
And the smile on your face!
Jackie Seidl, Grade 7
St William the Abbot School, NY

Mediocre

Not so in between
Stableness slipping out of my reach
With misfortune coming close
Carolyn Lau, Grade 9
The Bronx High School of Science, NY

Dissipation

Their lies dissipate
When formed inside
And they can't deny themselves
That they believe the truth
They try and succeed
In convincing others
That the lies they speak
Are not really lies
But the truth
The whole truth
Their motives?
At best, a myriad of them
For various reasons, of course
Some ignorant and harmless
Others deceitful and malevolent
But they try
And perhaps just for a moment
They may believe it
But again, in the end
Their lies dissipate when formed inside
Jared DeCesare, Grade 8
Little Falls School #1, NJ

Ode to Vacation

If it is in the snow or in the sun,
Vacations are always fun.
On a boat or in a desert,
Vacations are always a treasure.
A time to relax,
Or a time to seek.
It could be a month,
Or only a week.
Visit a museum,
Or read a book.
Or maybe go on a bus drive,
And just take a look.
It is always fun,
To lay in the sun.
Or you can just chill,
And hang out by the grill.
Your mind is the treasure chest,
That holds the memories and great times.
And you are blessed,
To have these memories for all time.
Diana Graziano, Grade 7
Cedar Drive Middle School, NJ

Bad Boy

You're so bad,
But you're also so good,
But I want to know why
You hide inside your hoodie!
And instead of hiding in your hood,
You should try to be good!
Anthony Winter, Grade 7
Ocean Academy, NJ

Why I Am Drug Free

I don't know why people take drugs
They know it's going to kill them
Because of drugs people lose their family
People lose their friends
People lose themselves
And most importantly
They are turning away from God.
Nicole Castiglione, Grade 7
St Stephen's School, NY

Fall

Standing underneath a colorful tree,
All the autumn leaves falling on me,
What a wonderful sight to see,
I hear the leaves under my feet crunch,
See them piled up in a bunch,
Autumn leaves falling down,
Autumn leaves on the ground.
Shahzail Bhatti, Grade 7
All Saints Catholic Academy, NY

Who Are We?

Who we are,
It's not what we know,
And it's not what we do.

Who we are,
It's how we react to what we know,
And is defined by what we do.
Juliet Ramdass, Grade 9
St Francis Preparatory School, NY

Love

Wrapped inside your arms
That's where I'll always belong
You're forever mine.
How can't you call this love when
I look up at you
And see myself in your eyes
Till the day we die?
Brianna Rinaldi, Grade 9
Raritan High School, NJ

Fall

Leaves fall on my feet
As the wind blows past my face
Finally it's fall!
Nicolette Morales, Grade 9
Raritan High School, NJ

Writing

A pen to a page
Ink appears, showing our thoughts
The page is filled up
Daniel Evancho, Grade 9
Raritan High School, NJ

Picture Frame

You rest on the shelf holding a moment from the past.
Maybe of someone's graduation or of a newborn baby.
People admire your companion.
They ask the owners questions such as,
"How was the trip to France?"
Or comment, "What an adorable child!"
But that innocent child does not live inside you.
She stares back at what you border.
She wonders, "How did I get stuck in there?
Will I ever move?" But you won't let her.

Now as an adult she still stares. She gets lost inside her own eyes.
She wants to step inside of you and wave to the other people,
To stand where she once stood. While she studies the picture,
She realizes that the girl staring back at her is different.
She sees the girl that laughed at everything.
The girl that didn't have a care in the world.
She begs to be that girl again, but those dreams are shattered glass.
Overwhelmed with frustration, she separates the two of you like ripping out a soul.
She leaves you empty, starving from loneliness.
Now you represent no memories and you stand without a purpose.
Stephanie Ingraldi, Grade 7
Fox Lane Middle School, NY

A Day of Hunting

About 5:30 a.m., I am still half asleep,
Inside my truck you would spot my father, my brother and me.
Across the road are the woods in which we will be hunting.
After a half hour, we are settled in our stand, yet I am still sleepy.
Around the tree, I see the sun starting to shine like a bright light bulb.
Beside me is my father.
Underneath us is the dirt on which we walked.
During the day we wait to spot any deer passing us by.
Past that tree is where I spot a doe sprinting like a fox.
Without hitting my target, I was a turtle with my slow-moving hand.
By now, it is time to head home; we can always come hunting another day.
Throughout the day I was a sleepy bear, but I can't wait to come back next week.
Jessica Dorf, Grade 8
Clinton Public School, NJ

Little Ducky

I don't remember you at all.
My mom said I loved you completely,
but I don't remember.
She said I loved you more than anything.
More than biscuits or vanilla.
I'd take you anywhere I'd go.
I don't remember you or anything.
But one day I forgot to take you with me,
and I blamed it on you.
Now my mom said she threw you away because I would never use you.
I wanted to see what you looked like even though I've outgrown you.
And it was my entire fault that you were thrown away.
Sorry.
Thomas Girgis, Grade 7
Schuyler School, NJ

The Mysteries of Childhood

The mind of a child is a marvelous machine
A living piece of art
Where colorful, creative, and wild thoughts
Flow honestly from the heart

They frown and they cry, and they jump up again
They've already forgotten the past
It is something that adults are jealous of
And grow out of way too fast

Innocence glows in their bright, joyful eyes
Fire runs through their veins
A flood of wonder, peace, and awe
Absorbs their blessed little brains

The world is a playground to a child
Where they leap over every obstacle
They know they can be whatever they want
And nothing is impossible

Children always want to grow up
But adulthood is strange and wild
A child always wants to be an adult
And an adults wants to be a child

Sarah Lynch, Grade 7
Holy Innocents School, NJ

Martin

As funny as he is
As cute as he may be
Never underestimate him
His determination goes farther than the eye can see

His personality shines throughout him
He never runs out of heart
He lives every day to its fullest
His mind is truly a piece of art

Imagine not knowing
What tomorrow will bring
His future is uncertain
His life is such an unpredictable thing

It is not on the outside
But it's the bravery within
Martin has many hopes and dreams
His faith shows through his determined grin

Leukemia is a serious thing
Take it upon yourself to find out more
Martin's my inspiration
Courage is what he stands for

Cathryn Cole, Grade 7
Little Falls School #1, NJ

Eternal Fire

I have a powerful fire flaming inside my heart
It will stay with me until my very soul departs
Never giving up for me is almost like an art

Everyone fights their own internal war
Who is the victor, no one knows for sure
Even when kicked in the ground, I will fight even more
A problem residing within is something I refuse to ignore.

We won't give in until we find the light
No matter how long it takes, 10 years to even one night
God's Word as a sword of truth shining bright

In this war, no one will actually die
Truth somewhere between tears and lies
Look up and see a golden sky
Pour unto me all your happiness, all mine.

Set our existence to something much higher
Something worth all a worldly desire
God come to me, my need is dire
Away with all the fakes, all the liars
God sustains me, His grace I want to aspire
I will never give up, with this holy eternal fire.

Christopher Ortiz, Grade 9
Bishop Ford Central Catholic High School, NY

The Music

Music…What is it…Can you hear it?
I can feel it. It's all around us. Can't you see.
All you have to do is listen.

Listen to the wind as it sings. Everything
else will feel like a dream. Open the soul and
let it in. For once don't think about anything.

In my heart there's a piece that's missing.
A dream ready to be reality. But when
the trees start singing it feels like a blessing.

Music…It's not in books…You can't learn it.
You have to feel it…It gives you the freedom…
To be all you can be. All you have to do is believe.

Listen closely to the beats of rain. The
clouds cry out their tears of joy. Love is always all around,
the music always makes me whole.

Soon there will be a new beginning, a time to
rise up from the ground. And the raindrops dancing I feel
all around. And music's all around. Can't you see.
All you have to do is believe.

Imani R. Williams, Grade 7
Our Lady of Trust School, NY

Step to the Beat

In the corner of an immense, dull, blue room,
A stereo is blasting an upbeat tune.
My feet are stepping to the beat of the song.
Every other person is mimicking each other.
Our dancing synchronizes to the song.

After a long day in a diminutive, blue chair at school,
It is a relief to clear your mind and dance without rules.
Dancing is the best way to relax and eliminate stress.
Some dance is calming while others are exciting,
But they are all of significant importance to me.

Jazz allows you to express your inner feelings calmly.
Hip Hop is a way to convey your rage.
Ballet and lyrical are as sweet as sugar.
They are exceptionally relaxing and allow you to be yourself.

All of your worries fly away,
And the music flows through your veins.
You feel each step you take.
But, all dances call for your feet to step to the beat.

Sarah Neydon, Grade 8
Hillsborough Middle School, NJ

Young Women of Grace

This is dedicated to the women of grace
Trained to be leaders and knowing their place
Modestly dressed with elegance and taste
Moving in the right direction, not a minute to waste
Leaders guided you at just the right pace
Allah gave us this earth with so much
People to advise, so listen well
A world to travel, be vigilant and observe
Allah's creation is a classroom
Learn, learn, and learn
Be prayerful every second
Don't miss an opportunity to show gratitude
With these tools and more
You're headed for greatness

Sadiqah Mekki, Grade 7
Al Ghazaly School, NJ

Life

Life
So precious
Yet so fragile
Fleeing so quickly
But yet staying forever
Life continues on even in the darkest of hours
Or the brightest of days
Grabbing pulling and fighting
People claw at its very substance and existence
Even if this world ends another starts a new
This is life at its finest moments

Anthony Pham, Grade 7
William Davies Middle School, NJ

My Angel and My Hero

I am blessed!
I am lucky!
Why you ask?
Here's my story,
My angel married my hero.
They love me,
Guide and support me every day.
I always knew that.
I always felt that.
But then, I really learned the truth
When the enemy struck,
Was it a thief?
Was it a murderer?
Was it a terrorist?
It was all of the above;
It was Cancer!
But my angel and hero never gave up helping me,
Loving me, and healing me.
I am blessed!
I am lucky!
Because my angel and my hero are my parents!

Angela Villota, Grade 8
New York Institute for Special Education, NY

A Terror to All

It all started in my basement, is was a cruel life down there
Constant movements in that room were common
Although they were thought to be the air conditioner
Every night when I was hearing noises in my slumber
I told myself it was just a pesky mouse
One night I even heard a sharp shriek
I had trouble convincing myself it wasn't me
Little by little I begin to hear pots and pans in the kitchen
And my mother vacuuming
I don't know how this is possible
Because my basement is practically sound proof,
I feel relieved.
I'm awake.

Julian Worden, Grade 7
Holy Innocents School, NJ

Enlightenment

Sad, lonely, confused
Unsatisfied with his life
As he stares out the window
Wondering waiting for his life to change
Why is he so blue?
He has no clue
As he waits
He cannot wait for enlightenment to find him
He must find it
His eyes have seen
His ears have heard
The wonderful sights and sounds of enlightenment.

Faith Lawson, Grade 7
Holy Innocents School, NJ

It Made Me Want to Cry

On the morning of September 11, 2001, there was a tragedy
It made me want to cry
Both towers collapsed in two hours
It made me want to cry
Another plane crashed into the Pentagon
It made me want to cry
The last plane crashed into a field in Pennsylvania
It made me want to cry
There were 2,996 deaths,
There were 2,977 victims
It made me want to cry
200 fell or jumped to their death only 1,600 bodies were identified
It made me want to cry
It was sad and so many times
It made me want to cry
10,000 bodies were unidentified
It made me want to cry
These people went through a lot and that
Made me want to cry

Destiny Rivera, Grade 7
Public School 232 The Walter Ward School, NY

Some Secrets Aren't Worth Sharing

It started with a day I would never forget
Oh how I wish I could regret
Telling that secret that wasn't meant to be shared
Knowing that it hurt someone who cared

It wasn't supposed to get out
But how was I supposed to know what that was about
It was never meant for me to tell
And when it got out, my heart fell

I saw all the tears
They brought back all my fears
I closed my eyes and counted to ten
Wishing I could go to what was back then

So next time you tell me a secret
Don't bother worrying if I'll keep it
'Cause someone will be hurting
While the other one is blurting

Alexa Locke, Grade 8
Our Lady Queen of Apostles School, NY

Autumn Is…

Autumn is the feeling of the crisp air on your skin.
The leaves turning into bright vivid colors.
Feeling the leaves crunch beneath your feet.
Seeing the warm colors of red, orange, and yellow.
Hearing little children say "Trick or Treat" on Halloween.
Eating a wonderful meal with your family on Thanksgiving.
Making piles of leaves then jumping into them.
That is what autumn is.

Isabella Valentini, Grade 7
St Mary School, NJ

Frogs

All kinds, disgusting and ugly
With BIG, bulging eyes.
All fat, bumpy, and green skin.
Tree frogs
With those funny looking orange toes
Living high in the trees.
They come out at night to seek their prey.
Itty-bitty dwarf frogs,
Floating on the water
With their very small bodies.
Nothing spectacular but they don't sink,
And their skin is bright green.
All frogs able to jump at you.
When they get close, you want to scream!
They get all over you with their slimy bodies.
They get your attention by croaking.
Brrribit!
Brrribit!
Brrribit!

Andrea Curbelo, Grade 7
Terence C Reilly School #7, NJ

New York City

The rush of morning taxis,
The many diverse people,
The spectacle of commuters pouring out of Penn Station,
All while the City opens her eyes.

The splendid tourism,
The smell of pretzels, hot dogs, and roasting nuts,
The angry shouting and furious honking,
All while the City eats her lunch.

The business people in their offices,
The people with big shopping bags pushing and shoving,
The tourists rushing to dinner reservations at five-star restaurants,
All while the City enjoys her evening.

The commuters and tourists get onto their trains,
The shops' lights are closing while their doors are locking,
The sun is setting, but the city will never sleep,
Because she is New York City.

Brianna Califano, Grade 7
St William the Abbot School, NY

Man's True Best Friends

Stepping down hard on pavement,
the rough leather cushions the impact,
as it should be…
Sticking to anything glutinous littered on the ground,
life is rough for these old Reeboks.
Walking, running, and even jumping,
they take a lot of use.
Shoes really are man's best friends.

Brent Hofmann, Grade 8
New Providence Middle School, NJ

Dream

I close my eyes
and I drift away.
A movie begins, as I press play.
It's a whole new world,
a story to be told.
It's the story of me
and the story of you.
You hold my hand,
you keep me close.
We kiss through highs and lows
We laugh together,
we smile for hours.
But then the corners blur,
the edges fade away.
I open my eyes,
and acknowledge that dreams are fake,
but it is something that your heart makes.
Emily Wilbur, Grade 8
Odyssey Academy, NY

Home Run

A home run
is like a firework.
The loud boom
grabs everybody's attention.
Watching the burning
ball fly up into the air.
Reaching its highest point.
Then rapidly descending.
Hitting the ground over the fence
or landing on the sandy beach.
The crowd roars
as I round the bases
or as the grand finale ends.
I cross home plate
my teammates hit my head.
The people watching
leave with big smiles.
Cory Aufiero, Grade 7
Cedar Drive Middle School, NJ

Drug Free

I will always want to be drug free.
Others might not.
It's a really great thing I have.
I can do things
Many others can't.
I'm not stuck in a hospital
Like many others are.
I'm so happy I can do sports.
I feel for those who can't.
I will always be drug free
And I will stay this way
Forever.
John-Paul Bobak, Grade 7
St Stephens School, NY

Love

Love is like a dream
one that could never be touched
one you think you have with someone but really don't
Love is one goal we all have
it's never complete
it's never enough
love always turns to hate
everyone has the longing to be love
the longing to have it
the longing to be loved
the never ending passion of it once you found love
Love is great once you have found it
but turns to evil later
it's sometimes unfaithful
love is sometimes your best friend
love could be your worst enemy at times
but everyone falls for it at least once
Michael Perez, Grade 9
Brooklyn Preparatory High School - Harry Van Arsdale Campus, NY

Time of Day

What would you do if you woke up one day,
in another person's body?

Would you take the chances you never could by yourself?

Would you take the chance with the boy who never gave you the time of day?
Or would you slap the girl who thought she was better than you?

If you were shy, would you be more outgoing?
If you were loud, would you be more muffled?

If you were pretty, would you try to be perfect?
If you were ugly, would you try to be noticeable?

You know what I would do…
I'd breathe and remember my old life while making my new one.
Amanda Springer, Grade 8
Schuyler School, NJ

Life

Life is given by God.
Life is not wrapped in a huge box with ribbons or bows, but it is a gift from God.
The Lord leads us to light, love, and laughter in life.
The journey of life is a staircase with its ups and downs.
Life is not always easy.
Life is like a waterfall, sometimes you get pushed off the edge.
You start to hear water rushing, gushing, and pushing you to your limit.
When this happens, you have to be strong like a bear.
You have to roar and growl at your enemy and can't be scared.
Life is like a chapter in a book, if you have any questions turn the page and take a look.
Life doesn't always have to be hard.
Just count your blessings, like lines in a card.
Life is like a rainbow, it has a beginning and an end.
Kiana Lopez, Grade 8
St Clare School, NY

The Boot

You better be glad, don't be mad.
They don't give a single hoot,
And if you do they'll give you the boot.
If you try to be cool and hip,
They'll just give you the big pink slip.
Those bosses are really tough,
Boy, can they be rough.
So do your work and you'll do good.
Or else you'll be living under a car hood.
So beware the dreaded boot,
If you want to escape it you have to scoot.
You better be glad, and don't be mad.
Beware the dreaded boot.

Andre Pugliese, Grade 7
New Egypt Middle School, NJ

Being Drug Free

Losing control,
Losing friends,
Dying,
Those are all effects of drugs,
Is being drug free important?
Keeping friends,
Graduating school,
Having a normal life,
Drugs can kill you,
Something that nobody deserves,
Take a stand,
And say
NO TO DRUGS!

Sabrina Mistriner, Grade 8
St Stephen's School, NY

Swimming Race

Hearing the whistle blow.
Tells me that it's almost time to go.
I adjust my goggles and swim cap.
My friend gives me a friendly back slap.
I hear my event and step up on the block.
When I hear, "Go!" I'm off.
And they start the clock.
I give all my might.
The race is tight.
When my race is done.
I want to see if I won.
I check my times and am pleased.
I pack my bag and get ready to leave!

Annie Bubel, Grade 7
Regina Coeli School, NY

Hooky

He's perfectly fine,
until it is time for school.
That's when the tears start.

Kendra Myer, Grade 7
Cairo Durham Middle School, NY

The Balloon

Grasped in a child's hand,
The scarlet red balloon gleams in the sunlight as she skips along the pavement.
Bobbing through the summer air,
The sphere is lost from her grip and the silver ribbon slips from the toddler's hand.
Drifting in the breeze, dodging tree branches, soaring through the clouds,
The balloon floats out of sight.
Oh, what a loss!

Kelsey Turner, Grade 8
New Providence Middle School, NJ

The Beach

Making everyone go to the beach,
The hot day was welcome as summer began,
Swimming for hours,
We felt refreshed.
Burning from the sun, tanning on the colorful towels, talking to family,
I love the sand, sun and the seagulls,
Oh, what a fun day at the beach!

Jodi Bull, Grade 8
New Providence Middle School, NJ

Whoosh!

Twirling the chilly and crispy cool autumn air rustles though the trees,
causing the leaves to dance and sway on the branches.
Blowing the chilly autumn air,
sweeps by the people out and about.
Rushing past, flying by, and sweeping through,
the breeze refreshes the towns as they catch their breathes.
The autumn air is a wonder of the world!

Emily Eng, Grade 8
New Providence Middle School, NJ

Mr. Confusion

He is always there in your head waiting for that moment.
When that moment comes, he will strike without doubt confusing you.
You will wonder what just happened as your mind's a blur.
You might ask where am I, you might wonder what you were doing.
Meanwhile, Mr. Confusion is laughing, laughing at your misery.
Then he pumps his fist, realizing his great success.
And back again Mr. Confusion waits, waiting to strike again.

Christopher Wallentine, Grade 7
Cedar Drive Middle School, NJ

Summer

Hot air
Bright sunshine
Friends
No school
Freedom
Stay out late
Sleep for hours
Short shorts
Tank tops
Summer love

Aleksandra Dewa, Grade 9
DeSales High School, NY

Our Love

It was so strong
Nothing compared
Seemed it would never die
But it did
Must be some mistake
But it isn't
It seems that all I have left
Is a crumpled love letter
And memories that will never die
Unlike our love

Autumn Miller, Grade 7
Pulaski Jr/Sr High School, NY

Rose Petal Dance

Water rushes pass my ears
Wind rushes upon my back with wild vigor
And rose petals leap to be nominal saviors
I sing with it all
Without moving my lips, a melody of sweetness and pensiveness lost
In decay upon my audience's ears.
Splashing in the water are the naïve little tadpoles
Fluttering in the wind are the mindless butterflies
And rose stems stand tall, embellished with their intricate thorns
I dance with it all, motion and movement
To my rhythm, a silent and long one
To test my body's endurance.
At one with the sea, a body that captivates with its merciless waves
Flying with the wind to amorphous clouds tempting me
And sitting on a chair
I read to the song of dance and life
Of the rose petals' stories of their travels and strife
And listen to the accompaniment
My silent harmony.

Lucy Zhang, Grade 9
Montgomery Township High School, NJ

Blind

I was blind to the truth
The truth of my obsession
My brain shut out the real world
Refused to accept it, and all its cruelties
That's when the craving began
I devoured the oh so sweet printed words
My appetite was insatiable
The moon was my lone witness
As my feast continued, even in the darkest of nights
and in the darkness I formulated my plans
My plans to attain more of what held an iron grip on my mind
There were no lengths to which I wouldn't go
Bookstores went bankrupt
Libraries had to shut down
There was no helping my fevered brain
Then one day, it all changed
My brain found the cure it had long awaited
The veil lifted for the slightest of seconds
Before the true blindness set in

Tajreen Ahmed, Grade 8
Mount Hebron Middle School, NJ

Autumn

The breathtaking views of an open field.
The leaves flowing off the trees filled with vibrant and vivid colors.
Unquestionable beauty of the work of God.
The cool, breezy air when you walk outside in the morning.
All the dazzling beauty outside your own front door.
The feeling of walking on the crisp leaves.
The gorgeous beauty of it all.
One word describes it…autumn.

Nicole Cleary, Grade 7
St Mary School, NJ

Snowboard

When I look at the snow
As the wind begins to blow,
I think to myself
It is going to be great.
As I ride the long lift
I can see a far drift
Of the snow I will carve
With my snowboard and my pass lift card.

I wonder how I will do today.
Will I go off a ramp
Or simply drink hot cocoa
Next to my boots that are damp.
I hope that today I will find
To be very fast and agile
Off the hill of the Virginia Mines.
Me and my snowboard race to the bottom of victory.

Noah Scarpa, Grade 7
St William the Abbot School, NY

Friendship

Friendship is like a flower.
It will just continue to grow.
No matter how many ups and downs there are.
Friendship will always show.
Friendship is like a river.
No matter how many lumps and bumps there are.
Friendship will always flow.
Friendship is like a guitar.
Even though the music may sometimes be slow.
The strings will never say no.
The key word in friendship is friend.
Friends are like brothers and sisters God didn't give us.
Friends will always be there when we fall or succeed.
Friends always bring the best out of us.
Friendship is faith in each other.
Friendship is the strength and encouragement we need every day.
No matter what happens we will always have friendship.

Caitlyn Ahern, Grade 7
St. William the Abbot School, NY

The Door

Hello busy business man
Walking across the slaved office
That's busy like Times Square
You're trapped
In your cramped office
Typing away your life
Tracing the scent of coffee
You take a sip and savor the moment
Wanting to go to back home
Your hearing staplers, printers and phones ringing
I love seeing the work be done

Stephan Arias, Grade 7
Fox Lane Middle School, NY

Autumn

Hearing the rustling leaves,
The crickets,
The football announcers on TV.

Seeing all the vivid colors,
The scary Halloween decorations,
The days getting shorter.

Tasting the warm apple cider,
The pumpkin pie,
The turkey with stuffing.

Feeling the oncoming cold,
The heat of the oven,
The softness of the pile of leaves.

Fall is wonderful!
David Cook, Grade 7
St Mary School, NJ

The Opposite Morning

I woke up,

put on my piano
and practiced my clothes.

I ran down my breakfast
and ate my stairs.

Then I cleaned my hair
and combed my teeth.

I grabbed the door
and ran out my lunch.

All because,
I have to get to the bus.
Finn Witt, Grade 7
St Mary's Prep School, NJ

The Ocean

Full of mysteries
No one can solve
Full of life
No one can imagine
Filled with life
And other species
Creatures that bring joy to everyone
Creatures that try to kill us
In the nicest way possible
Never know what you will find
But always will be searching
The ocean filled with mysteries
Everyone tries to solve…
Mahpara Ahmed, Grade 9
Razi School, NY

I Care

Why do I care about you?
Why is it every time I see you
I get nervous?
Why is it that when we talk
I forget about the world?
Is it because I like you?
Is it because I care about you?
Is it because I can't stop staring at you?
But you really don't realize it
I'm that one book
on the book shelf
that you never read.
People ask me questions
and I say we're just friends
but it's hard to see that I'm not that person who you care a lot about
or that person you like to be just more than friends.
It's like I'm the dandelion, and you're the sun.
I need you, but you don't even realize me in a big world
I just imagine how it would be for us
but I think you can't even realize that.
Julian Izquierdo, Grade 7
Schuyler School, NJ

Small Wonder

Colorful leaves fall to the ground,
Cracking, crumbling in many a sound.
The leaves speak as a beautiful wonder
How anyone could miss them is such careless a blunder.

Magnificent leaves are colorful and turning bright.
Sadly, the wind will whisk them away in flight.
Each little leaf of a tree is not easily seen, but all the leaves as a one.
For they will come and go, and I will continue to marvel at them until my time is done.
Benjamin Theodore, Grade 8
Regina Coeli School, NY

Fire in the Night

Fire, what a wondrous and amazing phenomena
Its radiant glow shines brightly throughout the pitch black darkness
Its heat wraps around my freezing body
Keeping me warm through the cold, harsh winter night
Fire withstands every harsh wind that comes at it
Its blazing flame sends a warning sign to all nearby animals
Many logs keep it burning as bright as the morning sun
Its magnificence can awe everything in its sight
Fire can be helpful yet so destructive
Its strange crackling sound startles animals and man
A forest fire burning out of control
The cold winter gusts spread its destruction everywhere
Screams of terror in the night as people cower in fear from the flames
Trees burning, branches falling, leaving destruction in its path
No one would ever suspect such a wondrous sight could hold such danger
Fire, so amazing yet devastating
Admire its beauty but be wary of its wrath
Jeffery Wu, Grade 7
Little Falls School #1, NJ

Cycle Starts Again

Flowers rise again,
from the seeping rain,
that came once again.
The birds chirp a lullaby
which signals of the wind.
The light gains;
the dark fades.
And geese meet,
new geese.
Like an artist,
the brush of new thoughts,
on brown vacant branches,
accumulates with colors that were forgotten,
by a lover's heart.
Rain that brings nothing plain,
from which spring gains,
to its train of nothing lame.

Edward Michta, Grade 8
Hillsborough Middle School, NJ

A Crush

You make me smile,
But only for a minute,
You don't seem to see me,
It's like I'm a ghost.
I wish I could tell you how I feel or felt,
Because deep inside, you make me melt.
You look at her and I don't get what you see,
I have a crush on you obviously.
But to think of your response to my feelings
Would break my heart.
My heart beats like a stampede
When I see you,
Thump, thump, thump, thump
Like nothing else before.
But you will always be,
And only be,
A crush.

Kamaria Veerapen, Grade 8
St Clare School, NY

Tears in My Eyes

The tears in my eyes can't stop,
when I think about my beloved grandpa.
I remember those moments when you gave me a hug
And said to me the funniest thing there is.
Yes, I do regret for not caring,
and trust me I was young didn't know anything.
I always will remember
those times when you were there for me,
and I wish that you knew how much you meant to me.
Your smile will always be in my heart,
and then maybe my tears will stop.

Anett Cherkassky, Grade 7
Big Apple Academy, NY

Ocean Wish

A dream of mine is to live under the sea,
It seems like such a special place to be.
I prefer to be a clown fish,
Because I wouldn't have to worry about being served on a dish.
I could be a mermaid and have a fin,
Or an alligator with super scaly skin.
I could build my house out of sea shells,
And through the windows, get the beach smell.
I would have a pet lobster and a whale,
To me, this would be a fairy tale.
I could breath underwater,
And have a best friend that is an otter.
I could explore the ocean,
And would not need to use suntan lotion.
I could try many fish foods,
With different attitudes.
I could swim with lightning speed,
But I would have to watch out for all the seaweed.
But as much as I dream and as much as I wish,
I will just have to settle for a pet fish.

Samantha Brayton, Grade 7
St Mary's Prep School, NJ

Stop Bullying from Hurting Any Longer

We are in the darkness,
We are the shadows walking miserable,
Behind closed doors,
Nobody can feel the pain,
We feel, we are invisible to teachers,
Friends and families, they can't stop the pain
we feel, if we can just stop the pain
from hurting any longer,
So we can no longer exist from life,
The world we are walking from fear,
Not being like,
Disappointment, hatred, being laughed at,
And most of us being bullied.

Ashley Gibson, Grade 7
The Young Scholars Academy of the Bronx, NY

Autumn

The scent of apples hits my nose
As I step out of the car,
Even when I'm blocks away,
I can smell them from afar.

The delicious pie is being baked by my sweet grandmother,
The leaves I raked are now scattered around,
Thanks to my little brother.

I like the season of autumn
For I'll always remember,
My birthday that will always be the nineteenth of October.

Kaira Tragico, Grade 8
All Saints Catholic Academy, NY

Back Stabber

She could be my friend and bat her pretty, little eyes,
But behind me, all her niceness turns out to be lies.

She could care about me for a second,
And make a face another.

She might laugh with me,
And behind my back, laugh at me.

She only was my friend to know what my secrets were about,
And once she knew them, she spilled them out.

Little does she know,
That she cannot change me so.

She cannot shade my shining sun,
For I am my own person

How could I have not known before?
That she was the one who did not let me soar.

She kept me from reaching the sky,
I should have known that she kept me from flying high.

I don't need her to survive,
I have other friends in my life.

I have improved so much,
When I was out of her clutch.
The clutch of my so called friend, who was a back stabber.

Sarah Hussain, Grade 7
Al Ghazaly School, NJ

Music

Music is something that's always here.
It comes from a stereo "BOOM" it's there.

Music is something that's always clear.
It talks to you like it's one of your peers.

Music is not always your favorite thing,
But sometimes you just gotta sing.

Music is relaxing it soothes the mind,
Like going to the doctor and hearing you're fine.

Music is always the best solution,
Better than medicine there's no prescription.

Music is always fun to listen to,
But it's made for dancing and that's fun to do.

Now this is the end but don't start cryin',
Music's the best; I hope you liked my rhyming.

Terrell Julien, Grade 8
St Clare School, NY

A Star Inside

With every leap I take,
Every soar my feet do,
Every flap
Of my majestic wings,
I am alive.

I keep on prancing,
As I twirl,
Like leaves in the air,
But I never stop.

What am I,
You may ask.
I am not someone,
I am a thing.
I keep people going
After their disasters.
I live inside
Their hearts.

I am
Hope.

Sharon Chao, Grade 7
Nathaniel Hawthorne Middle School 74, NY

Learning

even as the day goes by,
we learn something that makes us fly,
the knowledge makes us soar to a new height,
and then life doesn't seem like a fright,

learning makes it beautiful for us to live,
it's kind of hard to believe,
that we see,
all that we can learn with glee,

learning makes life a breeze,
and this is not a tease,
because what we are to be,
is based on the learning we have now and forever!

Angie Puranda, Grade 8
Cunningham School, NY

How Poetry Comes to Me

Poetry comes to me like a clock. Tick Tock.
The Tick is an idea, the Tock is me writing.
The clock goes around from number to number.
Just like my brain going from one idea to another.
Tick Tock goes the clock.
I'm waiting and waiting
Where's an idea?
Then the hands on the clock move just like mine
I'm writing and writing away.
Tick Tock, Tick Tock goes the clock.

Amanda Iacono, Grade 7
Cedar Drive Middle School, NJ

The End

The World Ended —
A poem was written,
Everything stopped,
While the rhymes were flowing,
But an eternal glow —
Stopped all motion,
A silence filled the air,
While nobody was there —
To read it.

George Kennedy, Grade 8
Valhalla Middle School, NY

Home

When you enter
You acquire a big warm hug
Chills go through your body
As you escape from the brutal weather
The wonderful smell of dinner
Waiting for you on the stove
The peacefulness and quiet
As if no one is home

Joseph Fraone, Grade 7
William Davies Middle School, NJ

Changes

The leaves are falling.
The birds are calling.
The snow is coming.
The nature is changing.
Holidays are approaching.
The decorations are outstanding.
We are not far from a day that's amazing.
It seems like everything's changing!

Erin Jordan, Grade 7
Regina Coeli School, NY

Omar

Omar
Trustful, careful, kind
Brother of Uriel
Lover of ice cream, soda, and pasta
Exited, outgoing, energized
Who needs friends, family, and being active
Who gives advice, jokes, and laughter
Sarmiento

Omar Sarmiento, Grade 7
Hammarskjold Middle School, NJ

New Love

Heart to heart love's near,
Butterflies tickle my heart
My nerves twist in knots.

Annie Seward, Grade 9
Raritan High School, NJ

On That Wooden Bridge

A warm spring afternoon lures families outside
to bathe in the blissful kisses of the sun
and the playful jests of the breezes
that tease ripples in the pond water.
Two young girls race towards a bridge.
They tiptoe cautiously across the wooden planks,
careful not to fall through the cracks.
Peering over the railings, they spot them — the geese.
Reaching into the bag they'd brought with them,
they produce fistfuls of crumbly bread.
They fling the bread into the water,
laughing as the geese scramble to gobble it up in a cacophony of honks.
Before they leave, the girls wave their pudgy fingers
at their newfound friends.
Then they hurry back to their moms.
Years later, a girl of fourteen lies in her bed,
watching the silvery moonlight reach their fingers to her
and reminiscing…about the age of innocence and simplicity;
She vows that someday, she'll return to that park,
to stand on that wooden bridge
once again.

Julie Huang, Grade 9
Cherokee High School, NJ

Miracles of Life

A true miracle isn't something they put in the news
It's the little things that are miracles
Only the fascinating things like a bird taking its first flight or a bee's first sting
A miracle is life
The sun rising each day or the moon desert and return each day brings smiles to my face
It's a blessing we're here
The aroma of fresh coffee in the morning and the age of the cobblestone streets in Spain
Is a miracle
The life outside our house that breathes beneath the tall trees
Is a miracle
Life is a miracle

Emma Dillon, Grade 8
Hommocks Middle School, NY

Death Embrace

Death
What do we take it as!
It comes in several forms
A blade in the hand of a psycho path
or even a half naked lady
It could even be embedded
In the hands of an innocent child

They say death is respite for the soul
Is it really?
or could it be?
The beginning of a new life
Death is like a blanket
covering us in its lonely shadow

Alex Ambrose, Grade 9
Brooklyn Preparatory High School - Harry Van Arsdale Campus, NY

Fall

Red, orange and yellow leaves,
That are falling off the trees.
Little children playing in them,
Oh, what fun!

A nice crisp breeze,
Winter's almost here,
Everyone's getting bundled up,
Winter's on its way.

Arianna Paul, Grade 8
All Saints Catholic Academy, NY

Fall

Fall is a season of joy and wonder.
The leaves change color to yellow or red.
Like confetti they plummet to the ground.
Now I lay safely in my bed.

Sometimes in the fall it is cold and rainy.
Often the storm leaves right away.
Now it is warm and sunny.
And I can go outside and play.

Geovanni Williams, Grade 8
All Saints Catholic Academy, NY

I'm Only Me

I'm only who I want to be.
I used to want to be you.
I used to want to be her.
I just didn't want to be me.

I'm only who I want to be.
I'm exactly who I want to be.
I'm me, just me.
You can't compare me to anyone.

Sasha Shamblen, Grade 9
Waterloo High School, NY

In Time

In time we grow
In time we see
And in time we change

In time we watch as loved ones move on
And we heal because we must move on
For the world must move with our lives

Jacob Roman, Grade 7
Howard T Herber Middle School, NY

I Am the Raven

On black wings I glide
My options are limitless
I am a black bird

Raven Amato, Grade 9
Raritan High School, NJ

How to Make This World a Better Place

What will it take to once and for all make this world a better place?
To end all the strife.
To end all the suffering.
Our world has known peace,
But it never could last forever.
Light and Darkness have reigned supreme over our world from the very dawn of time.
To make the world a better place,
We must eliminate the darkness filling it.
That is the only way to truly change the world for the better.
How do we save our beloved world from the taint of evil?
There is only one way.
We must join together.
With one body,
With one soul,
With one mind.
Together we can do it.
Together we can prevail.
However, we cannot do it alone.
For together and united we stand,
Alone and bereft, we fall.

Jose Del Orden, Grade 9
New York Institute for Special Education, NY

A Magical Christmas

Anticipating Christmas day,
I sleep restlessly under my warm blankets as I wait for the morning's light.
Lounging in my living room,
I wait anxiously for the rest of my family.
Yelling to wake up my parents, sipping hot tea by our Christmas tree,
and unwrapping presents,
this is all part of Christmas day.
Old Saint Nick never disappoints me.

Elise Minto, Grade 8
New Providence Middle School, NJ

Imperfect Me

I'm great at dancing like Beyonce,
but sometimes trip over my own feet

I can play the drums like Justin Bieber,
although not quite on beat

I can write a scary story like R.L. Stine,
it turns out in the end I scare myself out of my mind

I can read aloud a poem like Mrs. Z sending my voice low and up high,
Although after a while my cheeks get rosy and I get quite shy

I can sneak a midnight cookie like old Saint Nick without a peep,
Until I step on the wrong floor board and out comes a loud CREEK!

I'm outstanding at portraying many things
but now when I look down inside I see
the one thing I'm best at is being imperfect me!

Krishonna Jordan, Grade 8
Keyport High School, NJ

The Just in the Closet

I wasn't tired yet,
Because it stared at me from the closet.
Two bright yellow eyes,
The size of peach pies.
Just staring, not moving, just staring.
My eyes swelled with fear,
Or were they just tears.
I just couldn't tell,
Because the eyes in my closet look like they were from hell.
Just staring, not moving, just staring.
Then they twitched staring straight at me,
I was scared should I flee?
A shriek came from the closet,
Like nails on a chalkboard.
Just staring, not moving, just staring.
Finally, it moved,
Its back was grooved.
It was my cat.

Tiffany Bautista, Grade 7
New Egypt Middle School, NJ

Dancing to Music

I
Don't want to make a scene,
But my dancing wants to break out.
Free
The creative sound of the beat,
Makes me want to move my feet.
Boom, boom, boom,
I move across the room,
La, la, la, la the music goes,
I feel happy and glad
and less sad.
I am moving as fast as a cheetah.
The beat is slowing down and so is my heart.
The temptation is gone,
but not for long.
I am motivated because this dance cheered me up.
It made me dance with such love,
now my dancing skills are high above.

Ashley Choute, Grade 8
St Clare School, NY

Unknown

Staring out my window as time passes me by
I feel like I've known you a lifetime, but I've basically just met you
You may be out of my world and sight, but never out of my mind.
If I had a star for every time I've thought of you
I'd only have one…because you never left
I shouldn't be sad you're gone; I should be happy you were here
For that short time that felt like forever.
When you went away, I felt like every day it was raining
But I live life and try to smile as much as possible and move on and
Live every day and life to the fullest.

Breana Rogers, Grade 7
Holy Innocents School, NJ

Siblings

We love each other, but fight like we hate each other
We'll laugh together, we'll cry together
We'll fall with each other, then rise like no other
We won't give each other the time of day to say I love you
But the little things we do will show just how much I love you
You'll teach me how to ride a bike
I'll teach you how to jump rope
We'll play hide and go seek
And before you can even imagine
You'll teach me how to drive a car
And before you can even see it
We'll take a ride through our favorite childhood place
Then we can look back and smile
About how crazy and wild we were
The mistakes we made and the ways we learned from them
But as long as we know our feelings are true
I'll tell you I love you
Just to hear you say it, too

Krystal Coppola, Grade 9
Bishop Ford Central Catholic High School, NY

Dear Mom

You are as pretty as a diamond ring
The sound of your voice makes angels want to sing
I would never ask for a mom better than you
You make me smile, even when I feel blue
You make the evil want to be good
You would take the sick under your hood
Whenever I need your help, you're always there
To find a mom as amazing as you would be incredibly rare
The sun shines its brightest when you're around
When you're gone, there's never any stars to be found
I miss you when you're not near
Losing you is my biggest fear
Anyway, now let's think about thoughts that are good
You do things that normal moms wish they could
You help me out every day
You'll always look young, even if your hair turns gray
Every day, you help me shift my life to the right gear
And remember, if you ever need anything, I'll always be here

Casandra Fitzpatrick, Grade 7
East Islip Middle School, NY

Summer Fun

S oothing, warm sun beating on my skin
U ltimate experience, no school, no stress, no worries
M ost likely to be filled with joy and fun
M agazines filled with pictures of beaches, and swimsuits.
E ternally, warm, and sunny.
R unning, and splashing around in a pool.

F UN, FUN, FUN all summer is about is having FUN!
U mbrellas are never needed; there is barely ever rain in summer
N ever any nonsense or drama.

Briani Griffin, Grade 7
William Davies Middle School, NJ

381

In a snap, they're out of my mind
Why would you be any different?
You're the same as the rest
But yet you're still in my heart
You hurt me multiple times
Not physically but mentally
That hurts even worse
Can my heart miss a beat?
When I'm with you or even touch you
When do I look left to right to see if you're around?
He doesn't deserve your tears
That's what they tell me
But I can't seem to stop hurting
Why do you care what people think?
Does it really matter?
I don't think it does
Do you like hurting me?
No. Then why do you do so
Then why do I still have these feelings for you
3 words 8 letters 1 meaning
I love you!

Brenda Ferrer, Grade 8
Keyport High School, NJ

School

My guide for life
Molding my life to think certain ways
Even though it interferes with my personal situations
I take full responsibility for my work
Take full blame for any I don't complete
Handling everything and anything in a mature way
Taking notes of every little life detail
To inhale absolute perfection
Expecting only the utmost best I can do
Eventually creating a young-independent-learner
Help me achieve
My American Dream to go to college
Setting me up to be a successful adult

Giovanni Vargas, Grade 7
Terence C Reilly School #7, NJ

Final Call

These people be drunk of riches,
High of power.
That's why people took out the towers.
They'll crush you like an egg
So they can go up on the food chain.
It's insane.
They don't know what it means to feel pain.
You'll know their name
Because they'll be the end of all.
This is the world's fall.
Prepare because
This…this is my final call

Mitchell Kundert, Grade 9
Bishop Ford Central Catholic High School, NY

Napping at the Beach

Resting in the soft sand,
I admire how it covers the beach
Like a blanket covers a bed.

The sea is joyful today
The sounds of the gentle waves
Crashing on the shore are my rocking chair,
Easing me to sleep.

The squawk of seagulls
Searching for food
Is a mother's lullaby.

My eyelids grow heavy
While white, foamy water
Rolls up the beach
Barely reaching the tips of my sandy toes.

The wind whistles
As it blows an airy mist of salty sea water onto my face
Tickling me like long feathers.

I finally drift off
Hoping I will be able to witness
All of the sights and sounds of the beach,
From my dreams.

Claire Bainlardi, Grade 7
Fox Lane Middle School, NY

Unknown Future

What will the future hold?
What will it be?
What history will be told?
What will become of me?

The future is unknown,
that's the frightening part.
Each day can be a milestone,
or tear me apart.

The future is unclear,
constantly changing.
Someday it will appear,
like a bird chirping.

Life will be different,
I'm sure of that.
Possibly like the present?
Or in an altered format?

What will the future hold?
What will it be?
What history will be told?
What will become of me?

Edona Ahmetaj, Grade 9
Bishop Ford Central Catholic High School, NY

Paradise

The waves surge
As the sands merge.
The shells tumble
As the oceans rumble.

The sun is blazing.
The scenery is amazing.
The winds are whistling.
The ocean is glistening.

Jeremy Waters, Grade 8
Regina Coeli School, NY

Snow

Snow is falling everywhere,
It falls down from the clouds.
Snow lands gently on the ground
And covers the landscape all around.
The sound of the crystals falling is peaceful.
How white everything is,
How innocent.
The scenery is amazing,
The snow is beautiful.

Colin Flynn, Grade 8
Regina Coeli School, NY

Fishing

The freezing wind stinging my eyes
The frigid water splashing against my skin
But I ignore it all and get ready
I tie the hooks
But the bait
And rig the lines
Soon we make it to the spot
We begin to fish
And I never want to stop.

Bart Alseika, Grade 8
Holy Innocents School, NJ

Autumn

Colorful, vibrant, art from God,
Dazzling incredible masterpiece,
Outrageous astonishing work of art,
Sensation upbeat of colors,
Crisp, breezy, lively feeling,
Satisfying, brilliant time of year,
Time for family, friends, and feelings.

Andrew Colucci, Grade 7
St Mary School, NJ

When?

When is it my turn
To love the way others do
Hate to be lonely

Samantha Salvato, Grade 9
Raritan High School, NJ

The Loss of My Shelter

In the coffin he lay except he wasn't nearby
Only his body was. his spirit was long gone.
Gone farther than anyone could imagine
The angel that lived within him,
Had taken its flight back up to heaven all alone
there was nothing I could do now.
I couldn't go back in time to say sorry,
To take back my vile words I hadn't meant to cry.
But my words must have killed him.
Because now he's gone he was my comfort and now I had none.
If only I could take back the simple "I hate you" I forced from my teeth.
If only I could replace those words with "I love you."
I wouldn't have killed him. I murdered him.
Maybe not physically but emotionally
I saw the torment in the masterpiece he called his eyes.
He only saw perfect in me. I will never forgive myself.
I will never find a shelter from this everlasting storm.
Now as everyone is dressed in black,
I explore humanity for relief from the remorse that floods my soul.
All because I said one simple thing I didn't mean.

Liv Winnicki, Grade 8
Holy Innocents School, NJ

Mind Puzzles

I was a genius, because I knew that inside a TV remote,
lived a village of exponents, and marching numbers which
advanced inside the maze of a magnetic field, time and time again.

The numbers, originally bundled with variables
were laid out before us like nails in an old man's workshop.
We were trapped between rain and thunder —
between decapitated TV remotes and bitten supreme pizza slices.
The rain outside fell hard but the equations fell harder.

Our eyes were scuba divers, exploring the depth of the Earth
and our minds too, were underwater.
It was too foggy to remember but too dark to learn,
that these numbers, meant death.

They were violent, stabbing our brains with their sharp edges,
pulling our limbs apart, one by one, then re-gluing them back together
as if I were a jigsaw puzzle, as if they were human
and I, a physics problem, an equation.

Laura Wind, Grade 8
New Egypt Middle School, NJ

Thanksgiving

Steaming as it came out of the oven
The turkey looked succulent, it sat on its platter
Tantalizing the group,
the mash potatoes, and gravy were also placed on the table.
Sitting silently, waiting for the carving blade, becoming the center of attention
The turkey sat proudly on the table.
Thanksgiving feast is always a treat.

David Sann, Grade 8
New Providence Middle School, NJ

I Want to Be Drug-Free
I want to be…
A designer,
An artist,
A drug-free person.
Peer pressure will try to get me,
Drugs will too,
I will ignore them,
I will over rule them,
I will be drug-free.
Drugs can get to anyone,
They tell them it's great.
I will ignore them.
If I ignore them,
If I stay away,
If I stay drug-free,
I will stay drug-free,
I am drug-free.
Julie Klein, Grade 7
St Stephen's School, NY

Nine-Eleven
Nine-Eleven
What a day?
Not so happy, but rather sad
many we lost
many we couldn't save
most of all,
A big part of our city
came down crashing.
From some furious flames.
The normal, regular day
turned upside down
in just a flash!
But what can we say?
May we never experience
such a disaster.

God Bless America!
Linda Banbahji, Grade 8
Ahi Ezer Yeshiva School, NY

Autumn
Candy is
Free for
Candy Halloween Apples
Decorate with Jack-o'-lanterns
Fall is football season so let's go Jets
Kites fly free in the windy weather today
Leaves everywhere of orange red and green
Costumes of witches, ghosts, and ghouls
Pilgrims and scarecrows in November
Turkey and gravy on Thanksgiving
You eat mashed potatoes too
Autumn is very cool
Jeffrey Seggio, Grade 7
St Mary School, NJ

America's Hearts Sank
America's Hearts Sank
It was like an apocalypse had hit the earth
Dust and debris covered the floor
Helpless humans jumping out from windows and ending their lives on the concrete
Buildings were falling and so was America's spirit
America's Hearts Sank

America's Hearts Sank
Courageous men running into the deformed towers hoping to notice survivors
America stood in awe watching these tragic events
Even God had Cried during this Epic Day
Nobody was safe, evacuations spread throughout the country
Everyone knew this would be a start of a new age of war
America's Hearts Sank

America's Hearts Sank
Passengers of flight 93 spoke within each other hoping not to be heard by Al Qaeda members
They were aware of the consequences, but they had to save America
They sneaked into the passengers seat and overtook the Al Qaeda members
Their heroic act will live on forever, but their souls died passionately for America
America's Hearts Sank
Justin Pacheco, Grade 7
Public School 232 The Walter Ward School, NY

Sue
Sue
Fun, caring, outgoing, and artistic
Sister of John
Lover of music, tigers, and relaxing
Who feels excited to make new friends, most joyful when hanging out with friends
and most comfortable being with my family
Who needs more family time, less homework, and more knowledge
Who gives smiles to my friends, respect to others, and love to my family.
Who fears spiders, getting lost and bad grades
Who would like to get straight A's, have a bright future and be a winner of the poetry contest
Resident of East Brunswick
Lee
Sue Lee, Grade 7
Hammarskjold Middle School, NJ

Swimming
Swimming is my favorite thing to do.
In my pool or in the sea.
I will never disagree the water is the place for me.

I feel the water in my face so cool like ice.
I swim from day to night never alone. I don't bite.
I play these games you'd thing are lame when you play you won't be ashamed.

The air so warm you'd think you're toast.
Sun so light you would hate for night.
Putting music so loud you can hear it in different states.
Swimming is amazing as you can read.
I would love to see you try to beat me.
Julissa Rosales, Grade 7
Schuyler School, NJ

Rain

Drops fall from the sky
And travel to Earth.
All those who walk
Experience a refreshing chill.

Water patters windows
Cleansing the glass
Making repetitive music
For all to listen.

Drops fall from the sky
And travel to Earth
Filling the land
With a wet sensation.

Jenna Sucato, Grade 8
Regina Coeli School, NY

She Dances...

She dances for the love
She dances when she cries
She dances because she knows it's right
She dances…

She dances like no one is watching
She dances when she falls
She dances in her own world
She dances…

She dances when she feels pain
She dances not caring what people think
When she hits the stage she dances
She will always dance…

Ashley Czarnecki, Grade 8
Our Lady Queen of Apostles School, NY

Living Life

Living life to its…
To its fullest
coolest
funniest
happiest
sunniest
loveliest
powerfullest
longest
smartest
prettiest
Live life while you have it
because not many
get to live it long enough.

Raquel Roque, Grade 8
Churchill Jr High School, NJ

Tree Tops

Swaying in the wind,
Pine trees are an exquisite sight.
Coloring as winter goes on,
The trees represent nature and all of its magnificence.
Glistening with the snow, shielding the ground below, boasting vibrant greens,
they always excite my senses.
This is what true beauty looks like!

Melissa LaPara, Grade 8
New Providence Middle School, NJ

A Luxurious Car

Gleaming in the sunlight,
The car stood there like a gift from heaven.
Accelerating the engine,
I gave in to the irresistible impulse to drive the car.
Shining with tinted windows, covered with fire vinyl stickers, and topped with a spoiler,
It was difficult to believe this vehicle was really there.
The time to experience driving a luxurious car is finally here.

Haris Zia, Grade 8
New Providence Middle School, NJ

Regaining Strength

Twirling towards the floor,
The flower loses its pedals one by one as the weather gets colder.
Covered in snow,
The bare rose waits for winter to pass.
Taking in the rain, blossoming its pedals, and standing taller than ever,
The young flower molds into a gorgeous sight in spring.
How beautiful it is when it regains its strength!

Lorik Berisha, Grade 8
New Providence Middle School, NJ

Music

Creating perfect harmonies,
I know that the audience can't tell the difference, but, to me, it means everything.
Telling the stories of my world
I tell it through crafted melodies.
Perfecting a piece, giving myself a voice, swelling of joy,
It's truly amazing.
What great powers music holds.

Corinna Cardone, Grade 8
New Providence Middle School, NJ

Home for Christmas

Gazing with wonder,
The young girl places the ornament on the tree as she thinks of her father.
Gleaming with happiness,
He unexpectedly comes home from the long war.
Bursting with excitement, running with anticipation, and embracing him with love,
The girl hugs her father.
Now the holiday is truly complete with her father home for Christmas!

Jacquelyn Keating, Grade 8
New Providence Middle School, NJ

Two Perfect Stars

The amount of perfection he has stored inside leaves me in awe
Just like your addicting affection
Your light golden eyes leave me hypnotized
Just like how his sweet angelic smile has me captivated
Each star shines brighter than I'd ever imagine
Always full of joy and mystery
Each never fails to leave me chasing after their streets
He leaves me in tears
You wipe them away with your addicting power
You leave my heart in pieces
He glues them back with his astounding persona
He is too stubborn, so frustrating, and too afraid
You are too intolerable, too complicated, and so locked up
And my heart is breaking
But they can't see the smile I'm faking.

Maheb Zamee, Grade 8
Don Bosco Technology Academy, NJ

Gone But Not Forgotten*

You are gone but never forgotten
You are loved and never hated.
You will always be in my heart.
Gone but not forgotten.

I remember when we laughed.
I remember when we talked.
I remember when you taught me how to walk.
Gone but not forgotten.

You love me with all your heart.
You made me smile when I was sad.
You will always smile down at me.
Gone but not forgotten.

Taylor Cherry, Grade 7
Global Concepts Charter School, NY
*Dedicated to my mother, Kimberly Taylor

I Think of You Every Night

I wake up, tears streaming down my face,
Thinking of when you said you'd love me,
But that was a made up lie. All of it.
I get changed and go to school holding back my cries,
But you walk past me and I give a broken smile,
Yeah well, under that smile is a broken heart.
You broke it…
Tears stream down my face,
'Cause I know you're someone I can't replace.
I wake up, tears rolling down my cheek,
But you will always be the one I seek.
I wake up, tears flowing down my face,
And I know, for a fact, that I was dreaming of you, again.
Only you. The one I thought I loved.
Only you, the one I think of every night.

Kristen Onorati, Grade 8
St Mary's Prep School, NJ

The Pristine Girl

He ran,
He wasn't a fan.

He played me as if
My feelings were like
A board game.

The way the Statue of Liberty holds her torch,
Is the way he held his pride,
Knowing that he scorched
A hole in the heart of a pristine girl.

He ran,
The man with the pride,
Hides the pain deep down inside.

Alexis Zaino, Grade 9
W Tresper Clarke High School, NY

The Final Piece

So tropical it's another one of his fantasy dreams.
The buses pass, and the milk man comes up the steep street saying;
"Milk, we have milk!" like he's back in the mid 1900s.
The bell of the church rings.
He's put right at home,
He knew there was no experience like it,
Just like there's no place like home.

Walking downtown, the soft breeze hits his head.
He smells the burning pavement as he walks across the street
Grazing the pavement, his feet start to burn
And blister.
He can hear the street calling out to him saying "hello"
Like he was the final puzzle piece,
Waiting to be put back where it belonged.

David Cardona, Grade 7
Fox Lane Middle School, NY

Why I Want to Be Drug Free

Drugs will make me weak and ill
I would become depressed
Never would I be focused on any one thing
My mind would become useless and irrational
Nothing would ever matter to me
School work wouldn't be a priority
I would be sick for days
I would be poisoning myself
A slow agonizing death could take my life
I would end up on the streets
My life would lose its meaning
I would have nothing to live for
I would never take drugs
This could be my fate,
If I ever did drugs

Adam Frosolone, Grade 7
St Stephen's School, NY

Fall

I think the season of fall is stunning,
It is a great season for running.
When the leaves start to fall,
I try to run and catch them all.
I feel excited and dandy,
When I get a lot of candy.
I love this season a ton,
Because it is always a lot of fun.

Thomas Fioretti, Grade 7
St Mary School, NJ

Music

My inspiration and motivation.
It helps me keep trying until I succeed.
It's my stress reliever.
The way I forget about a long, difficult day.
My escape from the world.
It holds all the solutions to life situations.
I just close my eyes and listen.

Bryan Rodriguez, Grade 7
Terence C Reilly School #7, NJ

A Starry Night

The stars at night are huge and bright
I watch them twinkle in the dark sky
While all the dark gray clouds pass by
there's the big bright grayish moon
What it feels like inside
To be all alone with nowhere to go
And no one to talk to

Diamond Weedon, Grade 7
Holy Innocents School, NJ

Nothing

My brain is empty
Nothing in my mind,
Want to do something,
But there's nothing to do
Need something in my mind
Need something to do
So there can be something in my mind

Jordy Chamba, Grade 7
Terence C Reilly School #7, NJ

Angels and Demons

Angel
Pure, perfect
Illuminating, soaring, healing
Entirely good, extremely corrupt
Deceiving, conniving, despising
Evil, dreadful
Demon

Ryan Figueroa-Parsons, Grade 7
William Davies Middle School, NJ

Autumn Splendor

Summer was fun, but now it is done.
Beaches, vacations and hurricanes are now all gone.
Days of summer are now days of color,
and there's no more pool because now it is cool.
You put on your sweatshirts and get ready for school.
No more grilling, because now it's chilly,
so replace the barbecue with some stew and chili!

Leaves dance from the trees of amber and create a patchwork of color.
Crunch! Like a gymnast, you sprint and vault into leaves.
Sundays spent on hay rides and pumpkin picking,
looking for the perfect patch with your family.
There are busy schedules for football and soccer
and "It's the Great Pumpkin, Charlie Brown" is on television.

The clocks fall behind, but we gain time, while
the animals scurry like mice gathering food for winter.
Halloween is on the way,
toilet paper lacing the bare trees and ding-dong ghosting.
Ruminating costume choices and Trick-or-Treating at the best houses!
Autumn is splendid.

Allison Herdje, Grade 8
Hillsborough Middle School, NJ

The Battle Is Mine — Not Yours!

Snored like a pig.
Tossed and turned.
I glanced up into the sky.
Where the clouds look as if they were a battlefield between Good vs Evil.
The clouds began to scream and run towards their opponent.
Strapped up in the armor's protective goodness.
Ready to battle — ready to win.
I slash and grunt with my dignity in my hand.
As I sprint pass the foe that has spit on me with her words of doubt.
At the finish line my team lifts me up and shouts my name.
While I hold the key to my success — that glows in my hand.

Kiarrah Johnson, Grade 8
Galloway Township Middle School, NJ

Stages of Life

Taking his first steps,
The baby only makes noise,
With which he cannot express himself.
Learning his first words,
He can now start to speak,
But he is very limited.
Growing up, acquiring vocabulary, and learning grammar,
He can finally speak fluently and use words powerfully to express himself;
He is now a musician who uses the art of expressing emotions.
It's fascinating how a mere noisemaking baby,
A beginner,
Can turn into a fully grown, expressing adult,
A musician
In just a few years!

Rohan Mallya, Grade 8
New Providence Middle School, NJ

Summer Spectacular

I have been standing here all winter,
You are running,
But somehow avoiding me.
Travel my tracks,
Are you frightened of my drops,
As large as the super-sized sun?
My tracks are fun,
My turns are like an out of control race car.
My flips wink at you,
You can't sprint forever!
Why don't you give me an attempt?
There's one more shiny seat,
Run,
Faster,
Win that spot,
Treasure it like gold,
Please come ride me?
Before the winter comes,
Again.

Matthew Horne, Grade 7
Fox Lane Middle School, NY

My Dystopian Sunset

I searched what's left
Of the astral streams
Voyaging to landfall
On a crater not fit to float
A destination on hazy grounds
Can I continue to meet
The demands of my waking vibe?

When clutched crows
Are screaming
The hollowed floor
Is seeping evermore
The curse that
Plagues this dirge
My epiphany conjures, weeps
To conjure a scheme
To cast
This feeling nevermore

James Sanchez, Grade 8
Don Bosco Technology Academy, NJ

Fall

Fall is my favorite season,
But don't worry, there is a reason.
With so many different colors around,
And all the leaves upon the ground.

It's like God is painting the leaves,
Then, just letting them fly off of the trees.
Fall is a season to adore,
It's awesome, it's great, can I say anymore?

Maria Daly, Grade 7
St Mary School, NJ

Klick-Klack

The pounding noise of your landing,
Sounds like underweight quarters,
Slowly tapping each sturdy panel of the rooftop in a rhythmic way,
I continue to listen silently, like a ghost on Halloween night
Awaiting but not wanting your rooftop tap dancing to seize.
The house is a mall on Black Friday; both busy and crazy,
People's laughter and chatter filling every soundless moment that my ears heard.
I admire your predictability,
But I dream of your surprise attacks and startling ways.

People are scrambling like miniature mice,
In effort to move everything inside and protect it from you,
Yet you remain consistent and I remain motionless,
Ignoring all and every action; trivial or important as difficult as it may be.

My affinity for you is stronger than a mother's for her baby.
I can't seem to understand how or why people wish for your absence.
Thunder booms and bite-sized flashes of lightning begin to appear
Then you romantically dim the lights and the rest of the power
And as if you became a war general and demanded it,
People light candles and sit silently listening to your hypnotizing klick-klack.

Kylie Dickinson, Grade 8
Hillsborough Middle School, NJ

The Baseball Field

I walk up to the majestic baseball complex.
An unusual feeling bursts throughout my body.

I can't help but admire the beautiful setting of the baseball field.
The soft, radiant sun struggles to shine over the scoreboard in center field.

The crowd breaks out into a boisterous roar as I enter the field.
Thousands of fans come to this enormous arena just to see me and my team…

The Philadelphia Phillies.
Only, this is just a dream.
Maybe, just maybe, someday, this will happen.

Vincent Naurath, Grade 9
Holy Cross High School, NJ

My First

It felt good off the bat
It was my first
As I jogged around the bases
Emotions built up in me
My body felt heavy
I heard my mom screaming
It felt like forever but I finally rounded third
I jumped and stomped on home with my teammates there to greet me
They all pounded on my head
One of my greatest memories
Finally the game was over
I received my game ball
I held it tight into my hand

Kevin Passaro, Grade 9
Holy Cross High School, NJ

Greasers: Golden Goodbyes and Unfair Lives

As I catch my breath, I started to realize, these guys weren't the preppy, high-class jerks I've heard about
With the grease in the hair, a look in the eye that showed without a doubt they've had more goodbyes than care
Goodbyes to some of the people they love, who had shown them to be golden
To the people who never got to warn them about the Universe's complications that come racing down the road unexpectedly
Worn-down and bruised up, kept walking keeping their chins up
God bless them, I thought, with no parents to turn to, thank God they have each other
I felt mad at the Universe, for giving them these lives
Why throw these amazing people these awful experiences, and those horrific goodbyes?
Unfair, I thought, sad unfair lives that will leave scars on them forevermore
Hopefully making the golden colors inside them start to shine
After they get through with the hurt, it can heal them all
Showing people that no matter how hard your lives are, you always have a choice
You don't have to be an angry, mean Soc, they were just raised that way
And unfortunately, their choice in life was wanting to make people pay
Their golden time is going to be delayed
But in time they will understand, maybe change their old ways
And shine like a sun, that's been fueled by the good energy of the spirits of people
Who taught some of the most hurt Greasers
To always stay golden, even in the most horrible of days

Gemma Farquhar, Grade 8
Oaklyn Public School, NJ

Family

What a powerful and loving word.
A group of people who love each other, more than anything else on this planet.
People who appreciate the things you do and care about you even if you did something right or wrong.
Family
They will help you along the way from birth to adulthood.
People who care about you, trying to put a smile on your face when times are tough.
People who brought you to this magnificent world.
Family
People who will do anything for one and other.
They will protect you no matter what.
People who tell you stories from past generations about their family.
Family
I love the word family.
They help me through a lot of things, whether it's having a brother going to war or helping me with my academic career.
They still always find a way to make one and other smile
Family
What a powerful and loving word.
A group of people who love each other, more than anything else on this planet.
People who appreciate the things you do and care about you even if you did something right or wrong.

Kamil Pietras, Grade 8
Kawameeh Middle School, NJ

Scary Movie

The screen is portraying scary images
Fear, and a rush of thrill takes over my body
I squeeze my eyes shut, but still hear the murderous screams of people acting like they are dying
The sounds and images play back in my mind like a broken record
I can't fall into a deep sleep, constantly waking up because of the nightmares the film is giving me
I fear the dark, because maybe a killer might jump out and murder me
But then, Mom reminds me that they are just actors
And everything goes back to normal

Jacqueline Petroski, Grade 7
Hammarskjold Middle School, NJ

Planes

The engines of the plane
Are savage beasts
Roaring too loud
To listen to your favorite songs
You can't surf the web at 35,000 feet
You can't read
Due to the tough turbulence tumbling the plane
You can't watch TV
Otherwise
You'll bring down the whole plane
Like a meteor
All you can do
Is read the back
Of the cheap, dry peanuts
Given to you
By flight attendants who reek of perfume
Over
And over
And over again
For five hours

Thomas Bell, Grade 7
Fox Lane Middle School, NY

Winter

Snow has covered the trees.
No more sign of the honey bees.
The birds went down south.
No more singing from their mouth.
Rolling hills of pure white snow.
And in the night you can even see them glow.
Winter is here.
Every year.
Replacing warmth with cold.
Stories by the fire are told.
The snow continues to fall.
This is winter after all.

Ilya Enochs, Grade 7
Regina Coeli School, NY

Things That Go Bump in the Night

The groaning steps creak,
The spooky ghosts shriek,
Time to go home,
Vampires moan,
What's under your bed?
It's not little Johnny with a mask on his head.
When you begin to snore,
The creatures of night roar,
The werewolves howl,
The monsters growl,
They all go bump in the night,
BOO!

Joel Reiter, Grade 7
Hammarskjold Middle School, NJ

The Cycle of Evolution

In the beginning,
Men roamed the earth.
Lacking fire or light, the crippled race,
Wielded only sticks and clubs.

The prehistoric creatures evolved;
Becoming stronger and mightier.
They invented the wheel,
Shed light on the future.

A civilization emerged, a mole from its hole.
They became genius and developed weapons.
From monkey to caveman,
From caveman to man.

Before with the light bulb,
And now with the jet.
They came from the bottom,
To the top of the food chain they rose.

They emerged from an animal,
These intelligent beings, the praying mantis of the mammals.
Neanderthals or humans,
Now technology leads the way.

Eric Graber, Grade 8
Hillsborough Middle School, NJ

Racism

He is walking to the store
He holds his head high
No one sees him anger
No one sees him cry

They laugh at him and call him names
They yell and point and jeer
He doesn't pay attention
He has nothing he needs to fear

His skin is dark
Their skin is light
He doesn't want to get involved
Or maybe start a fight

He smiles at their insults
He giggles at their glares
He grins at their shouting
As if no one really cares

And so he walks with dignity
He will keep his pride
He knows it's not about what people look like
It's about what is inside

Noelle McManus, Grade 7
St William the Abbot School, NY

Beach

Waves racing onto shore
Grains of sand rubbing my toes
Sand the color of shaved gold
The breeze kissing my face
Seashells swiftly slipping into the sea
The water as blue as the sky
On a sunny day
The beach
Where I go to escape
My flaws and mistakes
And where I feel perfect for once

Vanessa Bermeo, Grade 7
Fox Lane Middle School, NY

Flight of a Pegasus

Free as the sky
Strong as the land
Look to discover it

Mysterious as the ocean
Power as endless as space
No one can assist you in this quest

Will you find
The Pegasus
Inside you?

Justin Pereira, Grade 9
W Tresper Clarke High School, NY

New York City

I am New York City
I hold a big city upon me,
I hear all the yelling and screaming,
From young to old,
From short to tall,
I hear everything.
I soak up the cries of the skies.
you can barely see me on,
A map.
I am that tiny red dot.
I am New York City.

Ryan Miller, Grade 7
SS Peter & Paul School, NY

A Day at the Spa

Towels, bathrobes, slippers and so
Set up some polish, ready, set, go
Put on slippers, fluffy is nice
Light up a candle to add up some spice

Call up a friend, to make it more fun
Spas are better when there's more than one
Paint on a mask, dry, then peel
Spas can be fun, pretend or for real.

Rebecca Theodore, Grade 7
Regina Coeli School, NY

September Eleventh

The eleventh of September is a day we should always remember
Through all the months, such as November and December
We must remember the courageous people and deeds that were done that day
We must honor them, in each and every way
Those planes that day which out of the sky emerged
Made people worry, run frantically, and through the city surge
That sorrowful day felt so weary and long
But all it did was make our country strong
People can try to knock our country down
But we will stand up for ourselves and turn things around
We now have memorials and services, books too
About that terrible day that was oh so blue
We must look toward the future, not live in the past
Even if people are still gloomy and aghast
September eleventh was indeed a terrifying day and sight
People will forever hold in their hearts the pain, sorrow, and fright

Caitlin Doht, Grade 7
St William the Abbot School, NY

Earth Is a Wonderful Place

Earth is a wonderful place,
It's full of different ethnic races,
However, together we must join,
To keep Earth cleaner than a coin,
Clean without a piece of flying debris,
Tidy so it's a better place to be,
Hygiene so we may all survive
We'll all work together like the bees in a beehive,
It's the least we can do 'cause remember that Earth can continue life without us,
And no one will ever know who made all the technology,
Or who even studied biology,
Who could have made all the pollution and litter,
Without any hesitations.
So in that instance, we must all keep a distance from polluting,
And the people will not only be saluting the United States,
But honoring us for our achievements that we are capable of.

Ashni Kemraj, Grade 8
Queens Gateway to Health Sciences Secondary School, NY

My Room

Most of the time people explain themselves by comparing themselves to something.
But, what really explains me is my room.
Why you ask? Well, it's really simple.
It's because you will come in and say, "It's a mess!"
But, if you ask me where something is,
I would know right away where to find it.
Yes, I agree. It's a mess but that mess is pretty organized.
If you look at it from my understanding and point of view
I'll admit it's weird.
My mom is always telling me to clean it up. Then, she cleans it.
Then, I just get mad because I don't know where everything is.
I need to have it at least a "little dirty!"
The best part is that I don't have to compare myself to someone else.
I keep my identity in my room.

Sharon Moreno, Grade 7
Terence C Reilly School #7, NJ

Love You Mommy

I miss her like Mary missed Jesus.
Plop! As the teardrops fall,
No more texts, no more e-mails, no more calls.
Does she remember how I look?
Is she a criminal, a crook?
She's been gone for over 9 years
At last once every month
An overflow of tears.
My phone…it calls me, it tells me to call her,
"She'll pick up! I promise!"
But does she ever?
No.
I'm crying and trying
But nothing ever works.
I just want Mommy to know
I love her.

Kaliya Greenidge, Grade 8
St Clare School, NY

Ocean

The ocean is wide, a giant pot of water
I look at it and think about it
The indigenous animals swim about and walk their way.
I love to look at them and watch them all day
The serenity of the ocean is always there
For people like me to sit down and stare
The waves tumble over each other on the beach
For one can hear their shout and feel it on their feet
The power of the ocean is raw and large
Depending on mother nature's mood
It can be devastating or beautiful
It's unpredictable, for it is crude
And it smothers our Earth, and paints it blue
There will always be something new
For the ocean is growing while we live
For we barely understand something so big

Sean Faison-Ince, Grade 9
Bishop Ford Central Catholic High School, NY

Declaration of Independence

A bright sunny day in a
Quiet court room
With beautiful pieces of paper on a desk.
Fathers of our country prepared to sign it.
It seemed like nothing could disrupt
This peaceful evening
Patriotic soldiers standing tall and proud,
Because they finally broke free from the chains of Britain.
So many losses,

So many deaths,

But with many more to come.
Because of this never ending war for freedom.
But, it was all worth it because
These pieces of paper will change the Thirteen Colonies forever.

Nathan Wenhardt, Grade 7
Terence C Reilly School #7, NJ

Leaf

We frolic around
The other leaves and I dance
to the loud beat of the wind
dressed in glamorous gowns
of gold, red, orange and green
spreading the joy of the fall ball
before winter creeps around the corner
and waits until every one of us drains our color and turns brown
wrinkling and fragile like the skin of an elder
as we curl ourselves up
and huddle together to keep warm
in the brutal breeze
I hobble over to the front door of a house
hoping to be let in
for who knows if I will still be here
in the spring

Grace Bailey, Grade 7
Fox Lane Middle School, NY

My Dog Estrella

When I first saw her,
Never thought I could be filled with so much joy.
I knew taking care of her wouldn't be easy.
When she was a puppy, I trained her.
Teaching her was always difficult but I never gave up.
I once stepped on her but she still trust me.
When she hurt me, I still loved her.
Because I was entrusted to take care of her,
And she know she needed me
Together we became a team.

Gian Villacorta, Grade 7
Terence C Reilly School #7, NJ

Homeless

I just stare at him
He looks so poor and homeless
I give him a bill
He shakes his money around
I walk away as he stares
Should I go back there?
I slowly walk back and smile
I look in his eyes
I put more money in his jar
It's not much, but it's a start

Monami Waki, Grade 7
Nathaniel Hawthorne Middle School 74, NY

Crash

At night I see shooting stars
And flying cars.
Sometimes I wonder,
I wonder if they collide, in midair.

Outer space car crashes!
Shooting stars strike!

In the morning, I ask my dad.
I tell him,
Explaining all my thoughts, and ask,
"Do they collide?"

He simply smiles.
Puts his arm around me.

15 years later, I'm in an accident
And my dad won't get the call.
He won't know that I grew up, and that
I'm thinking about car damage, not UFOs.

I regret making that step, growing up.
I did it too soon, too fast.

Every time I think about it,
I feel like one of those shooting stars,
Always worried that someday, I might just…Crash.

Daria Chaplin, Grade 7
Vestal Middle School, NY

The Vanishing Sun

All day the sun is big and bright
But where, oh where, does it hide at night

Does it go home and lock itself inside
Where can something so big hide

Maybe it hides behind some giant hills
Or possibly takes some disappearing pills

Maybe it hides in a secret lair
Or simply vanishes into thin air

Perhaps the moon is on the other side
Or was swept up in high tide

Could it be hidden behind the stars
Or was it stolen by people from Mars

I think it was covered up by clouds
Or perhaps wrapped up in a dark shroud

I've got it now, all around the world it has to run
Because after all, everyone needs the sun

Jonathan Nendze, Grade 7
Little Falls School #1, NJ

Fall

The majestic leaves fall,
Breeze sneaks in between the branches.
Why what a wonderful season is fall,
When everything is so relaxing.

Fall is when you see some of the most beautiful colors of the year,
Shades of orange, yellow, red, and even brown.
It is so nice to see all of these colors,
When we go outside and play around town.

Little children jump in piles of leaves,
Or they may want to go apple picking.
Grownups take long walks in the park,
There is always something to do with the family.

Don't you love it when a leaf gently lands in the water?
Or even when you step on a wrinkled leaf?
I just really enjoy fall,
When everything seems so free.

Jazmine Keene-Prieto, Grade 7
All Saints Catholic Academy, NY

The Angler's Triumph

Ra's royal radiance kissed my rod red
With colors able to raise the dead.
My line was cast, my mind was at ease,
Pausing to glance, I surveyed the seas.

Patiently I waited, prepared for a fight,
When a herculean fish struck with an unyielding bite.
With a fast furious flick of my wrist, I began to reel in
And glimpsed its glimmering green gills, and a fin.

I was a knight who had emerged victorious,
Hence a fleeting moment in time had transmuted to glorious.
A feeling of honor and vigor abruptly seized my mind
And urged me to fling the ichthyological beast back with its kind.

The ocean now lay as calm as night is black,
And the fish had no longer the courage to attack.
As I gathered my paraphernalia to make my way back home
Ra's royal radiance metamorphosed to chrome.

Anthony Zannella, Grade 8
Hillsborough Middle School, NJ

Waves

Crashing down,
Monstrous waves hit the sand of the shore
Where I am standing.
Roaring forcefully,
Another wave crashes.
Rising up, plummeting down, splashing everywhere,
The waves wash up and tickle my toes.
Look, here comes another one!

Alex Zeto, Grade 8
New Providence Middle School, NJ

Jolly Jingle Bells

The perfect nip is in the air,
The scents of holidays brewing.
I walk down the crowded streets,
People littered with bags head to toe.
Jolly Jingle Bells are ringing,
For the nearing of Christmas has risen.

The faces of many turn bright and warm,
Red with joy and glee.
The spirit of the holiday is near.
Jolly Jingle Bells are ringing,
For the birth of our Lord is coming.

My smile does not fade,
'Tis the season to be merry and bright.
While the Jolly Jingle Bells are ringing,
And carolers spreading joy are singing,
Families all over the globe come together
For this Christmas night.

Gianna Venturini, Grade 7
Copeland Middle School, NJ

Dream Chasers

Dreams
Can be seen in an instant
Can be a memorable moment
In the flicker of an eye
It can pass you by
Suddenly —
All is lost and forgotten
Your mind is clear and awoken
Time flies, every day,
As your dream drifts away
Never knowing what it meant
Could it be Heaven sent?
Try chasing your dreams,
Whatever they might mean.
The message is always useful.
Don't take advantage; it's crucial.
It might be your fate;
You just wait.
Your destiny comes closer — dream chaser.

Pamela Loperena, Grade 8
Warwick Valley Middle School, NY

Snowball Fight

Wonderful colors everywhere
White all around
Lumps in the air
Jumped down to the ground
As I dared
Fired my first round
I was unaware
I got hit so now I am down

Kirsten Homeny, Grade 8
New Egypt Middle School, NJ

A Dream of Reality

The light radiates on the white walls,
creating an aura of serenity in a time of chaos.
It's the border between a dream and reality.

The golden light emulates the passionate sun in the sky and creates a hazy atmosphere.
I'm barely conscious of anything around me but my burning face,
the golden light,
and my drowsiness.

Everything is a blur. Everything is so numbing.
The golden light, almost blinding, forces me to squint.
My face,
from the sweating heat,
is turning a deep red.

I am lying on a mess of a bed.
The sheets are undone, layered on top of each other,
designed to make me feel the intense heat even more.
It's so uncomfortable; I want to move, but I can't.

I feel as if I'm in an ambient trance, restricted by my settings.
The mesmerizing light slowly shuts my eyes
and before I know it,
I fall into a deep sleep,
a deep dream of reality.

Ikaasa Suri, Grade 9
Horace Mann Upper School, NY

Racism

Did Martin Luther King Jr.'s speech go in vain?
Did Adolf Hitler cause no pain?
Did Osama bin Laden's actions result in all Muslims to be viewed the same?
Or did Mahatma Gandhi exaggerate peace just for fame?

Many individuals are facing racism today.
Many commit suicide so they can run away.
Young hands holding a gun,
And some thought they were just having fun?

Punched, kicked, pushed, shoved,
Why can't we all just be loved?
For how long will people see,
Black or White, Singh or Lee?

Why be racist when you also come from a different place?
Remember Emmett Till, did you see his face?
How long will it take till we look at each other as one?
And not segregate from skin or where we're from?

My fellow friends, today racism still remains.
For hundreds of years we are still yearning to be free from these chains.
It will not take only one person to stand up and fight.
But together we will have to unite.
Together we will have to unite.

Atinderpal Singh, Grade 9
Townsend Harris High School, NY

True Friendship

Friends come and go
But you are the only one
Who stayed close to me.
As time goes by,
Thank you for seeing me
Completely for what I am.
This friendship we have is like a gift
Making me feel protected and safe.
You never worry about us
Getting hurt or in an argument.
This friendship is a treasure
I will always keep close to my heart.
Thank you so much
For letting me have a place in your heart
I know our friendship will always be.

Fariha Pia, Grade 7
Terence C Reilly School #7, NJ

Fantasy

As I dream about a perfect life,
I imagine a life of love at first sight.
A world of peace and happiness,
But as I wake up into reality,
It slowly disappears.
Love is a word of empty value,
A fictional, fairy tale ending.
A journey of dark, dead ends.
A sweet fantasy,
As I open my eyes it slowly drifts away.

Love is a lie,
Hidden behind smiles.
Love is a lie,
Hidden behind happiness.

Miriam Albaneh, Grade 8
Global Concepts Charter School, NY

Dawn

Dawn has so many marvelous colors
that fill the whole sky.
You will never see anything like it.
There are so many varieties of colors
everywhere you look.
Yellow, red and orange are so vivid,
Blending together
Nature's painting on a canvas.
That changes every day.
You want to watch it forever.
It's really worth being awake

Seeing what artists can not duplicate.

Nature at its best.
Marbella Guzman, Grade 7
Terence C Reilly School #7, NJ

A Mother's Love

Lying on the misty blue hospital bed,
a mother holds her newborn baby
while she gazes at her beautiful face with affectionate eyes.
Holding a bottle of warm milk,
she feeds her precious baby girl.
Singing, admiring, and cradling, the mother caresses the infant in her loving arms,
sending her daughter into a quiet slumber.
Oh, how deep the mother's love is shown.

Rachel Kowalewski, Grade 8
New Providence Middle School, NJ

Small Steps

Careening off the wall,
The youngster wobbles towards his mother as she reaches out to catch him in case he trips.
Falling every two steps,
He tries desperately to get to her.
Half-crawling, stumbling along, spreading out his arms for balance,
The baby finally falls into his mother's arms.
What smiles there are on their faces!

Amulya Mummaneni, Grade 8
New Providence Middle School, NJ

Autumn's Task

The prongs of the rake scraping the ground in an awkward fashion
Piles of leaves forming like an island
Slowly and orderly
The brisk air swirling and surrounding the landscaper as he works on this task
The ruffle of the black garbage bag as leaves are being stuffed inside
This all pays off when you see your end result
A beautiful, clean yard

Jake Brief, Grade 7
Grand Avenue Middle School, NY

Rainbows

Following the storm,
The rainbow arched over the trees as the rain diminished.
Layered in bright colors,
It displayed itself gracefully.
Flashing cameras, smiling at the beauty, And wishing to seek the pot of gold,
The neighborhood gathered outside.
Oh how I love rainbows!

Kelly Jonovich, Grade 8
New Providence Middle School, NJ

Baseball

When I was little, I wanted to be one of the New York Yankees
Baseball is my favorite sport and this was before the Yankees' championship was a dynasty
In fact I found one of my World Series poems in my school portfolio
Baseball is my favorite sports
Left field is what I play
Maybe I'll be in the Hall of Fame
If I become a pro one day

Christopher Ferrus, Grade 7
Our Lady of Trust School, NY

Drug-Free

I am drug free
Because I want to be
The highest degree
I can be

If I get offered
I say no thanks
If I get reoffered
I say no thanks
I walk away

That is why I am drug-free

Luke Strott, Grade 8
St Stephen's School, NY

You

Your amazing smile
Your chocolate brown eyes
I'd like to hang with you awhile.
When I see you, all I can do is sigh.
I just wish you knew;
If you did, what would you do?
Would you feel the same way too?
Maybe you do know.
Am I being too obvious?
I just wish you were mine.
I can't help it;
It's just a smile, but it gets me every time.

Bianca Tatiana Vargas, Grade 8
Keyport High School, NJ

Fireworks

Boom crash bang!
The dark sky is set alight,
The glitter and the sparkles
Look so elegant at night.
The color in the sky
Is as bright as neon signs,
Others whistle by,
Just to help pass the time.
There really is no gloom,
But there's a ringing in your ear.
Then I hear a mighty cry,
The final zoom is near.

Zoe Kaldor, Grade 8
Hommocks Middle School, NY

Valentine's Day

Valentine's Day is arriving.
Grab your heart and —
Scattle out the door.
Give it to someone special.
Make their heart beat fast!

Austin Conner, Grade 8
Ocean Academy, NJ

Time

The clock ticks and the day is gone
Before you know it a week has disappeared
I sit silently thinking of the future and what it has in store
My footsteps pace across the floor as the clock rings and another hour is gone
I worry of the horror that might come, and the sorrows down the road
In the blink of an eye another day is gone
The future and the possible horrors that come along with it are quickly approaching

A bright calm day comes into view and the chirp of birds happily awake my slumber
I feel for the first time that time has frozen and worries have vanished
I step out of bed and feel as if a weight has been lifted off my shoulders
I slowly walk down stairs and look outside
The sun is so bright and the grass looks so soft
I walk outside and the sun beams on my face
I'm surrounded by wonder and amazement as birds fly past me
I forget about worrying about the future and its possible horrors
I take time to enjoy the present and life's gifts
Worries are gone and stress has vanished
The clock rings, but I don't care

Peter Korchak, Grade 7
St William the Abbot School, NY

New York City

Dreams really come true.
That was what I exclaimed on my way to New York City.
The sounds of the cab drivers beeping are already implanted in my mind.
There are so many things I can do around Christmas time.
I can go see a play, or a game or the big sparkling tree.
I could to ice skating or holiday shopping.
Or maybe I could take a trip to see the Radio City performance.
Oh what fun everything is.
Maybe I could take a trip to the highest point of the city
by visiting the one and only Empire State Building.
I could visit my dad at work
or go to one of the famous museums.
I don't think it's possible for me to get bored in this city of dreams.
With all of these great things,
I would have to stop time to fit in all in.
But once I get there,
I will sure try to do it all.
Wish me luck!

Ryan Dempsey, Grade 8
St William the Abbot School, NY

Falling in Fall

Swinging through the chilly autumn wind,
an acorn prepares itself for its eventual fall.

Leaping into the crispy air,
the nut finally detaches itself from its life on the oak.

Falling through the air, weaving through obstacles, and landing on the ground,
the acorn arrives at its destination.
Left unscathed, soon there will be a newborn tree.

Lawrence Chan, Grade 8
New Providence Middle School, NJ

Where I'm From

I am from music notes,
From voices and pianos.
I am from swinging on the swings,
(Wind whistling past my ears, flying higher than anyone else).
I am from the ceramic flowerpot,
The bean sprout
That grew and grew
As if it could reach the sky.

I'm from reading in a corner, from storybooks and imagination.
I'm from hiding under the covers, trying not to be seen.
I'm from begging my parents to take me to the ice cream shop,
From chattering with friends and nonstop giggling,
Trying to stop, only to start again.

In my backyard, there's a playground,
Worn and creaky from many years past.
It's hosted generations of families,
Families that have disappeared into the wind
And been replaced time and time again.

I am from those moments —
Trickle by trickle, surging into a rushing river.
Nothing will cease its flow.

Rebecca Lin, Grade 8
NJ

September 11th Through a Child's Eyes

When you say "9/11"
You think of bad luck, sorrow, and loss
But I was too young to remember it
All I think is "What was it like?"

As far as I know,
It was clear one Tuesday morning
No fire or smoking
Until in came Flight 11

It was flying too low and hit the North Twin Tower
"Was it an accident?" people had thought
But, no, this was no accident
Flight 175 headed for the South Tower proved it with one hit

The towers went tumbling
The Pentagon lost a side
Passengers on Flight 95 wouldn't stay seated
They overpowered the pilot just to make their deathbed

All this talk of loss and death was probably true
I may have been too young to remember,
But my family has it etched into their memory
Like a permanent marker

Rachel Sakhai, Grade 7
Public School 232 The Walter Ward School, NY

Beautiful

"Beautiful" is a powerful word.
It can give, or take away.
Those who have it can be so vain.
Those who don't seem to always be slain.
Should beauty be power? Did God mean it this way?
Beauty is a competition.
Don't deny you don't play the game
But vanity cheats, I swear that it does.
How else could it hold so much power above us?
Beautiful is an atrocious word.
It saddens so many things.
Weight and color.
Shoe size and more.
The way we look at each other changes each morn.
What you're wearing, not who is caring.
is what seems to matter more.
"Beautiful" is a powerful word.

Kirstin Horn, Grade 7
Haviland Middle School, NY

Sun

There's a beautiful star every day
It shines like no other star in the sky
With its intense light, my eyes melt.

You light our day up with fire
The heat warms my skin
And leaves me a tan.

You stretch out to hug us all,
with your warm hands
You shine more than the shiny slippery floor
Making the floor feel defeated.

If only you can stay up and play with me a little longer
Eventually you would disappear into the darkness
Good night my beautiful star friend.

Elizabeth Castillo, Grade 7
Schuyler School, NJ

Stealing

Sprinting as fast as I can,
I make a desperate attempt to slide into third,
All I can hear is the roar of the fans,
I get there on time,
Spectators going wild with joy,
I'm leading off of third,
There is a little boy,
Who's holding up a sign that says,
"Hit that ball out of this dome!"
I'm where I belong,
I am determined to make it all the way home.

Samuel Adamo, Grade 7
William Davies Middle School, NJ

A Spring Day

The wind is softly blowing,
Yet in the gentle afternoon sun
   It is still warm.
The bare trees hover over the earth,
While purple crocuses open
Their gay faces to the sun —
A strange comparison
   To the leafless branches.

On the playground,
Second graders are enjoying
The warm sunshine.
   Their shouts mingle
With the bird song
And the sound of an airplane.

Oh these joyous first days
   Of spring.

Tamas Gilbert, Grade 8
Green Meadow Waldorf School, NY

Wanting to Be Drug-Free

A healthy person,
A great basketball player,
A good volleyball player,
A great swimmer,
A fantastic Irish Dancer,
A good student,
A person who gets good grades,
A loving pet owner,
A kind friend,
A honest friend,
A trustful friend,
A good daughter,
A caring daughter,
All things that I am,
Which I love being,
Which I want to stay,
So being drug-free is the way.

Lauren LoTempio, Grade 7
St. Stephen's School, NY

Christmas

Holidays
Christmas joy
Jolly Santa Claus
Gifts
Snow
Reindeer
Hot chocolate
Decorations
Smell of pine trees
Vacation from school
New Year coming hurrah!!

Adam Bruno, Grade 7
Ocean Academy, NJ

Betrayed

I was once loved, but betrayed by my own friend,
Love is strong, but to many, it's just to say
The one I loved didn't know, but the boy did know,
I was once loved, betrayed by my own friend,
She was the girl of my dreams,
She had lots of thoughts about me.
So she said, but as the series of despair transcends,
Every single heart will soon descend.
She confused my heart with her words, and
now my heart is drifting away on a boat to no return,
I was once loved, but betrayed by own friend,
When my so called "Friend" considered helping and supporting me,
There was probably something else on his mind, but the support of me,
But hey, I once heard an old saying…
"The only way out is the way through"
But I Have rewired that saying…"I went around,"
The girl of my dreams has taken my mind on an endless journey of
Passion, worry, curiousness and most of all…
LOVE.

Saquan Taylor and Renauj Buckley, Grade 7
The Young Scholars Academy of the Bronx, NY

Meteorite

Who would be a meteor, who could help it?
Pointlessly circling the continuous cosmos forever.
If you crash down on Earth you will kill millions, cause a fracas.
That's how the cookie crumbles when you are a meteor.
Not able to control your motions, for you travel the abysmal void known as space.
Although you are a shooting star in the sky you lack the finesse,
And grace to be beautiful.
Some smart scientists say that meteors are the greatest piece of space.
The trail of stardust they left behind, and how the meteors are the horses of space.
Graceful, passionate, has a tail, these are the words used for the meteorite.
Destructive, beautiful, mean, gentle, hot, cold, and kind, but cruel.
These are the words I use to describe the meteor.
Like an out-of-control plane not knowing when or where you may land.
Biting at the bone of yourself you are nervous,
But do not fear, you are the horse in the sky.
With the skill and power you can be more than a hunk of space rock.
You could be a wishing star: the kind of stars used in shows, movies,
And in real life that people wish off of.
So forget being a meteor, and be glad you're human.

Eric Moul, Grade 8
Clinton Public School, NJ

Autumn

The leaves crinkle under my feet as I walk down the road
I see the reds, yellows, and oranges blending together all in one canvas
The view is magnificent from here
I just love the look of autumn
If you sit outside this time of the year it is amazing
Not too cold, not too hot, it's just right
You can have so much fun outside
I love the fall!

Carolyn Davin, Grade 7
St Mary School, NJ

The Pain

The pain the builds inside her
fills the souls of others with hurt.
The tears she lets go
fill the sky with rain.
Her anger and frustration
brings thunder around us.

When she walks down the street
the scene behind her turns gray.
Every heartbeat of her tainted heart
brings sorrow to the singing birds' song.

The power and strength she has over her mind and soul
have weakened.
The pain of her body and heart have increased.
She's always felt pain
but she always had the strength
until that one day.

Jenarose Zaletel, Grade 8
Warwick Valley Middle School, NY

Is It My Fault???

Anger, jealousy?
Matthew was or is his name
The name I named my lost twin
Tears. I cry tears, but are they of joy?
I'm stuck here wondering
Wondering if the loss of my twin was my fault.
I am told no, but what if that's not so?
What if I'm the cause of this loss?
Is this good; bad? Am I happy; sad?
Now I know this may sound silly
But it's not to me. I wish I knew him
God willing one day I will
I can just imagine what it would be like, to know…him
Arguments, love, awkward moments!
It's what every boy or girl hopes to have as a twin
Well at least what I hope or hoped.
So is it my fault? I guess until it's my time…
I will never know?!?

Rebecca Bucknor, Grade 8
Holy Innocents School, NJ

Life

Life is just a big cycle
Full of frustration and laughter
It goes by as fast as a bullet
And the work just keeps coming
If you don't try hard as a kid
You'll end up a buffoon
There won't be any money coming in as an adult
But if you do try hard you'll have an alliance with success
You won't live in a dirty or grimy house
And you will succeed.

Jacob Weber, Grade 7
William Davies Middle School, NJ

Friendship

Friends are a replica of you.
They accommodate you that is true.
They commemorate you in every moment of their lives.
Always responsive to what you say.
Never let you get in harm's way.

Never abstain away from you here and there.
For that shows that they care.
Friends are like a sanctuary when in danger
They aren't like a stranger

They will always be beside you
It's nothing new.
You and your friend form an allegiance of two.
Always relying on the other so true.

They aren't self-seeking, or greedy.
Always generous to you when needy.
You just can't live without your friend
It's something you can't comprehend.

Juhana Habib, Grade 7
Razi School, NY

Stuffed Away

Where did you go?
No one can find you.
I miss your furry hair, your big blue eyes and stuffed paws.
Now, you're gone.
Nowhere to be found.
The dry soil covers you with its soft blanket.
I'm sorry I let you go.
I knew I shouldn't have.
Please come back.
Just give me one more chance.
I will brush your fur and give you a bath.
I will sew you up and squeeze you tight.
I will take you to school and you could sit and have lunch with me.
Peanut butter and jelly, your favorite.
I miss you.

Alexa Beam-DeSantis, Grade 7
Schuyler School, NJ

Narwhals

I am a Narwhal.
I live in the sea.
I swim in the ocean,
With my horn leading me,
All the way to Canada.

Yellow is my color.
I wear unicorn horns.
Unicorns and whales,
Are who I like to be with.
Narwhals, narwhals swimming in the ocean.

Sara Ruszczyk, Grade 8
Sts Peter & Paul School, NY

A Warm Welcome

Popping his ears up in excitement,
Murphy gets ready to pounce while his excitement builds.
Showing anticipation in his ears,
My puppy jumps up from the fluffy bed.
Eager for his daily homecoming butt rub, racing down the stairs, raising his ears up in realization,
he sees me.
Here comes my warm welcome!

Maggie Roughley, Grade 8
New Providence Middle School, NJ

Birthday Gifts

Untying the bow,
While all his friends watch,
Reading the card, he can't wait to see what it is.
Pulling off the ribbon, ripping the paper, throwing away the scraps, he finally sees the present
The boy gasps in excitement.
What a marvelous day it was!

Katie Tselepis, Grade 8
New Providence Middle School, NJ

Skiing

Flying down the mountainside on my pair of skis,
I go as fast as the wind.
The wind lashing my face,
causes me to yell with delight.
Blasting down the mountain, adrenaline racing through my veins, trees flashing past my eyes,
What fun skiing is!

Alan Wang, Grade 8
New Providence Middle School, NJ

The Love in Friendships

Friendship is to love,
To love you need friendship
A friendship without love is a wasted relation

A flower is beautiful,
As is a loving friendship
A flower is delicate and needs to be cared for,
And a friend in the loving relation

In life, friendship is everything!
Without it,
It's like a marriage without love,
Without the connection

I promise to always keep the love,
To always keep the strength,
To be the backup when you need it
To keep my faith in the loving friendship we share

To you my friend I love you still,
Established in 2007,
And the love is still there!
Friendship is everything and more!

Chrissie Wojciechowski, Grade 9
Brick Township High School, NJ

Never Shout Never

I have fallen in love
With the music that comes from his
Heart, mind, and soul.

I have tripped over the stars,
To plummet through the space,
Onto this glorified Earth.

I have seized to object,
To the butterflies soaring,
Within my soul.

I have sung to his words,
While my pulse flutters as he goes,
"Oh oh no. I don't know what I have been told..."

I have come to adore,
His voice as I listen sans judgment,
While my insides continue to swirl.

I have fallen in love,
With the lyrics that come from his
Heart, mind, and soul.

Kassandra Mendez, Grade 9
New Providence High School, NJ

Autumn

Autumn, the breathtaking colors of orange, red, and brown
The beautiful way it lights up the town
The sweet aroma of freshly baked pies
The migrating birds flying across the sky

The piles of leaves from yellow to green
The vibrant colors and the crisp breeze
Gathered around the fireplace at the end of a fall day
I love autumn in every way

Carolyn Kulick, Grade 7
St Mary School, NJ

My Family

My family may be different and I'm not really sure how
I didn't know if we were, but I was sure until now
I realized no two families are quite the same in every way
But a family may change, in as little as a day
I don't know if we're different, and really I don't care
I'm happy with my family, and I need not compare
Sure sometimes we fight
But it usually ends all right
No matter what, I always, forgive them by the night.

Timothy Malloy, Grade 9
Bishop Ford Central Catholic High School, NY

Fall

Fall is a breathtaking season of beauty,
Full of colorful leaves, crisp mornings,
Earlier nights filled with breezy winds to make you shiver,
Fall is an adventurous time of traveling all over,
Traveling on roads with trees as far as the eye can see,
Fall is a time to sit in front of a fire,
With hot cocoa and marshmallows,
Talking about how the day was,
Fall is one of my favorite seasons and always will be.

Maxwell Lenhart, Grade 7
St Mary School, NJ

I Want to Be Drug Free

I want to be drug free.
If not there's no singing for me.
I could die quicker.
If I take drugs I won't be able to breathe properly.
If I don't breathe properly then I can't sing.
Singing properly is a good thing for me because I love to sing.
I will hurt or damage my vocal cords.
I could avoid this by not taking drugs.
I will never take any drugs.

Virgil Castner, Grade 7
St Stephen's School, NY

Paper

Crisp and white you sound unspoken
The brisk fibers on you have yet to be broken
You lay in front of me, many stories to be told
I have yet to share them and let others behold
You are smart, you are strong
As my pencil smacks with a bong
Paper, oh paper, I must write upon you
for the school day is over
and dear paper, you're due!

Kayla Abella, Grade 8
Orange Avenue Elementary School, NJ

Autumn

I can hear the rustle from under my feet.
I can see my breath from its warm heat.
I can feel the wind, it's getting colder.
I know this means autumn and its coming closer.

Autumn is dazzling, with a breathtaking view.
With red, orange, and yellow, the colors hypnotize you.
But the colors are nothing, compared to what I see,
A big happy family, gathered around me.

Kayley Anthony, Grade 7
St Mary School, NJ

Tears

A situation causing tears
Swelling up inside your eyes
A stream of water dropping from your eyes
No one can really understand the feelings that go along with them
Looks like crystals
Rolling down your cheek
It's all about your emotions
I wonder what exactly happened
That made you cry?

Melanie Pazmino, Grade 7
Terence C Reilly School #7, NJ

Autumn

Autumn is here oh yes siree!
Every moment you would approach a tree,
the crisp fall leaves would fall upon thee.

The children were at play in their vibrant attire,
while mother came running with her warm apple cider.

When play time was over, they laid warm and snug,
All cozy in bed with their piping hot mugs.

Samantha Siriani, Grade 7
St Mary School, NJ

Oh! Autumn

Oh! Autumn, where will you go?
When all the white stuff comes,
What we call snow.

The leaves turn to brilliant colors,
Reds, yellows, greens, like no others.
The view is just breathtaking
It is worth the waiting.

Oh! Autumn, where will you go?
When it comes,
All that snow.
Alexandra Heim, Grade 7
St Mary School, NJ

The Will of Destiny

The more I ponder what I've become,
The more I wonder what I've done.

Death isn't who I am,
But controlling my life is my only plan.

No one will ever change me,
For that is certainly in my voice.

But I will take the reins of my destiny —
For now it is my only choice.
Zachary Ruffin, Grade 7
George Jackson Academy, NY

Basketball

Time of tip off
We won the tip
I took two hours to get up the court
Thump, thump, thump
Sound of the basketball dribbling
Seeing the hoop round like Earth
He shoots and scores!
Basketball is my favorite sport
Dribble, dribble, dribble up the court
Take the shot
And don't get blocked.
Andre Stewart Jr., Grade 8
St Clare School, NY

The Angels Above

You may not see them
But they are always there
They will guard and guide us
Thought the days ahead
Through times of doubt
They will understand
We will always know
That we are not alone
Kayla Hamler, Grade 7
William Davies Middle School, NJ

God Is Always There

Best friends are not who you think they are
You think you can tell them everything and they won't say a thing
Next thing you know the whole world knows about it
And you don't want to believe it's them
It hurts to know it was them
It makes you think
Was it an accident, on purpose or are they just trying to intentionally hurt you
And you cry day and night
You call your best friend every minute trying to figure out if it's true or not
And when you figure it out, it hurts you
It feels like a million pounds of metal fell down on your shoulders
You don't know any more who you can trust, who you can turn to
Who will always be beside you don't matter what
Who will be there with you through your ups and downs, your good and bad times
But remember this you'll always have God
So when you feel alone and you have nobody to turn
Turn to God 'cause He will always be there and He'll never turn on you don't matter what
So never lose hope and never lose faith because God is always besides you
Hajirah Gumanneh, Grade 8
Al-Noor School, NY

Falling for Autumn

Fiery red and golden yellow leaves covering the trees,
while the breezes gently showering the ground with the colors of Autumn
Smooth round orange pumpkins and green lumpy gourds
on tangled vines cover the dusty open fields
Brightly colored leaves gently flutter to the ground
is a butterfly gliding in the breeze.
The big oak tree cracking, brittle branches crunching and swaying in the
wind above me, like daisies swaying in the warm breezy wind
The crinkling of scurrying animals on the crunchy colorful leaves
that blanketed the hard cold ground
Gnarly branches clenching shiny red apples
like the fingers of an elderly hand
Warm apple cider with the crisp smell of cinnamon sticks
The aroma of pumpkin pie spices filling the air, baking in the oven
Sweet steamy apple pie bursting in my mouth with flavor
Juicy freshly dipped caramel apples exploding with every crisp bite
A cool crisp refreshing breeze on my face
while my arms wrapped in the warmth of my warm cozy soft sweater.
Jill Dieterich, Grade 8
Commack Middle School, NY

Halloween

It's that time of year again
When the leaves turn magnificent colors of orange, yellow, and red
The wind is blowing
First sweaters are being put on
Thoughts of scarecrows, pumpkins, and scary costumes come to mind
What will I be for Halloween?
Will it be scary or will it be fun
Bobbing for apples
Going door to door for candy
Oh how I can't wait for this spooky night to come
Mindy Weinstein, Grade 7
Hammarskjold Middle School, NJ

Christmas Has Arrived

Christmas has come
The joy and excitement have just begun
Let's celebrate just for fun
The holiday cheer fills me up with glee
Let's all decorate the Christmas tree
The birthday of our savior Jesus Christ
Let's go Christmas shopping no matter the price
It is Christmas eve everybody is so nice
The day we open presents
I forgot to mention
Santa Claus is coming to town
Don't yell, scream, or even give a frown
Making snowmen
With our own hands
It is the holidays
Let's all rock the night away

Joel Chan, Grade 8
Keyport High School, NJ

A Never-Ending Nightmare

What started off as a beautiful day
Turned out a nightmare with atomic rays
Radiation raced through the land claiming innocent lives
It was hard for almost any inhabitant to thrive
The moaning and groaning voices of the injured and dying
Made the others start sobbing and crying

The setting was like a world without man
Hiroshima and Nagasaki were planned
To be destroyed so that the war would end
Against a bomb no one could defend

The nightmare lives on until today
History is destined to repeat itself anyway
In March the tsunami was the latest bomb to hit
Will Fukushima ever get over it?

Bronson Rocha, Grade 8
Intermediate School 141 Steinway, NY

My Mom's Struggle

I'm living life with a struggle
That I will never overcome
But thinking of my mom
I'll always see a bright light
But not always do I see this light
Because inside my mom has a terrible anger
Lingering in her soul
I wish some way I can help her control this anger better
But until that I cannot help her
If only she could just accept it my help
But no
So now
As I wait thinking about my mom every day
Hoping my mom will take the help
But till that day
I will always wait.

Elijah Alvarez, Grade 8
Public School 232 The Walter Ward School, NY

Time for Spring

Spring is like a butterfly,
coming out of its cocoon.
The icy snow will melt away,
And our snowmen will decease.

A colorful world will be revealed,
And the birds will chirp once again.
Beautiful blossoms will embellish the trees,
And the flowers will awaken in radiant colors.

Our gloves and hats will disperse,
And raincoats and umbrellas will replace them.
A certain rabbit will come hopping,
Leaving eggs for one and all.
Spring is the loveliest time of year,
And I wish it would be springtime every day.

Samantha Matzerath, Grade 7
St William the Abbot School, NY

Delicious Dinner

Covered in delicious sauce,
The pepperoni pizza emerges from the oven,
As my stomach is growling of hunger

Burning from the oven,
It is delicious.

Oozing with cheese, steaming hot, covered in love.
Pizza is the best food ever.

I love pizza.

Nick Falkowski, Grade 8
New Providence Middle School, NJ

Being Drug Free

Drugs are very bad
For your health
They can make you have a premature death
Staying drug free is
Very important
If I stay drug free
I can have a better chance at life
I would be able to get a good job
I wouldn't go to jail
And I would
Live a lot longer

Patrick McCormick, Grade 7
St Stephen's School, NY

Why I Want to Be Drug Free

I want to be drug-free
because drugs are bad for me
I can't play sports
Or be active
It slows me down
And it's unhealthy for me
It makes me feel not free
From doing whatever I want
It can kill me too
Drugs are really bad for me
And everyone else
If I could choose
Between doing drugs or being drug-free
I would choose to be drug free
It keeps me healthy and happy
This is why I want to be drug-free!

Rachel Colan, Grade 7
St Stephen's School, NY

Original, Outrageous, Fall

The clashing of the colors,
The leaves, oh how they hover,
Coming down to the ground so great.

The hopes, the dreams,
On the wind like cream,
Until it dies down again.

The smiles on your face,
When you see the fireplace,
Sparking warm and hot.

The happy surprise,
When there is no lie,
Fall is here again.

Elizabeth Castellano, Grade 7
St Mary School, NJ

Home

My own dark
My own space
I love to be home
My space

The love, the laughs
Will always be remembered
My friends, my family
There forever

When gone
Or far away
I long for home

Home is where I will always stay

Ryan Valentine, Grade 9
Holy Cross High School, NJ

Are You Ready for Some Football

Across the Astroturf I run.
Around the defense I go.
Beside me is the cornerback; his arms reaching high are two skyscrapers rising over me.
Towards the quarterback is where I'm looking.
Outside shoulder is the target like a hunter stalking a deer.
Between the safeties are my sprinting legs.
Out my hands go automatically like a robot.
Below the ball are my hands like the sand in the ocean.
Throughout the catch I am running like a charging bull.
Into me comes the safety pounding for the ball like he is a boxer throwing an uppercut.
Except he comes up empty handed.
After being tackled I pop up with the ball, but all that's in my mind is excitement.

Jacob Berg, Grade 7
Clinton Public School, NJ

Lurking in the Dark

Dark as day and bright as night
Because in day criminals seem out of sight

But night people start to feel fright
Because those criminals begin to bite

And people try not going out in the dark
Because if you do they'll leave their mark

So don't go out at night cause your dog starts to bark
Because they'll smell you from a mile away like a blood thirsty shark

Benjamin Ramos, Grade 9
Bishop Ford Central Catholic High School, NY

Picture-Perfect Moment

Falling down, as if sent from heaven,
a gentle mist rains down to earth
while the sun is glimpsing at the water.
Striking the puddles,
the powerful rays of light skip across the lightly saturated areas.
Clearing the air,
breaking the darkness with light,
winding down to a halt,
the drizzling rain clears and the sun peers out of its hiding place behind the clouds.
Thus, the picture-perfect moment is created.

Kathryn Gomez, Grade 8
New Providence Middle School, NJ

Christmas

C arols sung together as a family
H and-knitted sweaters from grand mom
R emarkable memories permanently stamped into everyone's minds
I ncredible food cooked with love
S now falling on the ground as gentle as a feather
T ree covered in ornaments of green and red
M ountains of kindness for all
A s far as the eye can see are smiles forever staying on everyone's faces
S nowmen made with twig arms and button eyes

Melissa Vargas, Grade 7
William Davies Middle School, NJ

Moon Pool

Why is it that we can't touch the stars?
They remain in the heavens above though we wish them near
As children they sing us to sleep
As adults they separate us from our loved ones
And as we age to become elderly, they show us the way home
Even though we
Call
Dream
Hope
And pray
They will never answer
As dark as night can be
The stars shine even more bright just to be seen
But the one thing that we can do is watch
They display themselves every night
Even though they tantalize us,
Sometimes the only things that can keep us sane on this planet
Are the small beauties that we cannot contain

Sarah Ross, Grade 9
Pequannock Township High School, NJ

Time Passes

Time passes by me
Here I am, aging by the minute.
Alone, in this dark world
Filled with danger and hatred.

Never again, will time come
Back
The people we once met,
We will never see again.

People live and die
Plants live and die
Animals live and die
Time brings loss, but it also brings life.
It brings the people we love together as one
That's why I love time.
Time passes by me
Here I am, aging by the minute.

Aritzy Garcia, Grade 8
Intermediate School 51 Edwin Markham, NY

Why I'm Drug Free

At first drugs seem fun and cool
But when you take them you're a fool
At first people think they'll be fine, succeed and be cool
But trouble starts when you fail school
Later they cause pain and death
You better pray because there's nothing left
Every day people die
Because someone just wants to be high
Don't take drugs to be a wannabe
Drug free is the way to be!

Elliott Ziolkowski, Grade 8
St Stephen's School, NY

The Roads Least Traveled

There is a reason why the roads least traveled are favorable.
Laced with all kinds of adventures;
Big, small, exciting, depressing, or new,
You will always find one that fits you.

The roads are nearly boundless, with twists and turns,
But just around each corner,
Or with each new sunrise,
Something pulchritudinous might arise.

The roads can be rugged, with hills and valleys,
Or chasms, walls, cliffs or abyss'
And sometimes it appears the road will end,
But, in fact, it is just another bend.

It is your decision to compose.
Taking a path where no one went,
Full of adventures and merriment,
Or a path hammered down by thousands of feet,
All keeping pace with the monotonous beat.

Mackenzie Smith, Grade 8
Hillsborough Middle School, NJ

That Night

He came home late every night. Mamma
is starting to notice something wrong.
Mamma went to work and he took us to
Kingsburg with another woman.
Everything just felt wrong. When I looked at them
they were holding hands.
That night I went home and cried into my pillow.
He screamed at me the next day and called
me a liar for telling my mom. He left that night
and never came back.
Now, I can't look at him the same anymore.
I always get into fights with him now,
and never regret what I say or do to him.

Courteney Chew, Grade 8
Schuyler School, NJ

Gold Ring

It's something valuable between two people.
Something that unites them.
Represents them.
Brings them closer each day.
A gold ring
Representing a promise.
A gold ring
Representing their love.
It wraps around their finger
Representing a band of promise.
A band that can't ever be broken.
The only thing that would make them think...
"If it goes wrong where would I be now?"

Sabryna Morales, Grade 7
Terence C Reilly School #7, NJ

Springtime

Flowers smelling sweet
Fresh, warm breeze through my window
Signs that spring is here
Elizabeth English, Grade 9
Raritan High School, NJ

Music

The pounding bass line
Drowning out noise around you
Beats fill up my soul
Kacey Amato, Grade 9
Raritan High School, NJ

Autumn Breeze

The gentle breeze is
Flowing slightly through my hair
And whistles through trees
Emily Darakjy, Grade 9
Raritan High School, NJ

Love

Love is like a rose
It grows and looks beautiful
But ends too quickly
Carson Smith, Grade 9
Raritan High School, NJ

Books

Exploring beyond
With the turn of a page
Books become another world
Holly Varrera, Grade 9
Raritan High School, NJ

The Beach

Soft sand on your feet
Waves crashing on the sand
The smell in the air
Karry Bennett, Grade 9
Raritan High School, NJ

Beach

Footprints in the sand
The kids playing volleyball
Strong smell of sunscreen
Alana Peace, Grade 9
Raritan High School, NJ

The Pasture

Free to roam the fields
The chains are now vanishing
Tyranny gone at last
Bipra Kundu, Grade 9
The Bronx High School of Science, NY

Love

Love is a passion
Love is something you hold in your heart and spirit
Love is also a joy an everlasting experience
Nothing can break and stop the power of love
Love is what you truly feel about people
Your soul and mind is what should be set to love
As life goes on people's love grows stronger with them and never weakens
As we come across life's challenges we realize that sometimes love is the only hope

As we walk down the streets in our everyday lives we see love all around us
Love can mean many things
A mother's hug to give comfort or support
Or
When a new father looks down and sees in his hands a little child looking up at him with
Their big eyes and not having a care in the world, that's when you feel love
Love is a community standing one by one with each other

Love is something great and powerful that not anything or anyone can break down
Love is like a force of gravity that pulls you in
Love is all around us and we just need to open our hearts to see it
Love is a gift
It is the smallest gift of all, but can last a lifetime
Sarah Mantione, Grade 7
St William the Abbot School, NY

Jordan

Jordan
Outgoing, athletic, friendly, funny
Brother of Andy
Lover of Jets, Nets, and basketball
Who feels excited when the Jets win, annoyed waking up really early for school,
and joyful when I meet all my friends again on the first day of school
Who needs more sleep, a better phone, and practice basketball more
Who gives treats to my dog, laughter to my friends, and care to animals
Who fears hurricanes, tornadoes, and terrorists
Who would like to score a lot in basketball, go to a Jets game, hang out with my friends
Resident of East Brunswick
Vespoli
Jordan Vespoli, Grade 7
Hammarskjold Middle School, NJ

Colors of the Morning Sky

Colors are new
color are old
colors fade away,
making way for new ones.
They arise in the morning making way for new ones,
colors of pink, yellow, red and orange.
They burst into the morning sky like paint being spilled onto the floor,
the colors mix, creating vibrant colors of the sky,
The sun rises and the colors melt away
they disappear
and I wait, I wait for the next morning.
Just to see its vibrant colors spill across the sky.
Nicole McCarthy, Grade 7
Schuyler School, NJ

Essence

A drawing is not just a picture to an artist
A drawing is not just an image of reality or imagination
A drawing is not just a series of lines and curves
It is something more.
As soon as the pencil hits the paper,
The artist's heart beats faster
Adrenaline courses through them
Their mind is suddenly read and alert.
The rush, the feeling, the sensation.
That is what creates a drawing.
Even before the first line is drawn.
The material has become a part of them.
The image becomes attached to their body
The picture becomes a part of their soul.
Every line and curve is forever etched into their heart.
But when that drawing is stolen
Or ripped, or made fun of, or lost
It is as if the artist's soul is being ripped away
A piece of themselves is truly dead.
That is what others cannot understand
The true connection of art and its artist.

Madjena Joseph, Grade 9
Bishop Ford Central Catholic High School, NY

Who You Are

Everyone has inner beauty
It doesn't matter if you're a cutie
No one needs makeup or hairspray to show who you are
Because inner beauty makes them a star

Everyone has their own personality
It's all originality
Don't put up an act
Because your personality makes a big impact

Everyone is special in their own way
It's something that will never be taken away
So don't say au revoir
Because inner beauty and personality makes who you are

Emily Ko, Grade 7
Nathaniel Hawthorne Middle School 74, NY

Fall

Breathtaking colors from red to orange to green.
Even yellow, you can jump into the leaves.
Sitting near the fireplace feeling warm and cozy.
Eating popcorn, roasted chestnuts, and autumn pies too.

Truly phenomenal, joyful, and extraordinary,
It becomes cool by day and night.
You can feel this crispness and you want to hold on tight.

The season that is fall,
is one of the best of them all.

Ally Torres, Grade 7
St Mary School, NJ

Basketball: The Sport

Something I like doing is playing sports.
There are many different sports you can play.
They can be played in fields or played on courts.
You can play them any time, any day.

There are way too many sports to mention,
but basketball, football, soccer, baseball,
track and field, hockey, and lacrosse are some.
You can play these sports from winter to fall.

These are all sports that are terrific fun.
I like getting to play them all in gym.
But basketball is my favorite one.
It's all so great; the ball, the net, the rim.

It's fun to play when the weather is great.
Sunny days for basketball are the best.
It's fun seeing the shots that you can make.
The best part's hearing the swish of the net.

Swathi Pavuluri, Grade 7
William R Satz Middle School, NJ

The One That I Love <3

I miss those days
When you were different
Jumping on your bed
Singing along to my favorite song
We used to have so much fun
But then you made a choice that changed everything
I wish that the old you could come and visit
Until then I will count down the days
Wherever in the world the old you is
I wish that is where I was
If I could go back in time…I would
If I could have stopped you…I would have
But there is nothing that can be done now
That person is gone and out of our lives
But I believe that somewhere inside of you is the old you
The one that was fun to be around
The one that I could trust
The one that *was* a good role model
The one that I love

Emily Morgan, Grade 8
Keyport High School, NJ

Broken

I'm staring out the wide blue sky
Thinking about all of the times that have gone by
My love was all for you
And you wasted it all on her
I've tried to get over the hard times
I've tried to deal with the pain
But it's too much to bare
Our love is broken

Nick Peroni, Grade 7
New Egypt Middle School, NJ

A Taste of Your Own Medicine

You're evil, cruel, and really quite nasty.
You walk around putting others down.
You think you're the only doctor with your malicious medicine.
Have you ever tasted it?
I think I know what it is that you need.
A taste of your own medicine,
That should do the trick.
That grotesque, potent smell
Of pure evil.
The hurt you feel,
The tears that come after it.
Will it make you cry?
You seem to think not.
Why don't we find out?
Here is a sample,
Of your evil, mean medicine.
Your eyes are getting teary.
Your fat, red lip quivers.
Your medicine has expired.
I think you should stop prescribing your bully-like words.

Alanna Harrington, Grade 7
Cedar Drive Middle School, NJ

Life Itself

I wake with the sun gazing at me
The birds fluttering on by
Leaves dancing in mid air
I am ever so lonely
I try to distinguish myself from death
so soundless and unmeaningful
Thinking there was a point in life
What my purpose is here, I don't know
I sigh so high and begin to frown
There must be a reason I'm here
The knock on my door echoes through the house
I dash to the window and witness something ever so beautiful
I open the door and glance at something that made life itself.

Cole Praitano, Grade 7
Holy Innocents School, NJ

School

Bells ringing
Children smiling
Children screaming
Children jumping around
Parents saying their last goodbyes
Children hugging their parents goodbye
It's such a sad sight to see
While as others might wonder why
Children hurrying and scurrying to the classroom
Teachers close their doors as bells sing like
Hummingbirds with a soft medley for school
Then it ends as it started with joy,
Cheer as it had been only a year already.

Samuel Paul, Grade 8
St Clare School, NY

Writing a Poem

Writing a poem can be hard
Trying to figure out the rhyming
And the perfect timing
Can really be aggravating
Sigh, maybe I should just write a haiku
But is that something that I can do?
I'm thinking and thinking as time goes by
Maybe there is some inspiration around me
But there is none I can see
Hmmm…
I've written a few lines so far
Maybe, just maybe writing the rest won't be hard

Writing a poem is starting to seem easier
Turns out my inspiration was right in front of my face
And I'm starting to get ideas in a faster pace
Then I proceed to write…
My hand is moving faster and faster
Like I am a poem master
I write and I write
As the thoughts flow out of my head
Will it, ever end?

Celeste Douet, Grade 9
Bishop Ford Central Catholic High School, NY

Mom

Most don't understand what I've been through
This world is empty when I don't have you.
I might not always see you but I know you're always here
I feel so insecure when you're not standing near
I love you very much and I know you love me too
You don't understand what life's like without you
You tucked me in at night, and loved me like you do
It's so impossible to replace a mother like you
You told me right from wrong and taught me "how to"
When I grow up I want to be exactly just like you.
I know you left so quickly, but I wish you came to stay
Every day I have to wipe my little tears away.
I miss you a bunch, and I hope you miss me too.
I love you so much, I wrote this poem just for you.

Patricia Fusco, Grade 8
St William the Abbot School, NY

Battle

I'm scared, lost, and lonely
I can't lose any more people
Or myself
I'm sick of explosions, popping my eardrums
I miss my family and friends
I want to stop this, but my power is like a powder puff
Trying to hide my fears, but it's escaping
I'm losing hope, but I can't stop now
Can't stop now, Battle on!
BOOM!

Alvin Hsu, Grade 7
Nathaniel Hawthorne Middle School 74, NY

The Battle

The bulky batter steps up to the plate
with complete confidence to eagerly belt the ball
He barks at me in challenge
There are thousands of thoughts
traveling through my head
but I try to focus on the game

I look at the dirt on the mound and kick it with my cleats
like I'm trying to scrape the
earthy bark off a tree trunk
I take a deep breath
to calmly clear my mind
I am ready to think of nothing but the
center of the catcher's brown mitt
It calls to me, begging for the ball

I am a rocket ready to take off
I release the ball and
before I know it, it has already completed its journey
The catcher's mitt welcomes the ball and SSTTEERIIKE!!
That batter was out like a light
after his ferocious fight was over!

Marcello Carelli, Grade 7
Fox Lane Middle School, NY

The Ski Accident

I was on the icy frigid ground, crying, screaming, wanting help
Tasting the salty tears running down my face
The skis tricked me into going on that trail
As they swooped down the slope
It was like a whole football team was trying to kill me
In a flash I was in the ambulance on my way to the hospital
Bumps were killing me
Like someone shot me right in the heart
I was here lying in the hospital
It was the scariest moment of my life
I was only eleven years old
Not knowing what was going to happen
Home at last
Imagine going through that

Taylor Cutroneo, Grade 7
Fox Lane Middle School, NY

The Watch

When he handed me that watch, my heart filled with joy
When he smiled at me, I was proud to be his grandson
When he took care of me, I knew he loved me
When he visited my house, I knew he cared for my family
When he died, I knew everything was going to be all right
When I pray for him, I know he is looking down at me
When I think of him, I know he is with me
This watch he gave me isn't just any watch
It's my grandpa
Who will always be with me

Joey Gervasi, Grade 9
Holy Cross High School, NJ

When Summer Ends (Fall)

When summer ends…
the greens and blues fade away
only to be replaced with crimson red and faded gold

When summer ends…
the red, white and blues of the joyous 4th,
melt into an orange and shadowy black
when the full moon rises on the spooky 31st

When summer ends…
the melodic lullaby of the blue songbirds become overshadowed
by the tormenting gawk of the black beauty, the crow

When summer ends…
the rambunctious playful laughs of innocent children are replaced
by enervate, dreary groans of a dilapidated soul

When summer ends…
the life of nature falls into a deep sleep
until the warmth of the sun reaches their hungry souls

Oh, when summer ends…

Matthew Jeremiah Sato, Grade 7
Galloway Township Middle School, NJ

I Am From

I am from street signs and gun shots
From frustrated mothers and disappointing fathers
I am from screeching tires and florescent lights
From sexual movements and rhythmic melodies
I am from graffiti and spray cans
From loving voices and anticipated screams
I am from rap and R&B
From rare feeling of love, care, success, and pleasure
I am from apartments buildings and gated windows
From notorious feelings of hate, spite, failure, and pain
I am from pregnant teens and STDs
From disappearing acts, nobody for me
I am from abusive relationships and bad break ups
From weed, cocaine, nuvo, and ciroc
I am from prostitutes and hoes being pimped on the block
From an anonymous pink carrousel and scented scrapbooks
I am from courtroom drama and courtroom orders
From violence and murder
I am from continuous moves
From smiles hiding secrets and secrets hiding smiles
I am from fatal reality

Lyric Anate, Grade 9
Millenium Art Academy, NY

The Sunset

As I lay and watch
Such a beautiful sunset
Seems right above me.

Joshua Gannon, Grade 7
Shalom Torah Academy of Western Monmouth County, NJ

My Binder

Starting this year we had to carry
a three inch binder
to help us stay organized in school.
And that's what it did to me.
My binder is so clean and neat.
I can find whatever I need when I need it.
I'm organized from periods 1 to 13.
It's all I'll ever need.
From my main classes in the front
to my special ones in the back.
I can't imagine how I would pass
any of my classes without my binder.
My binder keeps me on my two feet.
It's what helps me succeed.

Reinerio Amaya, Grade 7
Terence C Reilly School #7, NJ

Accessories

Accessories!
Accessories!
Why do we have them?
One-third are useful,
two-thirds are not.
Accessories come in various sizes.
Sizes small, medium, huge,
It goes according to taste.
Glasses, earrings, necklaces,
and a watch to tell time.
Accessories!
Accessories!
I will never comprehend why we have them.
But we wear them every day.

Aiden Martins, Grade 7
Terence C Reilly School #7, NJ

Fall

I love everything that happens in fall,
From the weather to the trees,
To the colors of the leaves,
The crisp feeling in the air,
Even the trees that are bare.
I love that we play in the fall,
In this season I love everything and all.
I like the reds, yellows and oranges,
The apple cider and the pie,
It's so delicious and I don't know why!
The extraordinary time of Halloween,
The amazing times of dressing up,
The fun times that we have in fall,
Will never end because it's a ball!

Shannon Burke, Grade 7
St Mary School, NJ

Fireworks

High up in the air,
fireworks decorate the sky when there is a special occasion.
Lighting up the dark,
they make a beautiful picture.
Exploding in the sky, breaking the silence, vanishing between the stars,
it is a wonder that everyone wants to watch.
Fireworks are worth seeing.

Ellen Zwartkruis, Grade 8
New Providence Middle School, NJ

Raindrop

Tumbling down from ominous clouds,
The raindrop splashes on a delicate leaf.
Barely hanging on as it slips down the slick surface,
It reluctantly drips away.
Plummeting once more, riding on a steady breeze, plopping into a silver lake,
The drop creates glassy ripples as the water swallows it up.
I love the rain!

Jillian Turner, Grade 8
New Providence Middle School, NJ

Little Kids

Explaining out-of-this-world stories,
little kids always know how to make you happy.
Expressing their wild imagination,
kids always seem to have the answer.
Flying to China, hopping with bunnies, fighting with Power Rangers,
small children always know how to have fun.
I love spending my time with little kids.

Claudia Lucciola, Grade 8
New Providence Middle School, NJ

The Light of the Night

Awaiting the thunder boom,
The lightning prepares for its big scene while anticipating its cue.
Showing people its true beauty,
The lightning is set free from the sky.
Heading toward the ground, shocking everyone, and illuminating the sky,
The lightning quickly disappears.
Oh, how fast something this beautiful can come and go.

Nicole Kelly, Grade 8
New Providence Middle School, NJ

An Early Summer Morning

Twinkling through the thin green leaves,
As the day begins the sun shines in its full glory.
Feeling short gusts of cool wind,
I am soothed as chills run down my back.
Hearing the silence, enjoying the setting, beholding the beauty,
Of this gorgeous grove of graceful trees,
Oh how lovely is the beauty of a forest on an early summer morning.

Cooper Hyde, Grade 8
New Providence Middle School, NJ

The Deep Blue

The glimmering blue moving across the horizon
Slow,
A group of curious mackerel
Lower to the ocean floor
Disrupting the angel fish from keeping their nests on the reef below

A graceful sperm whale glides by
The mackerel avoiding their unfortunate doom
Rising to the surface bubbles galore
As the whale chases and eats the mackerel

Green plankton floating by the current
The tuna coming to get a quick snack
The mackerel still trying to survive
Tiger sharks and black marlin approach

The mackerel swimming away
Futile but attempting
All of the mackerel
Are eaten except for two…

Morgan Evans, Grade 8
Regina Coeli School, NY

My Brother

I care about my brother
But, half of the time
I don't feel related to him.
He acts like a crazy ape.
He is annoying because he imitates me.
Sometimes he acts mature
By doing his chores and obeying our parents.
However, he always wants to be in charge.
Even though we still fight with each other,
I know he cares about me.
I'm never bored when he is around.
He protects me, always!
I will always love him.

Kamila Dasilveira, Grade 7
Terence C Reilly School #7, NJ

Why I'm Drug Free

I am drug free because I love sports!
Sports are my life!
If I didn't play sports I would be a Couch potato.
I will always be drug free because I love sports.
Drugs would ruin everything for me
I wouldn't be able to get a basketball scholarship.
It would just ruin my life.
I want to live long,
and stay good at sports.
I think drugs are just so not cool.
They put life to no good use!
I would always put my life to good use.
That is why I am always drug free.

Ireland Kramer, Grade 7
St Stephen's School, NY

Love

What is Love, but the pure sweetness of honey,
Tainted by the soul of man.
The essence of love is greater than any mortal capability,
Beyond the reach of any man, woman or child.
Love is mocked, mocked by all living beings,
Being imitated, so shallowly, so weakly.
Man does not understand what Love really is.
It can never really achieve true Love, for it is beyond them.
They can only wallow in their poor excuse for an imitation,
And put on fake faces of happiness.
So then, the essence of Love, what is it?
Is it a beautiful butterfly, or an elegant peacock?
Neither!
Love cannot be compared to mortal creatures,
For it is beyond anything they can or would imagine.
Never can Love be comprehended by me or you,
Only by forces beyond us can Love truly be known.
And to us, it is just a mystery that we try to decipher hopelessly.
We will never understand it.
Never.

Samuel Goldman, Grade 9
Pelham Memorial High School, NY

Dance

I am a dancer.
I hear the beat.
I hear the thunder of the music.
I preordain, practice, perform.
The beat of the music goes boom, boom, boom.
My feet go tap, tap, tap.
I may mess up,
I may fail,
But I keep trying.
Dance, dance, dance.
Dance is like a town tap.
Dance is like corks upon the waves.
Dance is life.

Zaneta Jackman, Grade 8
St Clare School, NY

Your Shadow

I do not have a face, or any clothes to wear.
I die at night, and am reborn as each new day is.
I copy you with each move you make,
Whether it is swift or slow.
I am one of a kind.
I have been many things before you;
A flower, a rock, an animal, a human.
I follow you around whether you like it or not.
I am darkness in the day.
You control me to dance or stand still,
Laugh or cry.
I am only but a shadow,
A replica of you.

Juliana Mastrolia, Grade 8
Holy Innocents School, NJ

911

Huge 767 planes flying low,
Everyone panics,
The second boom shakes the city,
Debris and smoke fill the air,
The northern building collapses,
A loud crackle alerts you,
The second tower falls,
No one can breathe,
Today we are still healing,
Now bin Laden is dead,
The memory is with us all.

Donald Longo, Grade 8
Keyport High School, NJ

Our Untrue Love

Our love was like a bottomless ocean,
As we swam with the fish all day.
The one day the thunder rolled in —
The waves crashed over me —
I was drowning —
Trying to get out of the storm,
I slowly started toward the surface,
Closer and closer —
The light started to appear
As I emerged on the surface —
Without you.

Carrie Miller, Grade 8
Galloway Township Middle School, NJ

Good Things

Good things always end
Good spirit, good mood, good friend
They wash away
In one quick day
Never to return again
People say
That in a way
Feelings won't ascend
But people are wrong
And feelings are strong
And good things NEVER end

Mary Heck, Grade 9
Bergen County Academies, NJ

Leaves

I live in the air,
Floating, drifting.
I always hang with my friend, tree.
I want to go on vacation,
But when I do, it never ends.
I will become one with ground,
Tree's friend.
Maybe we will be friends too,
Later…

Valerie Gray, Grade 8
Sts Peter & Paul School, NY

Second

I am your second everything and she will always be your first.
First kiss,
First hug,
First friend,
First love.
I am your second and forever will be
We cannot change the past.
When we are together I can't get myself to care,
When you're with her my insecurities eat me alive.
She was your first everything…
First kiss,
First hug,
First friend,
First love.
You said it ended long ago but how do I really know?
She still has feelings for you
It's easy to see you have feelings for me right now.
Can't she see the way you always kiss me, hug me, say that you love me every day
You tell me I'm your number one even though,
She was your first, and I am your second.

Devin Goldring, Grade 7
Cedar Drive Middle School, NJ

Lifeless

Falling from the sky
As if they were paratroopers
Midget ice crystals hit the ground
Landing harmlessly gentle babies of Mother Nature pile up on the sod.
Regrouping with lost friends,
Speaking softly,
Watching others rain on them,
These flakey creatures only want peace.
Lifeless little snowflakes are absolutely beautiful.

Zander Felezzola, Grade 8
New Providence Middle School, NJ

Life Is a Train

I get on in the beginning and don't get off till the end
As I walk through the train I make new friends
All with a story of their own hidden glory
Like life, the outside moves too fast even if we'd rather live in the past
The floor underneath me stays perfectly still
The outside world will move at its will
Like life things happen I just don't understand
They go as fast as an hourglass filled with sand
The inside of my life stays perfectly still
But maybe one day I'll pass over a hill
It will shake me up it will be abrupt
But remember life's a thrill
Don't live life looking out the windowsill
Treat life like a train look ahead to tomorrow
And leave behind your pain and sorrow
Because we all have a place to get
Even if we don't know it yet

Kate Carney, Grade 7
St William the Abbot School, NY

I Am a Pencil
I am a pencil
Rolling and writing.

I live in a crayon bag
When I'm not at work.

My job is to write,
All day, all night.

I like to wear yellow,
Leather jackets in general.

I go on vacation,
When I get dull and flat.

I like to go places,
Especially the sharpener.

My favorite holiday
Is when there is nothing to write.

I came from a tree,
But hang with some markers.
Conor Kellner, Grade 8
Sts Peter & Paul School, NY

The Riddler
T hinker
H avoc
E nigma

R iddle
I ntricate
D angerous
D eathtrap
L earned
E laborate
R ough
Jacob Roman, Grade 7
Ocean Academy, NJ

Fresh off the Boat
Fresh off the boat,
That's what we are,
Old from our country,
In a land afar.
Whether the West,
Or the Far East,
Whether from Roma,
Or from Beijing.
Fresh off the boat,
We all stand,
Entrepreneurs
From a foreign land.
Michael Brusca, Grade 8
Holy Family School, NY

Never Forget
We will never forget
The people we lost
The huge planes crashing into the World Trade Center
The screams of worried people
The destruction and explosion in our ears

We will never forget when
People jumped out of the building as their last resort
The taste of smoke in our mouths
Sirens of brave firemen risking their lives to save our loved relatives
Still today when they shine the two beams of light in the air on "Ground Zero"
We will never forget
Marlon Bennett, Grade 8
Keyport High School, NJ

JK
Jessica
Libra, creative, smart, active
Sister of Julia
Lover of theater, mystery, and writing
Who feels happy when they get their first pet, anxious to find out the role they got in a play,
Excited when they get a new "Diary of a Wimpy Kid" book
Who needs a skateboard, a nook, or a Mac book pro
Who gives colorful paintings to my family, treats to my dog, and hugs to my sister
Who fears black widows, death and fire
Who would like to be a teacher, a famous actress or win a million dollars
Resident of East Brunswick
Kimberlin
Jessica G. Kimberlin, Grade 7
Hammarskjold Middle School, NJ

Dining at Dusk
Gliding across the water,
the loon swims while searching for his dinner.
Taking a quick dip,
he pops up to the surface with a minnow.
Checking his surroundings, gulping it down, and swimming proudly away,
this fowl makes sure everyone knows he's eaten his prey.
"Looooooo" he cries out as day becomes night!
Colin Forbes, Grade 8
New Providence Middle School, NJ

Hijab
Why do you stare?
Just because I don't show my hair,
Because I don't wear tights and skinny jeans,
You might think I don't care about my sense of fashion or style,
But the hijab to me is a full cover-up,
It makes me feel modest and protected,
I wear a hijab to make sure no one looks at me as an object but rather as a human being,
To make sure people judge me based on who I am on the inside, not how I'm dressed,
I wear the hijab because I want to, not because someone forces me to,
Hijab is my freedom, and my identity,
It's who I am.
Fatima Shifa, Grade 7
Al Ghazaly Elementary School, NJ

Halloween
Cauldrons and witches,
Frankenstein's stitches,
Children collecting their candy;
Pumpkins and fairies,
Monsters look scary,
And everyone else looks quite dandy.
We all look so silly,
Even though it's so chilly,
A coat would've been very handy...
At the end of the night, we snuggle up cozy,
Warm from our toes, to the tip of our nosey.
This year was so far the greatest I've seen.
I can't wait 'til next year,
Next Halloween.

Courtney Whyte, Grade 7
Hammarskjold Middle School, NJ

Jazz
Listen to the sweet sound of the sax
The blare from the trumpet, too
Feel the rhythm from the drums
This is what jazz is made of

Louis Armstrong's voice of wonder
Scott Joplin's hands of gold
Miles Davis' birth of the cool
This is what jazz is made of

The trumpets scream
The guitars follow suit
The rhythm section keeps the tune
So go and listen to jazz music soon

Lily Krietzberg, Grade 7
Cedar Drive Middle School, NJ

Puzzle
I must link the puzzle together
I need an answer now
The search can't go on forever
Ask me but I don't know how
There's always a hint or a sign
There's Jesus to lead the way
No one else to draw the line
Nothing someone else can say
I know if I am going in the right direction
And I will do the right thing
There will never be perfection
But the sound of trying will always ring
I will finally put the pieces together
And we will all live peacefully forever

Samantha Schlinger, Grade 7
St William the Abbot School, NY

Autumn Calls
Golden leaves dancing in the breeze;
Thin branches falling off of the maple trees;
Jack-o-lanterns glowing in the night;
Candy is the only thing in my sight!

Snapping twigs blanket the ground like snowflakes on a cold winter day;
Whispering wind throughout the town enters my body in such a way;
School bus engine is a lion's roar, loud as can be;
Pulls up at 7 in the morning "Stop wait for me!"

Burnt pumpkin pie can be smelled across the country
It's one of those fabulous foods made just for me;
Chimneys bring smoke throughout the air;
Campfire stories that might give you the scare!

Chocolate and candy is what I enjoy the most;
On Halloween day I walk the whole east coast;
Pumpkin seeds sizzle in my mouth;
They go down my throat, to my stomach, and out!

I hike, I bike, I run those trails with the birds;
The pain in my muscles can't be described into words!
Autumn is a season that I like best;
It's when my five senses are put to the test!

Ian Rubin, Grade 8
Commack Middle School, NY

Stapler
Who would be a stapler, who could help it?
People push down so hard.
The stapler tries to get away, but she does not succeed.

Staples go into the paper and the kids run away, again and again.
Just like she's a toy you only play with when you're bored.
Loquacious kids wait in line to use her;
No one knows how much it hurts her to push the staples out.
Since staples come out though, everyone uses her.

The stapler is far too kind at most times.
Today happens to be different; the stapler is an angry giant that has been awoken.
People treat her awful, and now she is stuck.

The stapler has it rough, like a kid in poverty.
All she wants to do is eradicate the children and have some peace for once.
As soon as she gets unstuck, she gets jammed again; this time she gets stuck on purpose.
Because she gets jammed, everyone smacks her to get her working again.

The stapler is an angry businesswoman now.
Everyone is smacking her and hurting her.
Now she decides to stop working completely.
Finally there is some peace.

Melissa Weiss, Grade 8
Clinton Public School, NJ

Summer
I saw
the bright gleaming sunset over the steaming pool and the crashing waves break into my face.

I heard
strong winds whistling and angry water drops charging to the ground.

I smelled
juicy ribs sizzling on the BBQ and oily suntan lotion on my burning skin.

I tasted
the flaky frosting from my sister's 16th birthday cake and the scrumptious chocolate frozen yogurt from Yogurt Crazy.

I felt
sweat chasing down my face and an air soft shot that felt like a bee sting.

I said
"Yes! No school" and "I love sleeping to 12:00 noon!"

And it was the strangest thing:
feeling the ground rumble below me and rapid hurricane winds all in one week.

Zach Cohen, Grade 8
Commack Middle School, NY

On the Line
I am from the Lexus that was owned before my time
My mom's face when she learns that their pride and joy is a boy.
I am from the laughs shared during trivial pursuit —
The shock that came from Pa
The time spent to make manners a valuable resource.

From the first toy, to the first cell phone, to the first car, to the first house.
All these memories are remembered permanently etched in my brain.
A scar from the time before
My roots spread from the great wall to east Europe across amber seas of grain to the land of liberty
From the "Three Stooges" and "Who's on First"

From all the good times and bad.
From torn jeans and strange times.
From the great depression and the potato famine
From all the times that made us scream in both amazement and grief
And for all the times we've shared and will treasure forever
I am the one who hangs their head in sorrow when "Another One Bites the Dust"
As another loved one rides the "Stairway to Heaven."

Eric Burns, Grade 7
Schuyler School, NJ

Silence
Gliding down upon the taupe limb,
a wise, auburn owl perches himself as the ivory moon rises languidly in the star-scattered sky.
Ruffling his chestnut feathers,
gives a quiet hoot.
Blinking his fiery amber eyes, puffing his dappled chest, and unfurling his large speckled wings,
he swoops off the branch with elegance.
Oh, how enchanting it is when he vanishes into the silence of the night.

Caelynn Hogarth, Grade 8
New Providence Middle School, NJ

Being Drug-Free

Doing drugs is no good
It's never fun to see someone do them
If you do drugs…
You'll be done for!
If someone asks you to do drugs,
Say NO!
Even if you're pressured,
Always say no
If someone you know does drugs
Then that's not good
Remember,
Drugs affect your health!
And once you do drugs,
You can die!
So be careful making right choices!

Cindy Nguyen, Grade 8
St Stephen's School, NY

Drug-Free

You might feel left out,
Or you might feel sad.
You might feel scared,
Or you just might feel bad.
However,
Solving problems isn't really a drug's forte.
Brain cells are dying,
And your accidents are multiplying.
You have lost much interest,
And have horrible changes in appearance.
Once addicted,
It's so hard to stop!
It's a better idea to just not start at all.
So come on, let's keep ourselves clean,
Because drug-free is the way I want to be.

Ciara Vedella, Grade 8
St Stephen's School, NY

Just Like Him

A rose,
Just like him,
Beautiful and sweet,

A thorn,
Just like him,
Can take a harsh beat,

The words he says,
The challenges he face,

Just like him,
He.
Always.
Stays.

Cynthia Cheng, Grade 7
William Davies Middle School, NJ

The Pencil of Life

There was an orange writing tool on my desk,
I touched it gently while the wheel barrel began to roll.
The wooden pencil rolled off my shiny metal desk rim,
The stick created an echo in the hollow wide desk.
It rolled towards me,
So slowly even a turtle could go twice as fast.
I slanted the desk with my blue sneakers on the two front legs,
So it rolled quickly and made more progress.
Just like a person needs encouragement to one direction,
When all they have is a flat surface to go nowhere.
The pencil rolled even more towards me,
Now halfway through the desk that was the pencil as New Zealand in the world.
I stared inside the rusty old desk.
It was like the sewer underground with nasty garbage,
As in this desk curse words and pieces of torn lined paper stuck to gum.
Out of my sight the pencil dropped to my blue shoe,
And the skeleton ended his life.
I grieved the graveyard of my companion,
When it barreled down the classroom seats.

Jason Wong, Grade 7
Deerfield Elementary School, NJ

Amazing Just the Way You Are

You're just like a storm; every time I see you, you blow me away
And I would never waste the moments I spend with you,
Because every raindrop counts

You're just like the ground I walk on; always there when I'm not stable
And yet no matter what, you let me step all over you
To see what's hidden behind that hard concrete

You're just like the ocean's waves; crashing down and tearing apart my hopes and dreams
And yet for some crazy reason,
I can't help it but to love your currents

You're just like a dream to me; too good to be true
And it seems that every time I pinch myself,
I wish for this nightmare to end

You're just like a riddle; different and unique, not like any silly fairytales
And you're too hard to comprehend, easy to read,
But yet amazing in your own way

Elizabeth Rose Thornton, Grade 8
Keyport High School, NJ

Are You Scared?

I awakened at a faint sound. It seemed almost as if I was imagining it.
Then all of a sudden I heard "BANG!" then a slight gasp.
My body shook in horror. Who was out there?
I felt like I was paralyzed. I reached my hand onto my cold as ice doorknob.
I stopped like a deer in headlights. There were footsteps coming down the hallway.
I locked my door and floated toward my bed, my nightgown draping onto the floor.
The steps got louder and louder. My doorknob jiggled, then turned and opened.
I screamed as loud as possible but my screams were baffled by the sight of my…sister?

Savannah Gibbs, Grade 7
William Davies Middle School, NJ

Being Against Drugs

There is nothing more disgusting
Then the constant fussing,
About drugs
Drugs are evil, terrible, and sickening too,
Why people do them?
No one has a clue
When you're high
Everything flies by,
It will go to your head
And before you know it,
You could be dead

Peter Kroetsch, Grade 8
St Stephen's School, NY

Fall Is...

Fall is the best time of the year
Warm vibrant colors
Cool weather
Halloween and Thanksgiving.

Fall is about family
Sitting by the fire
Watching movies
Drinking hot chocolate.

Fall is filled with great things.

Demi Rivera, Grade 7
St Mary School, NJ

When Does Sunshine Leave

The sunshine is gone
The darkest days are holding on
Shadows where people whisper
Daylight sends a kiss to their soul
Undertaken breathes by those who love
Yet, the sunshine still does leave
The howls at the moon
And occasional screams at the night
The sunshine returns
Yet, darkness comes again

Jasmyne Medina, Grade 8
Keyport High School, NJ

The Football Life

I like to play football
And playing with my teammates.
Having fun running
Around with the ball.
I like being able to get on the field
And the RUSH
Of getting out there
With your team
And winning the game.
I love the football life!

Isaiah Bowman, Grade 7
Ocean Academy, NJ

To Live Is the Rarest Thing of All, Most Just Merely Exist

Combining talent, potential, and laziness,
Every day questioning what to make of it,
Me and my loved ones doubting me hating it,
Reluctantly though I agree with them,
I know what my obligation is,
Die trying or get rich but avoid the hood pit,
Leading to my alternative,
Get an education and earn basketball recognition,
Avoid lifetime on probation and sleeping with garbage bins,
But in this nation for the American dream that is so famous,
All you see now is homeless people without employment with hungry children,
Maybe I could rattle in a few buckets and spit verses and rerun it,
But am I gonna have enough effort when I'm older to make a life out of it,
Everyone repeating Timmy think realistic,
You're not strong enough, good enough, or fast enough, in the league to be major big,
Just in human form nothing more than a walking stick,
You're not talented and tough enough to put together a stellar hit,
You don't have big a heart enough to be forever iconic,
Living on a prayer though,
Through thick and thin always on God's link
My goal unlike others is to actually live, not just sit around casually and just commonly exist

Tahmid Chowdhury, Grade 8
Middle School 101 Edward R Byrne, NY

Mark

Mark
Fun-loving, funny, creative
Brother of Mena Ibrahim
Lover of laptops, Snickers, family
Who feels nervous on tests, happy when playing sports, sad when doing homework
Who needs more sleep, less work, more money
Who fears snakes, spiders, and bugs
Who would like to gets straight A's, have a statue of me and go skydiving
Resident of East Brunswick
Ibrahim

Mark Ibrahim, Grade 7
Hammarskjold Middle School, NJ

The Other Side of Your Ego

"Egos" they can sometimes affect our minds, thoughts, and reputations.
They are cast as the shadows of the night and troubles of the day.
They have a thin line between reality and make-believe.
Egos are our split personalities that we have no control over.
They are like curious babies roaming, and roaming,
And roaming with thoughts that you cannot tame.
With the pounding of your head and the beating of your heart,
You slowly begin to feel the tarnishing of your reputation.
You begin to fall into a deep depression from the blistering comments,
And thoughts of others.
These thoughts began to increase "louder, louder and louder" in your mind,
Wishing that it would stop at anytime,
But all it is, is your big-mouth ego,
It seems to be holding you back from the fact that all along
It was just an ego.

Camille Burse, Grade 8
St Clare School, NY

The Growing Child

I want the big yellow truck, Mom
I want the big bear, Mom
I want that big hat now
Can I have a book?
Can I have those shoes?
Can I go out to play?
May I get a chip?
May I watch television?
May I try some coffee?
I need to get those games
I need you to play a game with me
I need Dad to see something
I'm going to get some food
I'm going out to play with friends
I'm going to a party
You know what, Mom?
What do you want?

Justin D. Lee, Grade 7
Nathaniel Hawthorne Middle School 74, NY

August 20th

You told me you sung in the shower,
It took only a mere hour.
I was shortly hooked right in,
Only I didn't know that you'd be my biggest sin.
I held onto you so dearly, even when you pushed away,
I tried everything in my power to make you stay,
But with my words, your heart I could not sway.
I handed over my heart to you on a silver platter,
But with a soul as cruel as yours, it would never matter.
You've left me here, broken and bruised,
Never in my life have I felt so used.
A dirty rag thrown to the bottom of the pile,
Never would you stay longer than just a little while.
Always had somewhere else to be,
Always a place that didn't involve me.
I gave up my happiness, I gave up my heart,
But boy, were you my biggest mistake from the start.

Cambra Conover, Grade 9
Cape May County Technical High School, NJ

My Dying Flower

He is a dying flower — with nothing else to lose.
His deep ocean-blue eyes tell me his story —
Of how he lost the people he loves.
They were like roses, strong and beautiful…
Killed by the raging fire.
Now his story ends —
Before the last petal drops from his flower of life,
Wilts away — soon to die —
I take him into my arms and hold him close —
So close his heart beats in my ears —
Not letting go until his last petal falls.

Umara Malik, Grade 8
Galloway Township Middle School, NJ

Live, Laugh, Love

Life is a beautiful melody
You write the lyrics to your own song
Like a theatrical composer
Let the lyrics lead you in the life you
Want to live

A smile is a ray of sunshine
Peaking over the horizon
About to rise over the beautiful lands of Earth
Let your smile lead you to the lyrics
To your symphony

Love is like a butterfly
The more you chase it
The more it will avoid you
But if you turn your attention to other things
It will come and sit softly on your shoulder

Jayme Bryant, Grade 9
W Tresper Clarke High School, NY

Scars

Scars on my skin
Some pink — some red — some black and blue.
Hold painful secrets
that are locked in a box.
Secrets that nobody should know
Secrets that would ruin me.

They teach me a lesson, remind me of my mistakes.
Play on in my head like a broken record
Remind me of how painful it was to be born.

Scars will be with me forever.
Mocking me
Killing me.
Now I will bury them down in the earth
Far away from me
Leaving me with only their memory.

Arielle Schafer, Grade 8
Galloway Township Middle School, NJ

Cheater

I don't know what I was thinking when I said yes to you,
But now I do, now I got a clue
Now soon I'm going to make a fool out of you.
I know you're scared, I can see it in your eyes.
You said you loved me, but now that's just a lie
You look like you're going to cry
You better watch out because,
Baby, you ain't going to last much longer
I'm so much stronger
Baby, I can't hold it in anymore, I love you
And I forgive you. Please don't be mad.

Emily Digiorgi, Grade 7
St. Mary's Prep, NJ

Meaning of Life

My family is pretty big,
Altogether we have six.
You can say that is a lot,
Compared to the normal mix.

We have three pets,
One dog, two cats.
One cat is skinny,
While the other is fat.

I have one brother and two sisters,
They all try their very best.
Even if I do not show it,
They hold a soft spot in my chest.

Having a big family there is always something to do,
Video games, soccer, swimming,
Each day is something new.

Noah Welsh, Grade 7
New Egypt Middle School, NJ

Heaven

Alone I stand in a flowered field
Clouds of gold and silver line the skies
Shadows dance between blossoming trees
Streams of sunlight will light your way
And angels take your hands
Towers high, stacks of stone rise up
To greet the purple dawn and smiling moon
Children run, free of worry and care
Crystal waters meet rushing little feet
And suddenly stars begin to twinkle above
Galaxies swirl, be seated in your throne
And watch the clocks turn
With eyes like a hawk and legs made of stone
Seas deep and oceans strong
Nothing can hold you back from the place
Only you see within your dreams,
One only you can see, a place only you can be
Your Heaven

Catherine Ishimasa, Grade 8
Holy Innocents School, NJ

Wonderful Man

Can you be the man I want you to be?
The wonderful man who used to love me?
The father who will hold his son in his arms?
The stranger who will show all his charms?
The brother who will stand by his sister's side?
The son who shares his father's pride?
The worker who gets all jobs done?
The best friend who's always so much fun?
Can you be the man I want you to be?
That wonderful man who used to love me?

Somaillah D. Slack, Grade 8
Keyport High School, NJ

Concealed

Our faces are hidden behind a mask
in brilliant shades of pink
It keeps us from being judged by the outside world
it's much harder than you think!

We paint our faces as an artist would
but with shadows, glosses and blush
I think I'm ready to face the world now.
But wait! Just one final touch!

Is this really who I am?
Is my mind in the right place?
Is it right to conceal my face behind a mask
So that no one can see my true face?

Let's live in a world
where no one needs to hide
their personality, beliefs or race.
But we can certainly feel beautiful walking out of our house
without makeup on our face!

Isabelle Yazon, Grade 8
Holy Family School, NY

My Drug Free Role Model

My role model is my sister,
Who is drug free,
And I admire her for that.
She is my role model for many reasons.
One reason is being drug free.
She is drug free because drugs are harmful.
They can cause diseases,
Or even kill people.
My sister is twenty-one so she can drink alcohol,
But she is very responsible with that privilege.
Drugs can stunt growth,
Cigarettes can give a person lung cancer,
And more harmful things.
This is why my sister and I,
Are drug free.

Hannah Panzica, Grade 8
St Stephen's School, NY

The Wild One

The wild one rides away,
Through the sunny passageway,
Only he knows where he will go,
Through forests and streams that flow,
Through the season's bitter bite,
From little eggs to birds that take flight,

From sunsets sleeping on the sky,
To dawn when the birds awake and fly,
Through pumpkin patches and skies of gray,
Until the sun starts to fade away.

Caitlyn Manning, Grade 7
William R Satz Middle School, NJ

New Life

My baby,
Alone,
No one with him,
I can't face it,
Seeing him get hurt,
That note in middle school,
That one word,
Dead,
I ran to the house,
Hope was on my side,
I got there,
With the only words that were in my head,
I love you,
Now he knows how I feel for him,
Kissing all night,
Wanting and getting to be more than friends,
A true love's heart,
Gives a note,
Saying that care is one thing,
That is the key to the beginning,
The beginning of a new life.

Olivia Guardabascio, Grade 7
Toms River Intermediate School East, NJ

Fate

Fate hit me and I cried
Fate nailed me did I die?
Fate crushed me right before we won
The pain I could not overcome

I was carted off the field
But told the paramedics to yield
Fate was laughing his stupid laugh
It killed me, it crushed me

I wanted to hurt him but knew I couldn't
Fate could be stronger than an ocean current
I opened my eyes as I saw my x-ray
I yelled in disbelief and dismay

Kyle Prouty, Grade 7
New Egypt Middle School, NJ

Love

This is how it should be.
The way you and I are together.
I just want this to last forever.

I just love the way you are.
The way you look into my eyes.
I can't stop myself from loving you more and more.

I hope I can spend forever with you.
I will give you a feather,
The feather that holds our destiny.

Michael DeCarlo, Grade 8
Regina Coeli School, NY

Rude Awakening

When I close my eyes, my former life vanishes
And my thoughts and dreams take flight.
I am a drop of inky blackness
Slowly drifting skyward to a different dimension
Where anything is possible.
I soar above jagged mountaintops
The wind flowing across my body in ripples of joy.
But my irritating clock
Reaches up
And sets off the fire alarm
In my head,
Screaming at me to wake up
Like a freight train
Threatening to run me over
So I pull the emergency brakes
And realize how make-believe
Those adventures and achievements really were.
Simply figments of my imagination.
And that perfect little paradise
Is gone.
How I hate mornings.

Kevin Robare, Grade 7
Fox Lane Middle School, NY

The Beast of the Sky

Gliding in the clouds,
the eagle flies gracefully
as he spots his prey.

Eying his dinner,
he prepares to attack.

Diving towards the ground,
aiming for the tasty treat,
extending his monstrous claws,
the eagle snatches the mouse swiftly and fatally.

What a beautiful beast this creature of the sky is!

Jimmy Evangelos, Grade 8
New Providence Middle School, NJ

My Younger Sister

My Younger Sister
Gives me many problems
Sometimes a pain in the neck
Wants to get me in trouble
Have to take care of her when parents not around
But, on the flip side
Still glad to have her around
She can keep secrets
As she learns a lot from me
I have to be a good influence for her
But I still love her
I'm glad to have her as my sister

Johanny Lojano, Grade 7
Terence C Reilly School #7, NJ

Snow

Falling from above,
the snow lands on the ground while children play.
Covering everything,
the cold, white flakes fall from the sky.
Building snowmen, throwing snowballs, and sledding down a hill,
We enjoy the snow.
It is amazing!

Mary Kate Buckman, Grade 8
New Providence Middle School, NJ

The Sleeping Bats

Hanging upside down,
The bat sleeps until a loud bang awakes him.
Flapping around in panic,
The bat searches for the source.
Searching, flying, and screeching,
The bat uses his sonar to find the noisemaking culprit.
He finds none and goes back to sleep

Tyler Gazaway, Grade 8
New Providence Middle School, NJ

A Wonderful Welcome Home

Entering my house while carrying my backpack,
I am greeted by my dog.
Running toward me,
She almost knocks me down with excitement.
Wagging her tail, licking my face, and blocking me from leaving,
She shows me she misses me.
I love coming home to that wonderful greeting.

Juliana Ruta, Grade 8
New Providence Middle School, NJ

The Chase

Barking at the baby rabbit,
The young golden retriever dashed across the field.
Sprinting as fast as he could to catch his little prey,
The puppy soon tired,
Panting, whimpering, and resting was all he could do.
In the blink of an eye,
His eyes shut as he fell into a deep sleep.

Colleen Judge, Grade 8
New Providence Middle School, NJ

Beauty

Warmed by the sun,
The beach awaits me.
Coming with me,
Allie, my best friend enjoys it too.
Glistening sand, flying seagulls, and a surprising blue sky
The scene at the beach makes me melt inside.
I want to stay there forever!

Chloe Anekstein, Grade 8
New Providence Middle School, NJ

Golden Goal

Jumping into the cerulean sky,
he kicked the ball into the net, just as the game ended.
Landing lightly on his feet,
the scorer turned around and ran to his cheering teammates.
Complimenting him, praising his shot, and yelling his name,
they lifted him onto their shoulders.
They had won the game by a spectacular goal!

Mark Van der Merwe, Grade 8
New Providence Middle School, NJ

Sunset on the Beach

Sitting on the never-ending ocean blue horizon,
The fiery red ball of light begins to set as the day ends.
Producing rainbows and beautiful combinations of color,
"Helios" is getting dimmer and dimmer as night approaches.
Faded and calm, glowing a bit, reflecting beauty,
The sky now produces only light from the full moon.
A beautiful sunset is best seen on a beach.

Shannon Charlton, Grade 8
New Providence Middle School, NJ

A's

Leaping with excitement,
I saw my report card that I had just received.
Jittering black printed ink "A's"
Were printed next to each subject,
Jumping up and down, running around, celebrating,
I went wild.
Wait until my mom sees this!

Johnny Shahpazian, Grade 8
New Providence Middle School, NJ

In the Morning

Glistening in the sun,
The dew settled on the field while the birds chirped.
Shining so brightly,
It looked like 1,000 jewels.
Sitting on the grass, waking the world, watering the earth,
It brought peace to my soul.
Oh what a lovely sight!

Noah Kudman, Grade 8
New Providence Middle School, NJ

Buildings

Towering over the tiny people,
The skyscraper stands absolutely still, as people below walk.
Looking as amazing as ever,
The building appears like a gentle giant.
Looking fierce, being powerful, failing never,
The monument watches over the city.
What a sight!

Philip Catanzaro, Grade 8
New Providence Middle School, NJ

Fall

Leaves, leaves all around,
leaves, leaves full of sound!

Leaves, leaves such a treat,
leaves, leaves not so neat!

Leaves, leaves hit the ground,
leaves, leaves all are found!

Leaves, leaves piled high,
leaves, leaves in the sky!

Katy Nelson, Grade 7
St Mary School, NJ

Nothing

One square,
Two squares,
Three squares,
And four more.
How many squares
Are on the floor?
Wait, I can see some
Rectangles on the floor too,
I can touch them all
With the bottom
Of my shoe.

Robert Graham, Grade 7
Regina Coeli School, NY

Halloween

Screaming children in the night
Dancing monsters with such fright
Collecting candy one by one
Never ending 'til we see sun
Candy wrappers cover the ground
No one's stomach is very proud
Tonight the dead come alive alive
But only once a year surprise surprise
Bones shake skeletons awake
The moon comes out the wolf pack howls
And Halloween begins

Isabella Petrone, Grade 7
Hammarskjold Middle School, NJ

Winter Storm

Winter is here,
Now go out and play.
An ice storm is near.
"Wait, what did you say?"

There is an ice storm outside.
And you want me to play.
It's a storm we should hide.
Oh I wish it was May.

Conner Latimer, Grade 7
Regina Coeli School, NY

It's Raining, But the Sky Is Clear

In a melancholy atmosphere asphyxiating you
How can anyone dwell?
She does all alone into the vast night
Assignments smother her to death
No affection is returned
She stands alone in a truculent society
Life gets dysphoric and arduous
One day she shatters into a million pieces
Tears of pain rain down from her murky azure oppressing eyes one by one
Regret and disappointment echoes in her conscience
Her weeping seems as if it will never halt
In this secluded dark frightening corner
Everything loses their brilliant hues in her sight
She seems so distant from her friends
An outcast she is
She can't take the sadness any longer
At last he asks, "Are you all right? I'm worried."
Melancholy rain drops drench her smoky cobalt eyes
A benevolent light pulls her out of the vicious malicious black hole
The river of remorse and failure runs dry
But the stain is there forever

Alina Lou, Grade 8
Hillsborough Middle School, NJ

Fall

Fall; how could anyone resist the colors of the leaves changing;
The cool breeze at that perfect time;
Kids and even adults playing football in the yard;
And what's better than the happy holidays during this splendid season;
Halloween is for the kids who have a craving for sugary sweets;
Thanksgiving is for the families who love getting together;
Food, relatives, even a game or two of football;

Fall is the most peaceful, yet exciting season of the year;
That is until winter comes along.

Max Allen, Grade 7
St Mary School, NJ

As the Rain Keeps Falling

As the sun hides behind a cloud like a small child,
Across the sky dark clouds roll in like bugs drawn to a light.
Concerning the rain, it is a fierce monster.
Outside my house, the rain beats the porch steps.
Within the deep forest, the rain chases small children playing in the trees.
Throughout the long, long day the rain chases the sun around the sky;
The sun begs for mercy, but the rain just won't listen.
Up upon a hill, a child asks the rain to go away, so he can come out and play.
Until the rain has ceased its ranting, the boy will have to wait.
Off the ground and to the sky the rain continues to bounce.
Over fields and plains the rain passes through.
Beyond the cool breezes, the rain is an angry storm.
Through the tunnel, up the hill, he has not found his destination.
Near the end of his journey, the rain stops, satisfied with his work,
Before he leaves and goes to play somewhere else for the rest of the day.

Scott Jackle, Grade 7
Clinton Public School, NJ

The Final Flower

The day grows longer,
Her heartbeat grows weaker,
The flowers next to her bed are wilting like her,
She dies as they die,
Sometimes I wonder if they are her source of life,
Now she can barely open her eyes,
I know I must be with her at her hour of need,
Last night my Father ran away like my luck did,
I'm helpless, but I must stay strong for her,
I give her freezing cold water every day,
It is my attempt at healing her,
But all was in vain because nothing worked,
The flowers turn browner and lose more life.
I'm more scared than ever because her time has come,
I was with her the last hour and there was no sign of life,
Her finger moved ever so slightly as if she were saying goodbye,
As she took her last breath a dead flower fell off its stem,
At that point I realized I gave her water, but not her flowers,
My mistake was as clear as day,
Somehow, somewhere I knew I'd find comfort.

Nina Giacone, Grade 8
Holy Innocents School, NJ

Come and Go

When I was younger, Mommy always told me
"Friends come and go."
I never listened because, to me, Mommy was old.
What did it mean when she told me this?
I was as curious as a blind man to the world,
I got older and more mature,
Brought friends home and actually had a social life.
Mommy still told me, "Friends come and go."
Why did she see a need to tell me this?
Time passed and my friends began to fade.
Tick, tock, boom, thump!
Time lapsed as my heart mourned for them.
The clock spoke to me, saying
"Time changes; your friends are gone."
I remember asking Mommy, "Why do friends come and go?"
She said, "You'll know your true friends."
At the end of the day, I'm the size of the Earth.
Mommy's my true friend,
She has come and will never go.

Armani Langston, Grade 8
St Clare School, NY

Playful Puppy

As the front door opens,
The puppy runs enthusiastically towards his loving owner.
Wagging its chocolate colored tail,
The puppy lets her scratch his ears.
Licking her face, fetching the stick, and slurping his water,
The energetic puppy can do no more.
What a day the puppy has had!

Jen Maluso, Grade 8
New Providence Middle School, NJ

I Am

I am caring and curious
I wonder why the world is full of hate
I hear the fighting out on the streets
I see the violence spreading
I want to make a difference
I am caring and curious

I pretend that everything is okay
I feel like the earth is falling apart
I touch the soul of the people who are broken
I worry that the world will become worse
I cry when I hear about people's death
I am caring and curious

I understand that more help needs to go around
I say everyone can contribute
I dream the world will be a better place
I try to be a good influence
I hope more people could live in peace
I am caring and curious

Stephanie Da Cunha, Grade 7
Hammarskjold Middle School, NJ

Something More to a Dream

Something more to a dream.
A simply dazzling midnight scene,
but thus anyway I enjoy, the winter scheme.
With no snow or hopeless dream,
Nether, the wind of forever blows,
in the dead night show.
Together with star-touched rain.
An unreal reality, forever wanted by me.
With the beauty of the night in plain sight,
fit into a picture frame.
Heart despairingly blown away,
With the overpowering full moon.
Who dazzles all in its light.
Though unreal and nothing more than unreality
every now and then. I
find myself lost in my unreal dream,
but if hope still exist in this hopeless world.
If maybe beyond the sky there is light
then my picture-perfect dream is somehow…
REAL LIFE. Something more to a dream!

Adina Aamir, Grade 7
Al Ghazaly School, NJ

Once Upon an Unknown Time

It all comes back to me, a past I long wished to see.
The truth has been long lost, and hidden from me.
I have been separated by the bittersweet truth.
The dark secrets of the past, haunting me waiting to be discovered.
If only I had Known, if only I had known,
But it is too late now I can't help it now.

Iqra Khan, Grade 8
Grand Avenue Middle School, NY

As I Get Older

I gaze into my family's amazing eyes seeking advice from the wise.
They've picked me up while I was down.
They have let me know that everything will come around.
They tell me right from wrong to make me strong.
When I was lost they led me home.

Now that I'm older I hope to even the score.
Now that I'm older I do more chores than before.
Now that I'm older I am taller and bolder.
Now that I'm older the world seems a bit colder.
Now that I'm older they can lean on my shoulder.

As the years go by I will use what I have learned.
My family's love and respect I hope I will earn.
Life is not easy we all need a sage.
I hope to give guidance to all as I age.

Liam O'Grady, Grade 8
St William the Abbot School, NY

Over

She's over it
Take off the silliness and pettiness.
So sick of it, she's struggling
The shadiness the fakeness
Can you see it?
She's over it.
Protecting her heart like a window cover that can't be removed.
She's over it.
Many tears she has cried
That won't go away.
She's over it.
It takes a second to say hello, forever to say goodbye.
Thinking, thinking, thinking
I don't want you.
Move on, it's simple.
Love, happiness, care appear.

Hanna Oyetunde, Grade 8
St Clare School, NY

Your Love!

Your love,
Is a part of my everyday routine,
Like when I fix my hair
And brush my teeth.
Your love,
Is not only a part of my life but
also my soul,
The thing that keeps me whole.
When I hear your name,
My heart beats BOOM, BOOM, BOOM, nonstop
Thinking if I lose you,
I won't find anyone like you.
Your love is like music,
The more I hear it, the more I love it.
So please don't break my heart.
I don't ever want to be apart.

Alexa Pierre, Grade 8
St Clare School, NY

The Perfect Sport

Soccer is in the blood of almost all Hispanics,
Just like me.
I think it's the best sport of all.
That's the reason why I could talk about it every day.
Soccer is the perfect sport,
if you love to run and kick.
The feeling of preventing the other team
from making a possible winning goal

is stimulating.
Being with your friends
working together to score,
You just feel unstoppable.
The feeling of when you make a goal.
Winning the game!
It's sensational!

Carol Jimenez, Grade 7
Terence C Reilly School #7, NJ

Moonlight Journal

Before I even say a word,
The memories that I hold,
Will be written like a book,
And it shall be witnessed by the moon.
Though you cannot read it out loud,
They were memories that made me feel astounded.
No one can see these memories but me,
But that's all right,
Because every day, when I wake up,
Another page is written.

Roxana Ponce, Grade 8
St Mary's Prep School, NJ

Masks

Masks are gateways to self expression.
You can wear different kinds of masks
To go to different kinds of occasions.
Fancy masks are for balls.
Scary masks for scary parties.
Masks filled with color and life are for birthday parties.
Masks are made to hide emotions
Such as laughs, frowns and tears.

Masks are ways to get become something else.

Ancyto Valcin, Grade 7
Terence C Reilly School #7, NJ

The Power of Words

Every stroke is an unlocked door
Waiting to be opened.
Every line is a different secret
Shared but never stolen.

Every letter is a stepping stone
On the path to understanding.
Every word is the swing of a shovel
that digs deeper into your feelings.

Every page whispers answers
To questions long left behind.
And every piece you've ever read
Is a jewel in the crown of your mind.

Pooja Parwatkar, Grade 9
Hillsborough High School, NJ

Timeless

The old photograph
Of the relatives you loved
Rekindles memories that
Lay dormant for so long.

You remember all of it —
His face, her smile, and
The way that her eyes gleamed
When she was happy.

You relish the memory
And you try to recall more
But you're left just staring
At an old photograph.

Alex Parsells, Grade 7
New Egypt Middle School, NJ

Soccer Game

The whistle blows.
The ball is tapped.
Feet move fast.
Kids yell.

The ball is tapped
The ball is kicked with a "thump."
Feet move fast.
The ball hits the net "swoosh."

The ball is tapped.
Feet move fast.
The ball is kicked with a "thump."
The whistle blows.

Kyle Aaronson, Grade 8
New Egypt Middle School, NJ

Butterfly

Landing on soft flowers
The gorgeous butterfly relaxes and rests as clouds float overhead
Roaming the beautiful earth in search of nothing
It beautifies its surroundings
Flapping its small wings, fluttering around carefree, and soaking in the sun's warmth
This insect enjoys life
How amazing these magnificent creatures are!

Talya Bendarsky, Grade 8
New Providence Middle School, NJ

Mystery of the Deep

Pushing through the colossal waves,
I hold tightly onto the hands of my two sisters as the waves do silly dances on the horizon.
Awaiting the surprises that the ocean holds,
We laugh and scream to our hearts' content.
Diving through, floating atop, and getting crushed by the vast, powerful monster,
We never break our link to each other.
I wonder if I'll ever figure out the mystery of the deep, or if I even want to.

Keara Sullivan, Grade 8
New Providence Middle School, NJ

Daybreak

Casting a warm glow,
the sun illuminates the mystic black night as it grows brighter.
Blanketing the land with light,
the sun ascends into the sky, high above the valleys.
Inching its way into the clouds, hiding its face from view, shedding few rays of light,
it seems to disappear,
But then bursts into view again to announce the presence of daybreak.

Kara Dobias, Grade 8
New Providence Middle School, NJ

Waking Up

Blossoming petals
spread out as the sun shines.
Displaying its colors,
the flower comes to life.
Shooting up from the ground, reaching toward the sun, and discovering a whole new world,
it comes back to life from its slumber.
What many things a flower does to wake up!

Cristina Riccio, Grade 8
New Providence Middle School, NJ

Before Dusk

Glistening on the surface,
the ocean undulates gracefully as sunset reaches its peak.
Bursting with orange, yellow, and red,
the sky gives way to darkness of the night.
Sitting on the horizon, flaming with brightness, and painting the sky with a fiery tone,
the sun starts to sink towards the deep blue.
Darkness engulfs the sky as dusk approaches, and a new sky is born.

Audrey Suh, Grade 8
New Providence Middle School, NJ

Whiteout

Graceful powder glides from the clouds,
Falling onto a pink moist tongue,
Soon to be liquefied by the warm sensation of a mouth.

Wool that was once shed now warms your goose bumped limbs.
Coldness surrounds you, you cannot escape its grip.
Hands thawing by the touch of hot cocoa,
Toes get hit by a pin of pain by the fire.
Winter is here, and so is the shiver.

Ashley Brunner, Grade 8
New Egypt Middle School, NJ

Judgment

People will judge you
The negative storm clouds will never go away
It will always hang over your head
Some people give in
And get struck by lightning
But those who are strong
Get an umbrella
And ignore the cast judgments
Then the rain of judgment will fade away

Philip Thomas, Grade 7
Terence C Reilly School #7, NJ

To Make the World a Better Place

The way we can make the world a better place
Is not just to stare at it's face
To me it seems like a disgrace
To see no one getting up
Picking up garbage from the floor
So many people,
day by day going poor
We knock on doors getting people to come outside,
so we can join together and make the world shine

Jonathon Tehozol, Grade 9
New York Institute for Special Education, NY

Flying Out of Death's Bittersweet Trap

Saturated in sorrow,
I realize that until we meet again, I won't fly.
Drowning in hope,
I forget for a second that you are gone.
Staring into space,
Wishing with hopeless candles,
Drenched in death,
I remember your full face telling me that time heals all wounds.
I will fly, and when I do I will soar!

Jamie Riffel, Grade 8
New Providence Middle School, NJ

Autumn

Looking at the trees with breathtaking color,
A sight so magnificent unlike any other,
Crisp and joyful sitting by the fire,
Sitting with my family which I do admire.

Playing football outside in the crisp, cool air,
The aroma of pie everywhere,
Eating chestnuts wrapped up in a cozy blanket,
Autumn is of what you make of it.

Scott Misson, Grade 7
St Mary School, NJ

Life

The wonder of life,
Mesmerizing, powerful,
Bold, beautiful, yet filled with strife,
Rich, deep, and immensely full.

People search for reasons,
Though they elude nearly all.
Amazing, with so many wonderful seasons,
It can be seen in many things, big and small.

Hunter Savery, Grade 8
Regina Coeli School, NY

Fall

The crisp cool air outside in the sky
The lovely smell of warm apple pie
The magnificent colors of leaves in the trees
Sipping apple cider in the autumn breeze

Fall is the time of soccer my favorite sport
I wish the fall was not this short
Looking at the colors of leaves on the ground
Hearing the leaves blow and crunch is a wonderful sound

Daniella Tollevsen, Grade 7
St Mary School, NJ

Autumn

Fall, so vivid and beauteous
So many colors that capture the image
As I walk through the forest I think,
What could be so beautiful?

We are so grateful to have this sight,
As in God's image is so luminous.
The colors red, orange, yellow, and brown,
Really do bring out the brilliance of our world.

Mackenzie Herrlich, Grade 7
St Mary School, NJ

My School Day

Every morning I wake up in bed,
the beep of the alarm clock pounding my head.

I brush my teeth and eat some toast;
whole-wheat is what I like the most.

I'm not on time and I miss the bus.
O, my parents will make such a fuss!

My homeroom laughs as I come in late.
O, who would ever know I'd have such a horrible fate?

During school I'm in defiance,
probably because I'm horrible at science.

My day gets better when I go to math,
I know how to do it; I'm on the right path!

I take a deep breath and walk to Spanish;
all my worries about the day seem to vanish.

In English what we learn is very inspiring,
except when we get homework, we all start sighing.

Social studies is my favorite class;
I hate the days when it goes too fast.

I pack my bags and end my day.
"Hey, this wasn't so bad," I say.

Samantha Ferraro, Grade 7
St William the Abbot School, NY

Orpheus and Eurydice

Married, a word associated
with peace and joy, brings me
much hopelessness and sorrow, for
my love is gone, and
my heart is hollow.
Regrets will not
bring you back,
so I travel underneath
earth, underneath its core
determined, earnest, in search
of what I
came here for.
You, my love, is what I seek, to get
one more chance with you,
but they tell me do not peek, do not look back,
as she walks out, be trusting in the gods. But I longed one look.
So one look I took, and my heart was taken to the lowest degree.
Farewell you said, as you were stolen from me
back to the Underworld, no longer to be seen.
Music became meaningless, my limbs ripped apart,
but it was all worth it, for a finally substantial heart.

Natalie Varghese, Grade 9
Weehawken High School, NJ

Home Bound

She opened the mailbox to her surprise,
It laid in front of her right before her eyes.
A note from her husband that made her cry,
The first one since he said good bye.

She holds it tightly not wanting to look,
Every time she saw it she shivered and shook.
After reading the note she reached a new height,
Knowing the army had not taken his life.

She knew he was safe and sound,
But she did not know he was home bound.

Weeks later there they stand,
All together hand and hand.
They ran the fields,
They ran the land.
That day she knew she had her man.

Shannon Leahy, Grade 7
Holy Innocents School, NJ

Your True Self

Opening a door
Your biggest fears awaits,
Shadows of guilt and memories of hate
Lie mainly on this road
This road is called fate;
Wanting to be understood
You couldn't really understand
The deep emotions you've never had,
A baby has
Having seen through its eyes
Watching those that laugh and cry;
Who are they?
Who am I?
We've begun to lose these eyes
But we have the future
A door in which we seek
That holds our true selves
Locked away in a dream

Guerley Denis, Grade 9
Bishop Ford Central Catholic High School, NY

Rain

The cool colorless clouds kidnap and hide the sun
It begins to rain
The sky becomes a closet full of monsters in a child's room
The falling rain is ice cold
It is a different form of life
Establishing bodies of water
It is two-faced
Compassionate but harmful
When its enemy the sun comes out
It is overpowered and fades away

Anthony Sandoval, Grade 7
Fox Lane Middle School, NY

The Dynastic Cycle

There was an emperor, appointed by the gods
who swore to bring peace, order, prosperity to
the lands.

Over the bloodshed of the last dynasty, the new emperor,
promised people the golden age!

This is the great age!
The people cry.
And it is
for only a short time...

Disaster strikes!
The gods are furious.
People afraid of the wrath,
people revolt and say
the emperor is not worthy by the gods
Take him out!
They cry
A bloodshed is spilled. A new power rising.
And then

There was a new emperor, appointed by the gods
who swore to bring peace, order, prosperity to
the lands.

Ian Sun, Grade 9
Townsend Harris High School, NY

The Story of That Day

Whenever I think of that day I start to cry,
You were only 16, you didn't deserve to die.

Engraved in my thoughts
Like your name on a tombstone,
Your garden as pretty as you,
Your pretty brown eyes
Flash in my mind as I remember
The sound of the Boom Boom Boom.

Seeing Diego I wanted to cry,
You're stuck in his heart, as much as you are in mine,
You have an affect on all the people that love you,
Even though we can't see you, we know that you're there,
Watching over us, singing a prayer.

With the face of an angel and the heart of one too,
We love you Sofia,
But sadly there is nothing we can do,
If I could only go back to that day, I would,
I would find a way to keep you away from that party,
Where that gun shot went off.

We love you Sofia, and just want you to know,
You're forever in our hearts, and always in our souls

Mary Wilczewski, Grade 8
Global Concepts Charter School, NY

In Like a Lion, Out Like a Lamb

It is on the prowl,
You can hear it snarl.
Sound reverberates,
Like an echo in a cave,
Minuscule hairs on your neck stand at attention.
There it is again,
That distinct, distant rumble.

Pang! The flash of resplendent light impales you.
The incandescent brightness repeatedly flashes.
Again and again, incessant attack.
Each strike illuminates more of the landscape.
Monotonous rain downpours like a broken record.
The road, the floor, the grass, saturated to the core.
Precipitation will not cease.
A never-ending monsoon, until the sun and clear skies reappear,
Serenity reached.

In like a lion, out like a lamb.

Emily Thomson, Grade 8
Hillsborough Middle School, NJ

My Savior

My Lord, my Savior came to Earth
When the woman Mary gave birth
To a wonderful boy named Jesus
The one who came to save us.

He performed miraculous signs and wonders
The Pharisees' disbelief was one of their biggest blunders
They did not believe that Jesus
Had truly come to save us.

He endured torture and anguish
To save us was his only dying wish
For all would have been loss
If not for Jesus on the cross.

He died, was buried for three days
Then by God's power he was raised
For even death could not hold Jesus
The mighty one who saved us.

Josiah Lyon, Grade 8
Churchville-Chili Intermediate School, NY

A Baseball Diamond

Covered with golden dirt,
the diamond plays host to the greatest teams on earth,
as they battle to be the best.
Smothered in grass,
the ground is where the legends play.
Sprinkled by glory, topped with greatness, played on with pride,
the field is the greatest place to step foot on.
It is purely amazing!

Carter Stumpf, Grade 8
New Providence Middle School, NJ

Autumn

An ocean of color expands overhead as day turns to night.
Then…they fall
down to the yellowed grass,
still, not moving.
A breeze comes and carries them away,
wind makes them soar overhead
looking down upon the rainbow floor.
From the sky, children
heading home
bags strapped on their backs.
They walk with a hunch,
a shout echoes in the distance
breaking the dead silence.
Days, weeks, months pass,
color fades,
trees are bare.
The light breeze turns to a bitter cold.
Then, a white crystal falls from the clouds.
Many more follow.
Autumn
is over.

Ben Morris, Grade 8
Hommocks Middle School, NY

My Kind

Cute and fine in my daddy's mind
My homemade clothes
My thick lips
My broad nose
I do not like the skin I'm in
Although, I met a friend
Who taught me that true beauty was found within
She made me realize I was beautiful
Beautiful in the skin my mom and dad gave me
They have created a beautiful child
You see!
The skin I'm in is fine with me
Even though some may seem to disagree.

Simone Puryear-Flippin, Grade 8
Holy Innocents School, NJ

Deep Dark Night

Lightning strikes,
Thunder cracks,
Rain pours,
The house creeks.
You're home alone.
Fear wins over common sense,
The adrenaline rush increases the suspense,
You don't know what's there,
You're filled up with fright,
The day is gone and here comes the night.
You can't figure out what hides in the shadows
Of the deep, dark, night.

Victoria Brown, Grade 8
Holy Family School, NY

The Way I Am

I honor the past
But look forward for tomorrow
I Stand unafraid
As I face all of life's sorrow
I try hard and do my best
Believe what can't be seen
Open the door when opportunity knocks
'Cause success is in my genes
I refuse to listen to the voices of doubt
Anger and criticism
I only believe the victory cry of optimism
I know that dreams are real
Like people they may die
But if you trust and work hard
Like Jesus it will rise
I am a force unstoppable
My courage is incredible
My spirit is invincible
Even when I feel invisible
One day I'll reach my Promised Land
That day Destiny and I will hold hands

Michael Reid, Grade 8
The Young Scholars Academy of the Bronx, NY

The Piano Man

Every day I see that piano man
Who can play a song anyway he can
Every day I hear that piano anytime, anywhere
Every day I see him playing over there

The piano man is such a master
For this I am a huge fan
Who can play any key faster
Than any other man who can

Why'd the piano man have to go?
Without music, it gives me pain
Yet little did I know
I was driving him insane

Jarod Sinahon, Grade 7
Holy Innocents School, NJ

My Mind

The ideas that flow from left to right
Up and down and side to side
The thoughts that I generate every day
The place where I can get away
Getting lost for hours in an aquatic sea of thoughts
Everywhere I go they follow me
In my head or written down
Everywhere and all around
This is what goes on
In my one and only head
My mind

Altea Parlapiano, Grade 7
William Davies Middle School, NJ

Why?

Why did you leave?
I miss you, and your furry warmth.
The way you anxiously paced back and forth when we cooked meat.
Especially chicken,
it was your favorite.
You were spoiled,
you ate people food almost every night.
When we gave you dog food, you looked at us like we were nuts.
I miss your crooked teeth that went this way and that.
They were awful, but that helped to make you cute.
You weren't very well potty-trained either.
You were there all my life,
but all of a sudden you're gone,
and never returning.
You left the Earth and now rest in the heavens.
Along with other animals.
You play with them, frolicking through the clouds.
You watch over me, protect me.
But I miss you protecting me from down here.

Alexandra Dumschat, Grade 7
Schuyler School, NJ

The Ballad of a Video Game

Once I got a video game
I remember that exciting day
The games all looked the same
My pocket was full of money to pay

I went into the store
Some of the games were rated "E"
Others were "M" for blood and gore
But there was one game made just for me

The game had a lot of action
It was one big race
There will be no distraction
You were able to fight face to face

I finally paid for it
I became very overwhelmed
It was the perfect fit
As I walked into its virtual realm

Matthew Persad, Grade 9
Bishop Ford Central Catholic High School, NY

Holidays!

The holidays are coming, presents and all.
The Christmas tree that makes you feel small.
Thanksgiving with lots of food,
and New Years that emits a happy mood.
The long school breaks that kids just love,
and the cold winter breeze that makes you wear gloves.
Overall the massive family time,
and the bells gentle chime.

Xavier Scott, Grade 8
William Davies Middle School, NJ

Friendship

Alone I am sitting
Left to wallow with myself
'Tis not doing anything
But upsetting me more

Simmering in my depression
Does but more harm
I am deep and alone
Surrounded by darkness

Nowhere to turn
'Til helped to comply
Then the words flow forth
I collapse with relief

Falling to the ground
Many hands holding me up
Supported by many
Comforted by more

Tis' friendship that saved me: The strongest power of all

Ashley Harsanyi, Grade 8
Fords Middle School, NJ

My Dream of Reality

As the stars align my room at night,
I sit alone thinking, "Is this right?"
I can't stop thinking of you,
You've been on my mind since I woke up.
Your beautiful smile stays on my mind for a while,
And my heart breaks a little more each time I try to fake,
Losing you was something I could handle.
So what I'll do is light a candle,
And hope our fate is still at hand.
As I stare at the flames, I think, "Who's to blame?"
For all this trauma, for all this drama?
But now it's getting dark and I must be on my way.
Back to my dream world, where everything Perfect lies here to stay.

Antoinette Simone, Grade 9
Mount St Mary Academy, NJ

Heavy Metal Music

Heavy metal music
It is LOUD!
The drums go
BOOM! BOOM! BOOM!
Cymbals go
Crashing together.
The electric guitars
Six strings with an awesome range of sounds.
A symphony of noise.
YES, it is loud and sounds like noise to others
However, it IS THE MUSIC
That makes me happy.

Phillip Azevedo, Grade 7
Terence C Reilly School #7, NJ

My Brother

My baby brother,
The annoying fly by my ear
That talks s-o-o-o-o-o much
I want to tape his mouth shut.
Stubborn as a rock.
But, can be sweet and
He doesn't even know it.
Is very lovable when he chooses to be.
He distracts my mind of troubles
Like a pain killer to my headache.
Rids my sky of rain.
He is the colors of my rainbow.
He is my younger sibling, and
He holds a very special place in my heart.

Denise Alves, Grade 7
Terence C Reilly School #7, NJ

That's Nature to Me

Nature is worth something to me.
A place where I can roam and be free.
In the water, there's my reflection.
In nature, there's no protection.

In the dark, you hear a howl,
You also hear the hooting of an owl.
In the night, you wait a while.
But when sunrises, you wake up and smile.

In nature, you see the trees,
And you feel that beautiful breeze.
Nature's a place to roam and be free.
Then I say that's nature to me.

Mckyle Ahmed, Grade 8
Global Concepts Charter School, NY

Pokemon

I sat there
watching Pokémon
all day long,
hugging my favorite toy
wishing it was a Pokémon.
Charmander and Cubone were the best.
My parents thought I was crazy.
It was my favorite show.
Now, I barely watch it.
I've forgotten all the names
and never use the trading cards
or play the games.
Now, I think to myself,
I loved this show, why don't I like it now?

Katherine Suazo, Grade 7
Schuyler School, NJ

A Day America Will Never Forget

A day America will never forget
The day that America was under attack
No one expected it
A calm and peaceful Tuesday
People rushing to work, children going to school

Teachers preparing for the school day
"Wow, Look! That plane is so close!"
Maybe a little too close
BAM! Right into the north tower of the World Trade Center
Instantly killing hundreds of people

A second plane, right into the south tower
The next plane crashed into the Pentagon
A tragedy no one could have imagined
Especially after what happened in New York
But another one crashed in Washington D.C.

And then another one down in Pennsylvania
But the last one was different
Not only did the passengers stop the terrorists from landing in a building
They made sure no one other than the people on the plane died
So brave for doing that

Miyah Morales, Grade 7
Public School 232 The Walter Ward School, NY

A Broken Brick Wall

You were a brick wall.
Not merciful towards those who tried to influence you wrongly,
Who tried to destroy your sturdy eminence.
You stood a durable stance,
Fluently asserting yourself as a role model.

As everyone knew you were
Fiercer than the ocean tides crashing against the coastline,
Gentler than the wind slicing through the summer air,
Wiser than an owl during its nightly hunting hours,
Bittersweet like chocolate bliss,
The light of my life.

But suddenly you're not a good example anymore.
The hourglass in your heart empties.
It shatters to pieces as you discover the notorious alcohol.
I am ashamed of you.
Even in broad daylight,
I am blinded by your corruption.
And through the iris of my eye,
All I can see is the fire.
Burning your brick wall down like thin pine wood.
My respect for you disappears as your malevolent essence gleams bright.

Maryam Busi, Grade 9
Timber Creek High School, NJ

A Winter Snow

Little white clumps
Are thrashing down
and covering the ground
As blankets cover babies

The air becomes brisk
Sending chills through me
Giving a feeling
that ice is being dropped down my shirt

Young children scamper
With a look of anticipation and eagerness
While catching snowflakes
And tasting them as they melt.

Soon, the fun will be over
The blanket is pulled away
Children go inside
And life proceeds.

Sara McCloskey, Grade 7
Fox Lane Middle School, NY

Gossip

I take a breath
A gasp for air
I relax and calm down
But can still feel your stare

I hear all the whispers
I see all the glares
I cry all I want
But nobody cares

I walk through the halls
Scared and alone
Knowing the only
Safe place is home

I'm hurting inside
I'm ripping apart
I hope you all know
That you're breaking my heart

Abigail Rasol, Grade 7
Lewis F Cole Middle School, NJ

Letting Go

Opening the latch on her door,
My fingers pause as I hesitate once more.
Realizing that it's finally time,
I step back slowly to let her fly.
Fluttering uncertainly in front of me,
Hovering for a moment, then soaring free,
She's off to see what tomorrow brings.
If only I could grow butterfly wings!

Cindy Weng, Grade 8
New Providence Middle School, NJ

Remembering a Tragedy

A normal day, a beautiful day, a day full of dreams turned into a nightmare
While some saw their lives turn to dust right in front of their eyes,
Others responsible for the tragedy enjoyed as one by one America's pride vanished
Many just stared knowing that now nothing could be done about it nothing could stop it,
But they could save as many lives as possible right about now
America took action they had to do everything in their hands
Some just looked up at the sky eager to know if their family members were alive or not
Many were trapped under the rubble of New York's Twin Towers
As much as they tried to escape the burning flames trapped them
Down the veins of America flow rivers of sadness and endless news
As some are on their way to safety the tower collapsed all these souls become trapped
While many have been rescued and sent to safety
Others are still in the ninetieth floor waiting patiently to be rescued
Some write letters and call their love ones
While others pray to try to fill the emptiness and sadness felt by not knowing anything
They try to locate any family members to feel better
Would they survive or not they asked themselves
To most these memories are permanent they have scarred them for life
To America this will never fade, forever it will stay
In our lives, in our memories, and in our past

Frances Espinoza, Grade 7
Public School 232 The Walter Ward School, NY

Love, Wounds and Bandages

Love is an intriguing word.
You love your friends,
You love your family,
But sometimes, you get trapped.
Your heart cracks and shatters.
Your tears slowly fall to the ground.
Hands and body quivering as you cry.
My head is shrinking, you think,
As your brain pounds against your skull.

Why did I ever love him?
Why did I ever try?
Thoughts running through your mind.
Blaming yourself for things you never did.

The world, harshly spinning as your heart is cutting through you,
Ripping through your flesh and suddenly, darkness.
You become enclosed in black, face cold, sticky, and salty from the tears.
Sitting alone in a world, a world you never knew existed.
Is this what love is?

Julianna Bloch, Grade 8
Hillsborough Middle School, NJ

Roller Coasters

Built with fun in mind,
it has many turns and many flips as it speeds up.
Waiting at the top of the hill, people scream and yell.
Exhilarated to the bone, scared out of their minds, and filled with excitement,
people raise their hands to the sky.
The roller coaster is the ultimate ride!

Matthew Scharf, Grade 8
New Providence Middle School, NJ

9/11, the Day We Remember

It was a normal September day. The sky
Was blue, and clear everything seemed
To be in order…until tragedy struck
Which we all call 9/11, The Day We Remember.

Firefighters, police officers responded
To the 911 call, but it wasn't for long
A second plane crashed into the South
Tower and people knew this was not an
Accident.

That wasn't the only tragedy the Pentagon
And Flight 93 both crashed, on the same
Day, but it seemed the Twin Towers were
Much worse.

No one could believe that all four attacks
Happened on the same day, people kept
Asking questions who, what, when, where,
Why, and how it happened.

Graciela Negron, Grade 7
Public School 232 The Walter Ward School, NY

I Miss You Mom

She was my shoulder to cry on
My best friend
My partner in crime with each one of my troubles
but most of all we were so close
Like Oreos and milk
Now she no longer offers me her shoulder
I am too old
I am no longer her baby
We now have a sad distance between us
Now my shoulder to cry on is my dog
Now he's my partner in crime,
He's my movie and laughing buddy
What I used to be with my mom. I miss the old her.
The one that ran her fingers through my hair until I fell asleep
But that mom is gone and she might not ever come back

Emily Chingay, Grade 7
Fox Lane Middle School, NY

My World

The world I live in is full of life, safety and joy.

The world outside is cruel and drowned in pain.

My world is an escape from reality.
It is safe in there when I want it.
I wonder if I just created this world to hide the truth of the other
Or to run from what hurts me most?

Until the world outside is truly safe,
I will stay in this one.

Samara Adamson, Grade 9
New York Institute for Special Education, NY

The Doc Is in…the Basement!

Huddled on the couch,
Fear lurking through our souls
Disturbance from below,
That echoes static rock n' roll
Go to check it out,
But not a thing before our eyes
The room illuminates,
and we approached a world of lies.

"Séance!" I declare. "No one here, no one there!
The Doc, he haunts this room!
He wants to bring us fear and gloom!"
I become the medium,
As the crowd falls mute and numb.

"Doc, please go! You once dwelled here, but you must leave!"
My crowd bears a shiver,
As if a sudden breeze.
What is unknown, however,
Will become the best proof
That I can conduct a "ghost"
That sends their fear levels to the roof!

Vanessa Demko, Grade 8
Hillsborough Middle School, NJ

The Great Pumpkin Scare

Pumpkins are good and tasty too
They can make you feel happy when you're feeling blue
Their orange color reminds me of fire
When we go pumpkin picking I never tire!
We get home and carve out scary faces
We get creative and put them in all sorts of places!
I even put a pumpkin up on a tree
My mom was looking for it and she didn't see
The pumpkin fell down and splattered all over
I got so scared I thought that my life was over!
My mom screamed out what is all this sticky mess!
I can't believe this ruined my dress!
Now what can I say?
My mom doesn't know it was me till this day!

Danny Quiroz, Grade 7
St William the Abbot School, NY

What Is World History?

What was it like back then?
Why are we who we are today?
What has caused the world to be the way it is today?
Why are we who we are?
The answers to these questions
Lie in the story of world history.
Our world's history is a story
Filled with the most significant facts to understand.
When these facts can be comprehended,
these questions can be answered.

Dimitri Perdik, Grade 9
Townsend Harris High School, NY

No Second Chances

It has been too long.
The tick-tock of my heart has finally ceased to a stop.
My mind is elsewhere.
Two eyes are filled with tears,
And are too heavy to look up.

They said it was too late,
That old dogs couldn't learn new tricks.
But why was I to listen?
For no one was the boss of me!

Oh what a pity,
Oh what a shame.
A little kid who couldn't see that the fairytales were to blame;
Blinded by hope and by the memories once played.

One shot was given.
One chance was used.
No mistakes were to be made the second time through.

Arline Pierre-Louis, Grade 9
Bishop Ford Central Catholic High School, NY

A Pitcher's Dream

The pitcher always throws a curve ball,
to the bullpen, the coach will never call
but for all of us, it's strike one, two, three
and to the winning team, this is their victory.

Up and down, inning by inning,
telling his "soldiers" just like a king
that special man throwing strike after strike
just fanning the opponent batters alike.

That fireball just whizzing by
you could just imagine the other team's sigh
oh no! there's one far, deep, and high
but not for one man yelling "I got it, it's mine."

The crowd was excited and they arise
the opponent, temporarily struck with demise
and as that special moment came
a grounder to first, The Perfect Game.

Robert Samuel, Grade 7
Yeshiva At The Jersey Shore, NJ

Steaming Soup

Soup
Boiling hot on the stove.
The chicken noodle soup, it will be consumed when It is ready.
Bursting with flavor.
The meal is anticipated and I shall so hurriedly devour.
Looking down into the bowl, feeling the steam, smelling the aroma.
I ingest the chicken noodle soup.
How tasty it is!

Mingyao Xiao, Grade 8
New Providence Middle School, NJ

A Remembered Christmas

"Jingle Bells," "Jingle Bells"
'Tis the Season of exchanging new gifts and finding Happiness
"Jingle Bells," "Jingle Bells"
How can I remember this new Season?
As my Family and I already have everything

"Jingle Bells," "Jingle Bells"
Gave away all my old Toys
to a stranger's kid who had not

"Jingle Bells," "Jingle Bells"
Remembered my Dad said
He for many years also had not

"Jingle Bells," "Jingle Bells"
In Church this morning, I saw
The infant Jesus smiling back at me
Just when the choir started singing:
"Jingle Bells," "Jingle Bells"

Vincent Gecevice, Grade 9
Bishop Ford Central Catholic High School, NY

Corrupt World

Capitol, capitol boil and bubble,
Causing nothing but turmoil and trouble.
Money leads to despair,
And in the end you do not care.
In you all hope is lost,
You are shrouded in evil.
Nothing but greed and sorrow,
It's the same today and tomorrow.
Losing your guilt,
Hungry on pride,
Everyone sees your actual side.
You've lost your soul,
And your heart has a hole.
Those who know truth,
Have no respect for you.
Now we may be mellow,
But soon we will rebel,
And take back what has been stolen by you,
A world that was once true.

Christian Perez, Grade 9
Bishop Ford Central Catholic High School, NY

The Game

Football
Running up and down the field
The team got very tired during the game
After hard hits
Some of the players had to come out
Going for the ball, jumping for the ball, throwing it deep
The quarterback completed the deep pass to the wide receiver
Football, America's game!

Chris Tangreti, Grade 8
New Providence Middle School, NJ

Ten Years

Ten years have come and spent,
I didn't know where you went.
September goes by year after year,
And I don't know why you are not here.
I miss you morning, night, and noon,
And I pray that I will see you soon.
You were a hero and the greatest,
And it proves that God only takes the best.
We think about you every day,
And we miss you in so many ways.
I miss you, Dad with all my heart,
And I know this is only the start.
There is a brand new world beyond you and I,
Beyond the Earth and the sky.
Goodbye Dad; our family loves you so,
And there will always be room for our love to grow.

James Lynch, Grade 8
Orange Avenue Elementary School, NJ

My Ability

Wanting to be a pro football player
Am I capable?
People tell me daily
I don't have a chance
Even my friends and family say it's impossible
Because I'm short and skinny
Not a typical football player body
But for me nothing is impossible
So, what motivates me to keep going?
Is it my resilience?
Or is it having passion
So, giving up is not an option
Believing is achieving
Achieving is reaching my goal
To become a running back football player

Mohammad Musa, Grade 7
Terence C Reilly School #7, NJ

Envy

Seven sins together in glee
Out of them, one who is me
Envy's eyes stare into my soul
And whispers things I rather not have heard
"Look at her" she whispers in too-sweet tones
"Her beauty and charm outmatches yours."
With Envy's power, she clutches my soul
And in my eyes, I see her grow
Looking in the mirror
I stare at my face
Holding my hands in helpless fists
Envy sits beside me and smirks
"Beauty is clearly not a gift you have received."
So I shut my eyes and wish with hope
That beauty will flourish and get rid of this voice

Karie Sit, Grade 9
Manhasset High School, NY

We Are the Targets

I am Daphne Lyger
I am fourteen years old
We all have special gifts,
But mine is extraordinary,
I can read, change, and erase memories from minds
It hurts
I get head aches and nose bleeds
I get dizzy,
And a loss in vision
My symptoms and side effects go on;
Just like they do in Allegra® ads.
All seventeen of us have power
This weight,
Has been put on my shoulder,
To take charge, and be the leader
I feel as if I have to defend us, save us;
There's no one to protect us
They're scared of what they don't know
They think they are doing the right thing,
And for that I pity them
They are living with their eyes closed

Grace Axelrad, Grade 8
Hommocks Middle School, NY

The Season of Fall

The early leaves changing in September,
The sweet smell of freshly picked apples,
And the pumpkin patches all bright and orange,
As well as the breathtaking sunset.

The short sleeves end and the jackets begin,
And Halloween soon approaches later on.
Creepy crawly spiders appear spinning their webs,
And then suddenly it all ends right then and there.

The sweet smell of pumpkin pie right out of the oven,
Warm and cozy, laughing with friends and family,
And if you're wondering what I am saying,
Yes, I am talking about the season of fall.

Jihan Drummond, Grade 8
All Saints Catholic Academy, NY

The Shadow

Appears on sullen nights.
It lingers on the ground, mimicking its master's every move.
Its long delicate figure strides through the night,
Only revealing its gloomy outline,
Never its face.
Its true identity lays hidden.
Its silent footsteps creep in the night like a sly fox hunting for prey.
It towers over you, threatening your every move.
Creeps up behind corners, on doors, on walls.
At dawn the shadow crawls back into your soul,
Waiting till nightfall to rise again.

Arielle Putter, Grade 7
Fox Lane Middle School, NY

One Day

Life, isn't a fairy tale.
It's not like the movies or best-selling books.
Things don't work out perfectly and fate and destiny are myths.
Life, isn't a fairy tale.

The boy you've loved for three years loves your best friend.
No matter how much time goes by, it will never be you.
You won't end up together in the end and realize you were meant to be.
Life, isn't a fairy tale.

You'll never be put first, and you'll stand in another girl's shadow.
She'll always get the role, whether it's playing a part or just being the best.
People overlook you, and you're second best once again, not good enough once again.
Life, isn't a fairy tale.

Life, isn't a fairy tale.
But I guess what keeps us going is the hope,
that one day, you'll be the one,
and one day, you'll be good enough.

One day, you'll move out of her shadow, and you'll forget about the boy that forgot about you.

Sarah Moyer, Grade 8
Odyssey Academy, NY

All About Me

Thomas
Fun, sporty, creative, adventurous
Brother of Michael
Who feels pumped when he plays lacrosse, excited to go paintballing, nervous on the first day of school
Who needs to play lacrosse, be around family and friends, to get less homework
Who gives love and attention to my dog Buddy, love to family, food to friends
Who fears skunks, spiders, people who stare
Who would like to score more than 17 goals in lacrosse, win more lacrosse games, play manhunt at night
Resident of East Brunswick
Bahmer III

Thomas Bahmer III, Grade 7
Hammarskjold Middle School, NJ

Excuses, Excuses, Excuses*

Dear Teacher,
Remember the homework assignment you gave me yesterday? The one I moaned about…the first one I moaned about. I kind of accidentally left it on the classroom floor…I think. I am afraid the janitor swept it up accidentally not realizing what it was, you know, accidentally. If you really think about it, it is your fault because you should have seen it before you left. Since it was gone I couldn't do it. Also, you know the project you gave us a month ago, I lost the rubric the first day and I forgot to ask you for a new one. I think it is only fair that due to you not making sure I had the rubric you give me a new sheet and another month to do it. After all, if you think about, it really was your fault that I didn't get a new one. Lastly the class pet I took home Friday and never brought back, I forgot to feed it so the hamster died. Don't worry though. I buried it in the backyard and gave it a great funeral. I even downloaded a funeral song off of the internet and buried Billy with some snacks to give him a happy send off. Again, if you really think about it, it's your fault to trust a nine-year-old boy with a pet hamster. I really thank you for understanding and that due to simple logical reasoning, all of these issues are your fault. It's okay though. I forgive you.
Your Favorite Student,
Anthony

Sarah Kaplan, Grade 8
Candlewood Middle School, NY
*Inspired by Williams Carlos Williams

What a Twin Is

A twin is someone whose smile makes you smile
Someone who you stay up all night with camping out under the covers
Someone who knows what you're thinking without you even saying a word
Someone you can tell all your secrets to and know that they're never going to tell
Someone who has the same songs in their head while you have them in your head
Someone who you can have a sleep-over with every night
Someone who people get you confused with
Someone you can put your head on their shoulder and they will hold you while you cry
Someone that will stand up for you or fight for you when no one is siding with you
Someone who picks you up when you fall
They are the person you are unstoppable with
They're the person that since the minute you were born you were inseparable with
They're the person that when you were a baby you cried if you're not sleeping next to them
They're the person that since you were born were causing some kind of trouble with
A twin is the person who is getting cradled in the right arm while you are getting cradled in the left one
A twin is the person who makes your mom tear up when you say "I love you" to each other
They're the person that when you're not with them you feel like half of you is missing
They're truly your best friend sent from God that you know you're definitely meant to be with, and that you're a perfect match

Jennifer Mantione, Grade 7
St William the Abbot School, NY

Me

I am loved and grateful of what I have.
I wonder how people become who they are.
I hear cries of needy people.
I see happiness and sorrow surrounding me.
I want to give the needy what they need.
I am loved and grateful of what I have.
I pretend the world is safer than it actually is.
I feel hate and love inside and outside of me.
I touch people's hands around me.
I worry of how the economy is.
I cry for the sick and the ones in need.
I am loved and grateful of what I have.
I understand that I don't have control over many horrible things and I can't change them by complaining.
I say that the world will change one day.
I dream that one day we will live in a separate world as the bad people.
I try to make a difference.
I hope one day the world will be perfect.
I am loved and grateful of what I have.

Eve Cukor, Grade 7
Hammarskjold Middle School, NJ

Alyssa

Alyssa
Happy, sweet, kind, polite
Daughter of Rob and Diane
Lover of friends, family, and dance
Who feels nervous on the first day of school, happy when I land a dance move, and excited for going on vacation
Who needs time to study, to watch less television, and keep organized in school
Who gives help to other people, food for my pets, and love to my family
Who fears lightning, sharks, and tornadoes
Who would like to win a first place trophy at a dance competition for choreography
Rakossy

Alyssa Rakossy, Grade 7
Hammarskjold Middle School, NJ

Stuck in the Moment of Forever

Don't you ever wish that everything
Could stay like this
Forever?
Just the way it is,
Just the way it should be,
Just the way you like it,
When you're running and laughing
With all your friends,
Don't you ever wish for it to be that way
Forever?
When you're next to your favorite person,
Snuggled close,
Under the beautiful stars,
And you sigh,
Hoping it will stay this way
Forever,
That moment,
Capture it in your mind,
So it will stay with you
Forever.
Kiku Ono, Grade 8
Hommocks Middle School, NY

Molotov Cocktails

Protest
Contest
I question what you say
and you shoot back
I defend
so you offend
The boycott
the embargo
the sit down strike,
Molotov cocktails from
casual mixed drinks
slogans taken from placards
that I hurl at you
across smokey bombs that tear
my eyes. Sirens, alarms,
bystanders turn and run
Someone we don't even know
takes a photograph
that I will see eleven years later
and wonder how old I was then.
Christopher R. Liggio, Grade 9
Holy Cross High School, NJ

School

S witching
C lasses
New **H** omerooms
An **O** ther new year
More h **O** mework
A **L** ot has happened since last year.
Adam Kulikowski, Grade 7
Schuyler School, NJ

Winter Night

Silver white crystals
fall down from the sky
each one is different
none is the same

All is quiet
not a sound from the street
not a word from the door
all is quiet

The moon is shining
bright in the sky
a ball of light
not anything more

On this winter night
only one soul is here
that is me
enjoying this winter night
Mary Rose Thompson, Grade 8
Orange Avenue Elementary School, NJ

In the Garden

In the garden of roses, there sat a girl
Her face cherubic
Her hair with a curl
Eyes like the sea
As blue as can be
In the garden sat a girl.

She sat there without a care
The wind in her hair
She listened to the birds
As they sang to the air
In the garden was a girl.

As the sun set in the sky
An orange and red
The girl lay down
She rested her head
And she fell asleep to the songs of the birds
In the garden slept a girl
Alexa Castellano, Grade 8
Warwick Valley Middle School, NY

Sunset

Sunset
Glowing brightly
The sun starts to set, as it the ends
Shrinking fast,
It approaches the water, and it gets smaller
Glowing, shrinking, cooling,
It leaves the sky with oranges and pinks
How I love sunsets!
Leandra Cordiano-Mooney, Grade 8
New Providence Middle School, NJ

Replication

A stance beginning,
of those you're wishing;
Trials of indolence,
strength in reverence.

As your mind proliferates,
the inevitable obliterates;
Unreal it seems,
you do all but feign.

As life becomes rapid,
your vices become rabid;
Monotony encompasses,
a constant flow thrashes.

Feelings are gained,
your flaws renamed;
Lack of an owed clemency,
an ambiance uncleanly.

So you live to see defeat,
watching your morals too deplete;
Strength unknown,
your adroit crown.
Kira Marshall, Grade 9
St Joseph By the Sea High School, NY

Mirror Image

I look in the mirror
Only to see
A face just like mine
Gazing back thoughtfully

Each day I consider
That curious girl
Returning my gaze
As I scrutinize her

I long for that world
As I search for the key
Just out of reach
They enjoy teasing me

I can touch her fingertips
She smiles when I do
Yet she echoes my bewilderment
Lost without a clue

Discouraged, I finally give up
And start counting my sheep
That universe must be in dreamland
I conclude as I fall asleep
Bracha Rosenberg, Grade 8
SAR Academy, NY

Why I Write

I write to express the raging sweep of fire in my heart that contains the built-up passion of a lifetime.
I write to satisfy the craving of the hungry monster inside my chest that forces my fingers to type the words of a tale.
I write to give fictional characters a chance to live, to give made-up places a destination.
I write because I have nothing else to do.
I write to organize the many things on my list of To-Do's.
I write on the relaxing cloud of my imagination.
I write about what happens to me back on Earth.
I write just so the pencil tips would go blunt.
I write to get the wheels in my brain churning, preparing them up for my train of thoughts.
I write while wondering if the page before me will ever be revealed to the public.
I write in the hopes it would get more compliments than criticism.
I write because I want it to be a masterpiece.
I write with the fear of being laughed at.
I write knowing people will not always understand my narrative.
I write knowing how many other people can connect to the words I have authored.
I write believing that it is my one true savior.
I write just because it is a part of my soul.

Christina Chen, Grade 8
Terrill Middle School, NJ

My Fabulous School

School is a place to meet new friends
To learn Math, English, and even Spanish
You use pens, pencils, and calculators
To do exponents, fractions, and decimals
You get good grades and type reports
About stories, ideas, and personal experiences
When you get a good grade you jump up and down
Smile and yell I passed, I passed oh look at me!

All the teachers and principals are always there for you
No matter what you say and do
Our school is a place to learn and to be who you want to be
You can read a book from our school library
Play games on the computer along with doing a power point presentation
The smart boards are the best of all you write and draw in all different colors
School is not just a place to learn, but a family and a second home to all my family, friends, and I!

Alyssa Boll, Grade 7
St William the Abbot School, NY

Death of My Safe Haven

To turn to a new page, is pure bliss. Once a new treasure touches my palm, I come alive.
To be able to fold the corners of a page, gives me my own personal taste of heaven.
The stories contained in between two covers inspire me, make me cry, make me laugh,
and make me remember. The weight of a good story overjoys me.
Elation comes to me in every new word, the way a father welcomes a new child into his loving arms.
It is inconceivable to think that other people do not share my feelings.
New technologies are killing my only escape. Just as my love is recently becoming extinct,
falling to these so called better replacements, so should we be replaced by better humans?
No! I forbid it! No matter how much effort is put into these new versions of man,
It will not be us; it will not have the same quirks, imperfections, and words that make us individuals.
If those who seek to destroy my only portal into the world of perfect imagination,
they will also have succeeded in the death of my one, true, safe haven.

Brandon Wingfield, Grade 7
Holy Family School, NY

Change

Yellow eyes,
Peering out from behind black-tinged trees.
The snapping of teeth
Echoes through the silence,
An unspoken challenge.
Accept or reject,
Either way blood will shed.
Running underneath the stars,
Speaking to your God,
A beautiful harvest moon.
Change or be changed, either way it will never be the same.
Silent ghosts slipping through trees,
Screaming a wolves' curse
As the crunch of a spine, confirms a change.
Eyes glaze over,
In a surge of pain
And pelts fall away to reveal moonlit skin.
Claws retract, and jaws shorten
Bringing you back to a weaker version.
One that holds a memory
Of lost sanity.

Shelbi Wray, Grade 9
Parishville-Hopkinton High School, NY

The Book of Life

It has no answers
It has no guides
It has no directions
Just a straight line

It's not so simple
Nor is it hard
Just stay on that line
And never draw apart.

The Book of Life
Has no color
And it doesn't have comfort
But the Book of Life has a reward

Tiara Elcock, Grade 9
Bishop Ford Central Catholic High School, NY

The Skies Above

The sun is vibrant
The moon never rants
The sky is multicolored
The night has always fluttered
By and by night and day
I never wanted the birds to fly away
The trees stand very tall hiding the moon
Gentle glow
I hope one day they will fall
If I was the glow is it the sun the stars the moon
I will always spin this gentle tune

Justice Manns, Grade 8
Keyport High School, NJ

The Trumpeter

He takes a breath and exhales music,
Long and low and full of wisdom,
Knowledge of what is and was,
Passed down to us through him.
He waits and starts it up again,
Now, a sad and melancholy tune
About hopeless love and lost paradise;
A life filled with regret.
This followed by a lively melody,
Exploding light, so bright and cheerful,
Like the sun coming out after a long stormy night,
Rainbows in puddles.
And then some notes, so sweet that
They reach your heart and make you feel them;
Lingering in the heavy air,
It is life, and it speaks to you.
He finishes with one last feeble sound,
As fragile as an angel's touch,
That wraps its arms around your soul
And makes you dream of heaven singing.

Iriowen Ojo, Grade 9
Long Island School for the Gifted, NY

King Arthur

When King Arthur was a boy
He came upon a rock
He pulled out of the rock the Excalibur sword
Now him being King was his reward
With Merlin by his side and Guinevere as his wife
He was sent a Round Table which would help him rule his life
But before he married Guinevere he made a manly mistake
He was bewitched by Morgawse but that was his fate
Later he learned that Morgawse was his own half-sister
And she bore a son Mordred, that became his own little mister
By then the Round Table had spread East to West
To find more knights that would go on jousting quests
The most famous knight of all came from France
By the name of Sir Lancelot, but not by chance
Now Guinevere and Sir Lancelot were Arthur's best friends
Even though Arthur knew they loved each other till the end
Near Arthur's death he knighted his own son and treated him well
But Mordred did not love his father because of the spell
Arthur died when he had been defeated by Sir Lancelot
But he was still the best king England ever got

Nicole Schneider, Grade 7
Siena Catholic Academy, NY

A Solemn Goodbye

Setting down slowly,
The sun shines brilliantly, when I stare at it in awe.
Turning redder and redder,
The golden orb refuses to disappear.
Setting gracefully, disappearing suddenly, and fading majestically,
the strong sun resentfully disappears.

Tim Charatan, Grade 8
New Providence Middle School, NJ

What Happened?

After school is over I got to my house;
Toward my parents I go sitting at the table, seeing them all dreary and upset.
Between them I sit wondering, "Why so down?"
Until they answer with a cry, "Your grandfather died today."
Through the doors of my house I go crying with sadness;
Within two minutes my parents are walking up the stairs with worried faces.
Beside me they sit, telling the story of how it all happened.
Into my heart a knife goes, killing off the last part I had of him;
Since then, we have had too many scares and tragedies happen.
Beyond that we all think we will never leave our lives, but we all know some day it will be our time;
Onto the chair I sit listening to the Priest say his last words to our grandfather.
Upon the casket I see him laying sleeping peacefully with his eyes closed;
Outside I look up at the tree up above, behind me I hear my dad calling me to get in the car to go to the church.
Inside I sit waiting like a dog, to be commanded what to do.
But from then on nothing is the same without him in my life;
Against the doors I push like an ox with nowhere to go;
With my family I see my parents standing with nothing to prove.
To the car we go, in the rain that will never stop;
In the distance I see a family that is a troop, standing tall and proud, unlike us standing small and low;
Under the covers I go crying myself to sleep.
Regarding what just happened, I figure life is a roller coaster turns, spins and will always end.

Allyson Giordano, Grade 8
Clinton Public School, NJ

Nupura

Nupura
Persistent, smart, distracted, solitary
Lover of fiction, daydreaming, and sketching
Who feels excited when I get a new composition, upbeat with friends, and uncomfortable with a large number of people
Who needs to talk more to family, to manage my time better, to have my own library
Who gives advice to friends, a person to talk to, opinions where they are needed
Who fears elevators, cats, and new places
Who would like to sleep more, write a book, make something new that could change the way people think
Resident of East Brunswick
Ghude

Nupura Ghude, Grade 7
Hammarskjold Middle School, NJ

The Play

Inside the stadium full of fans the bleachers rose
Before the crowd the players readied; amid the crazed atmosphere
Within them their hearts swelled with the pride of reaching the greatest stage
Upon the signal the players leap into action until the whistle blows
Among the defenders the quarterback is surrounded yet amid the chaos he slips away like a ghost
Toward the receiver the ball slowly travels up in the air
Throughout the pass the crowd is near silence
Into the hands of the receiver the ball falls
Behind the receiver the defender leaps
Down fall both players, like raindrops from the sky
Onto the ground the ball never falls; the pass is complete
Across the stands a cheer begins
The whistle is a whisper
But, already the play is history and the next one begins

Will Staszeski, Grade 8
Clinton Public School, NJ

The Last Olympian

The war does not seem to be coming to an end,
Warriors have fallen, by swords and blades.
But the tower they must defend,
Though the enemy continues its relentless raid.

One child is part of a prophecy by Fate,
A messenger is sent to offer some hope.
The child must end the battle consumed in hate,
But the truth is none could ever cope.

With a war that could not possibly be won,
The enemy is defeated, not by the child of Fate.
Because though they were frightened, they agreed not to run,
They won because the hero within the enemy showed, but came late.

And even though what was done was set,
The warriors accept the enemies regret.

Olivia Mason, Grade 7
Visitation Academy, NY

The Storm in Our Life

If God cancels the spring,
Or it snows when it's summer
If roses never again are seen in a garden,
Or everything beautiful disappears
If that moment ever comes that you stop loving me,
Think about it because it's not normal;
The clouds don't fall from the sky as strong as the wind might be;
In our life there is stormy weather,
I promise everything will get better;
I've made mistakes which I'm sorry for but,
We can't just leave each other like this;
We've slipped a bit,
But that doesn't mean we should give up on our love;
Forgive me;
We can still find the medicine to cure this love;
I never lose hope of this storm passing,
And everything being like before.

Andrew de León, Grade 9
Bishop Ford Central Catholic High School, NY

Mother Nature

Nature as I see it
Is a very beautiful thing.
The plants are filled with life,
Like lilies, daffodils, roses and violets.
The branches on trees spread out real strong and bold,
Like towering skyscrapers,
Giving shade to those below.
Mother nature treats its children,
With clean water and fresh air.
So that we can all enjoy,
Mother Nature's greatest gift.

Brian Mendoza, Grade 7
Terence C Reilly School #7, NJ

Snow Day

Playing out in the snow,
Snuggled up to escape from the cold,
Building a snow man with my family,
Having snow fights and we all go crazy,
Settling down and going inside,
Sipping hot chocolate and it taste so fine,
Sitting in front of the warm toasty fire,
Thinking about how the day can't get any better.

Jasmine Newsome, Grade 7
William Davies Middle School, NJ

A Sunset

Standing on the beach,
I stare into the distance
as the sun fades from the horizon.
Sinking below the ocean,
it brilliantly shines.
Steeped with color, falling quickly, becoming invisible,
the sun is but a memory.
Sunsets are the world's greatest phenomenon.

Ivan Wolansky, Grade 8
New Providence Middle School, NJ

She Reminds Me of a Flower

She reminds me of a flower
So gentle and unique
She reminds me of a flower
So soft and sweet
She reminds me of a flower
Her smell and beauty
She reminds me of a flower

Sean Wade, Grade 9
Bishop Ford Central Catholic High School, NY

Dawn in the Spring

Shining brightly
The sun rises for the first time today, getting brighter and brighter.
Flying overhead chirping birds are heard,
And dew is caught on the light green grass.
Opening flowers, shining sun, and drifting smells
Describe the morning.
Spring is a season that should last forever.

Sara Misiukiewicz, Grade 8
New Providence Middle School, NJ

A Bowl of Surprise

Swirling and twirling the tip of the spoon,
I seek as if to find the mysteries.
Pushing away the tiniest of crumbs
As I look at the recently bitten-off Cracker Jacks.
Pushing, swirling, and eating away,
I finally uncover the little ring.
That was close. I almost ate the inedible surprise!

Saad Khan Khan, Grade 8
New Providence Middle School, NJ

Loose Leaf Wish List

Make me into an airplane,
and let me soar through the sky.
My body is a plot of land,
for you to cultivate your skills
or to bury your darkest secrets
Turn my blank body
into a radiant picture
like an artist.
Write on me a side of you, so that one day I
may sing it to the world.

Jonathan Baccay, Grade 7
Fox Lane Middle School, NY

My Dog

My pet dog named Max has died.
It makes me so sad, I could just die now.
And if I had one wish, I would have him.
He rests in peace in the soil.
He crossed the bridge, life to death.
I am happy he is in Heaven.
Laying on his side and happier now.
Getting whatever he wants to get.
Now there is a huge gap in my heart.
One day, I will be with him again.

Patrick Harrigan, Grade 7
St Mary's Prep School, NJ

Drug Free

Why I want to be drug free
Is because of all there is to see
The cities, the streets
The bright Broadway lights
And the friends I could never live without
I never want to be in a phase
Where the world is a big craze
And I feel like drugs
Are
The only answer

Emily Westfall, Grade 8
St Stephen's School, NY

When She's Away

Every night I lie in bed awake
Thinking about her as my tummy aches
Whenever she's not by my side
I feel like running away to hide
Hoping she'll come back to me
Hoping she'll come back to New Jersey
I want her to know
I will always love her so
I cry that she comes back eventually
But all I can say is we'll see

Timothy Anthony, Grade 7
William Davies Middle School, NJ

Swimming Competition

Drip!
Sweat beads my forehead.
Adrenaline pumps loudly through my vein.
Boom! Boom! Boom!
My heart pounds like a hammer in my chest.
Every part of my body seems ten pounds heavier.
Those four words cause my body to shake,
"Racers take your mark!"
I crouch down into starting position.
Whee!
That one loud whistle blow echoes in my ear,
Just like somebody pulling a trigger on a gun.
Whoosh!
My reflexes cause me to shoot off the diving block, like an arrow off a bow,
As my body spears through the water.
My arms pull and push wildly but still maintaining rhythm,
While my legs kick, taking turns splashing in the water.
I feel like a torpedo seeking my target as I approach the finish line.
Victory,
The greatest feeling in the world.
It makes the endless laps that I did during practice much more meaningful.

Britney Cheng, Grade 7
MS 74, NY

Time

We had our good days and we had our bad ones
But it seems like times are changing before our very eyes
Our memories are slowly fading away and times may change
But we just have to hope that someday things will be okay
These times are changing
But I guess we can't hold on to the past anymore,
Because even if we want our past to be part of our future we don't know if it can be
And as we all shed one tear we still live in fear
That we will all lose everything in the end
But we will all try and keep hope and keep it until the end

Jennie Chalakee, Grade 7
William Davies Middle School, NJ

Poppies in June

The Papaveraceae bulbs dance through the freshly moist silt
Eschscholzia go to the creek to surround it in the most picturesque of ways
The Hunnemannia glide to the marsh to sprout up near the whirling cattails

Young poppies flutter to the luscious field to stain it
dots of crimson
and black speckles
the red velvet tickles your ankles
as you dash through the cherry flecked field

But fall must come and nature's wicked winds and spit
shall thrash and rip these poppies from the roots
But even though they will die soon
Nothing is nicer than poppies in June

Emily Hurley, Grade 8
Hommocks Middle School, NY

Turkey Day

Praying together in synchronization,
the joyful family articulates grace
as the snow batters against the foggy windowsill.
Slicing a thick layer of meat,
the knife slides through the breast of a steaming turkey.
Slowing the knife, snatching up a platter, and transferring the turkey piece to the china plate,
the grateful father eagerly serves his entire family.
It's time to celebrate Thanksgiving!

Kevin Dackow, Grade 8
New Providence Middle School, NJ

Courage

Hearing the chatter and comments they never hide,
accused of a lie, you cringe to hide the tears but they stole your strength.
Watching your every move to dig out all of your flaws, so if you slip up even one time they win,
they will spread it everywhere, to everyone.
Building up every day, wanting to speak up, and screaming for help,
You take the first steps to getting out of their brutal grasp, forever.
Don't ever let them win.

Samantha Leonardo, Grade 8
New Providence Middle School, NJ

Run, Stallion, Run

Cantering through an open field,
the beautiful beast never glances once in my direction, as I let his glory engulf me.
Mane flowing like a silk flag billowing in the wind,
the stallion conquered the land and demanded attention, with sustaining grace and composure.
Hooves crushing each blade of grass fiercely, muscles becoming more defined with each gallop,
and crazy determination fixed in his big eyes,
he gradually increases speed.
Oh, how I'd love to watch that creature swiftly turn and endlessly run with ease all day long.

Laila Stedman, Grade 8
New Providence Middle School, NJ

Piano Player

Sitting alone on the bench,
She makes her pen glide across the page as it listens to the silent notes that are written.
Being performed only for herself,
Her work of art is not yet completed.
Humming the notes, sweeping fingers smoothly across the ivory keys, and making music after noise,
She remembers that error can only improve a piece.
What a wonderful piano player she is!

Deborah Besser, Grade 8
New Providence Middle School, NJ

Strike, Swoosh, Score

Gliding along the turf,
The soccer ball reached my feet as it came across the field.
Soaring through the air,
my shot took off.
Flying over the goalie's head, going right under the crossbar, swooshing into the back of the net,
the white sphere landed.
The crowd roared, and we had won!

Natalie Zagorski, Grade 8
New Providence Middle School, NJ

A Future Lifeguard's Day at the Beach

The sun is rising in the East.
The alarm goes off, lunches packed; it's time to head to the beach.
Driving around the tower, the ocean comes into sight.
Just me and my dad — it sure feels right.
The sand's between my toes, we're setting up ropes, the flags are flying high, the sun's way up in the sky.
"Put on sun block," he yells, I pretend not to hear.
Just one quick dive in the ocean, the water's so clear!
I get out and dry off, then put on sunscreen.
Go for a walk and find beach glass — brown, clear and green.
The waves are getting bigger, they're looking really fun.
The lifeguards are going to play, so I get my board and run.
Boy, I'm exhausted; it's been a busy day.
I close my eyes to rest, and then the seagull comes my way.
The whistle blows, running lifeguards wake me from my sleep.
They have to save a little girl; she's gone in way too deep.
They bring her in safely, her mom was so afraid.
I can't wait for five more years when I do this job and get paid!

George Ritter, Grade 7
St William the Abbot School, NY

My Heart, My Soul, Myself

I am the wind and I am the rain, I am the sun and I am the pain.
I am the song and I am the sea, I am the leaves high up in the tree.
I am a poem and I am a sob, I am a painting and I am the mist.
I am a pair of eyes, blue as the sky, watching and waiting, loving and singing, dancing for tomorrow.
I am a delicate flower in spring, spinning and twirling in the wind.
I am a whisper, I am a dream…I am hope.
I am the silk of a spider's web, laden with dew.
I am free, I am silent even as my heart sings to the night.
I am a star, shining bright, shimmering for a chance…a light, a life.
I am always and never, here and not, now and forever, always forgot.
I am a flickering candle, I am a wish…and I hope that I am a jewel.
I am a moment of time, a breath of forever, a glimmer, a shine, a heart, and a feather.
I am one in many, many in one, all, no one, and you.
I am when, who, where, and how.
I am a strand of hair, a warmth, a chill, a treasure.
I am an individual lost in a sea, original but the same.
I am me.

Brianna Riggio, Grade 8
Warwick Valley Middle School, NY

Shadows Don't Last Forever

Shadows are nothing to the mere eye but a black presence that diminishes the light of our lives.
They also seem to haunt us like ghosts of the afterlife, looking for their "companions."
They feel as though they're always lurking behind you; always there with you.
Shadows are like stalkers; predators
Using their hawk-like eyes to watch over us as if we're their prey?
They are just ignorant, arrogant, and inconsiderate people that try their best to make us fail.
They are always trying to hold us back, trying to make us feel as if we aren't exceptional
Nevertheless
When we learn to ignore those people
That shadow then blossoms into a bright light that illuminates the path of your choice
We then begin to realize the fact that shadows don't last forever and…
NO ONE CAN HOLD US BACK!

Quaheem Griggs, Grade 7
Terence C Reilly School #7, NJ

A Lick of a Lollipop

A lick of a lollipop, so pleasing, so sweet,
Even better than a wholesome treat.
No need for long journeys, they sell them in stores,
Once you have one, you'll be begging for more.
They taste so good, so sweet, so sour,
The more you have the more you devour.
You can get them hard as nails or even chewy,
Half of the time you can get them gooey.

A lick of a lollipop can make you crazy,
Too much of it will make you lazy.
Cherry, grape, apple, and watermelon,
You can make a good fortune trying to sell them.

A lick of a lollipop makes you feel good,
Like riding a bike in your neighborhood.
Learning to skate or learning to cook,
Or catching a fish on your first hook.

A lick of a lollipop is not so tough,
Crave so much, but it's not enough.

Mannesah Georges, Grade 8
Hillsborough Middle School, NJ

Baptism

The water could quench the thirst of many.
It was pure and clean.
The water reflected back a person of the past,
But it could cleanse them of their sins.

It was pure and clean.
The water was chilled and would make the young cry,
But it could cleanse them of their sins.
The water could give birth to a new man.

The water was chilled and would make the young cry.
The water reflected back a person of the past.
The water could give birth to a new man.
The water could quench the thirst of many.

Lauren Harper, Grade 8
New Egypt Middle School, NJ

The Perfect Spring Day

How perfect a day it is.
Bouquets of clouds perfectly align in the sky.
To feel the spring air rub up against you.
The sun we never see seems so far away.
Always taking advantage of the day.
As the sun sinks in the water,
The moon rises.
And the stars glisten in the sky.
To hear the waves pounding against the shoreline,
I lay awake.
And at last, an orchestra of crickets sings me a lullaby to fall asleep.

Jane Baker, Grade 7
Sts Peter & Paul School, NY

Endless Possibilities

I woke up in my bed wondering what to do today,
Maybe I'll go to the park and play.

I could go for a good breakfast,
Or play a quick game of *Tetrus*.

Maybe I will go to the zoo later,
Or get the old game *Space Invaders*.

I could go to the aquarium and see,
All the fish staring back at me.

Maybe I will go to the Lego Store,
Where they have Legos from the ceiling to the floor.

I could go to the city by taking the train,
Unless there is a chance of rain.

I could see a new release instead,
Or read a book in my very own bed.

There is too much stuff to do in one day,
It might take from today until May.

Oh no, there were so many ideas going through my head,
That I never did get out of bed!

Brian Doyle, Grade 7
St William the Abbot School, NY

The Maze of Life

Life is a maze
Each day a new journey begins
Twisting and turning to a new path
Who will help me through this *maze* of life?

Tears flowing down my rosy cheeks
Needing the comfort
Of a mother's touch
Please help me through *this* maze of life!

My mind begins to swell with numbers and letters
There is too much to process
Time ticks away as I study each day
Please help me through *this* maze of life!

Like a puzzle piece
Try to fit in
Wanting to be popular, smart, athletic, and musical
So much for one to achieve
Please help me through *this* maze of life!

Family, friends and teachers, too
Will help me through *this* maze of life
And so can you.

Hannah Varghese, Grade 7
Nesaquake Middle School, NY

Nieces, Nephew, and Cousin

Every weekend my nieces, nephew, and cousin come.
Their laughs and screams come along, too.
All under the age of eight.
Each one having his or her own small creature personalities
One is always jumping from one wall to another.
The other is dancing to every song that he hears.
The smallest takes everything she sees and says it's hers.
The five-year-old acts like a diva wherever she goes.
The oldest follows me everywhere.
Asking me the strangest things like,
"Why was everyone born?"
The youngest gets me nervous
Whenever she is shedding tears.
But I can't help but love them all.
Relief comes when they all go home.
AHHHHHHHHHH!!!!
Peace and quiet at last.

Daniela Duran, Grade 7
Terence C Reilly School #7, NJ

Colors

Blue
Glistening, sparkling water
The gaze of the glorious summer sky.
Yellow
The sun, the fiery baking ball in the sky
Peeking over the horizon.
Green
The day on which brings luck
Four leaf clovers spread across green pastures.
Orange
The sweet taste of the bright orange spheres.
Purple
Small little circles filled with a squirting outstanding flavor
The smell of lovely petunias.
Red
The fluid that circulates throughout the vein.
Colors

Joselene Regilus, Grade 7
Terence C Reilly School #7, NJ

Halloween Night

Halloween night can be pretty spooky,
With all the things that are very kooky!
The owl goes, "Who? Who? Who?"
While the trick-or-treaters say, "Boo!" "Boo!" "Boo!"
The disgusting witches fly,
Right across the sky!
The black cats yowl,
And the green ghosts howl!
The creepy-faced pumpkin,
Wanting you to eat it like a munchkin!
On this night, don't drink a lot of caffeine,
Because I'm hoping you have a successful Halloween!

Bhoomika Jain, Grade 7
Hammarskjold Middle School, NJ

Lunch

Slithering smooth
Scaly scoundrel

    Silly scampering
    Scrappy scurrying
    Scoundrel
Together   Together
We hide   We hide
In the   In the
Field   Field

Slithering slurping
Helpless mice

    Scampering scavenging
    Escaping snakes

YES   NO
I've got one   He's got me

    Stupid
    Slithering
    Demons
Hello!   Good bye.

John Michael Knoetgen, Grade 8
Hommocks Middle School, NY

A Teacher

What many people may not see,
Is how great a teacher can be.
They share laughs and make a great memory,
That's why they're special to me.

You always see them smiling,
And greeting you with a hello.
They fill your head with information.
To help you learn and grow.

A teacher is a friend,
Who is there through thick and thin.
What many people may not see,
Is how important a teacher can be.

Niña Cabahug, Grade 8
All Saints Catholic Academy, NY

Swim Team

Atop the block, I'm ready to dive.
Off the starting block I go…splash like a dolphin.
Beside me are my enemies, as ready as I am.
Among me are my opponents, and they are out to beat me.
In the distance, my parents cheer me on; I hear nothing.
I have one thought in my mind: to win.
Under me is nothing, but water.
Above me is only the air I need.
Behind me are sharks trying to beat me.
Before I know it, it's all over; I'm on top of the world.

Lily Battell, Grade 8
Clinton Public School, NJ

Fall

Pumpkins, apple cider, candy, oh my!
Fall is the greatest I cannot lie.
A joyful time for family and friends
I hope fall never ends!
Halloween is a fright fest,
picking pumpkins is the best.
Getting a costume a goblin or ghoul
which friend will I now fool?
Getting candy from left to right,
a man just scared me I jumped up with fright.
Raking leaves is a pain
but when I jump in them it is a game.
Playing sports outside with all my friends
but when it's night time all the fun ends.
When I wake up I know it is still fall
I go outside and have a ball.

Michael Schondel, Grade 7
St Mary School, NJ

8th Grade: Class of 2012

Remember when we were little babies in 1998?
Then we reached to fourth grade in 2008.
We were turning one in 1999,
We were turning eleven in 2009.
We dreamed of going to school when we were 2,
We all started Pre-K in 2002.
In 6th grade we all turned 12,
In 8th grade we're the Class of 2012.
I'm going to miss the good times in the past,
I can't believe the years have gone by so fast.
We'll say goodbye to our old school,
We'll say hi to our new High School.
We will never forget about our friends,
We'll always be together until the end.
Even though our good days together are almost done,
We'll always be friends, together as one.

Nicole Magpantay, Grade 8
Holy Family School, NY

Possible Thinking

Always dreaming a better dream,
Come on people, you know what I mean.
Sitting on a cloud, relaxing all day,
Thinking the impossible and having it my way.
Swimming in the air, walking in the ocean,
In dreams, the sky is not the limit.
You can go up, up, and away without a care,
Then land in the sand and party all night.
Anything is possible, don't listen to what people say.
Just close your eyes and dream away...

Cosette Boulanger, Grade 7
St Mary's Prep School, NJ

Healing

In your arms you cradle my heart
Mending it after it broke apart
The warmth you hold soothes the pain
And to let you go would be insane
Little by little you heal the wounds
Your heart beats like a lulling tune
Wiping away the tears cascading my face
I wait for the impact of your embrace
Love and happiness is all I feel
Because you have my heart under a seal
Your kisses set me ablaze
And you maneuvered into my heart like a maze
But what I fear
Is you'll leave me in tears
For now, all I will say
Is I look forward to being with you every day

Donna Tran, Grade 7
William Davies Middle School, NJ

Nightlife

Shadowy streets,
Empty roads,
The animals are waiting.
They wait for everyone to fall asleep,
In the night

So they can roam free.
Without any problems
And no one to tell them to stay away.
They crowd in the streets
They no longer feel threatened in their territory.

A splitting howl
Like a coyote
The cold wind blowing in the air.
The eerie sounds of the animals hunting for their prey.

Calista Robertson, Grade 7
Global Concepts Charter School, NY

Little Midnight

Lounging lazily in the grass,
the tiny kitty spies a lightning bug nearby
as the sun begins to fade.
Following the prey with his large yellow eyes,
Little Midnight begins to slowly crawl through the grass.
Stalking, waiting, and then pouncing,
he captures the small insect in between his paws.
Little Midnight has finally caught his
snack.

Caroline Schlobohm, Grade 8
New Providence Middle School, NJ

A Violent World

Our earth's a wounded person,
Gashes from war all up its arms.
All the bullying cracked its neck
And September 11th stabbed its heart.
Instead of loving, we are hurting
Instead of caring, we are pitiless.
All this hatred has caused a cancer
Inside our precious earth.
It's suffering and waiting for its doctors to arrive
With a cure.
We are the only doctors that our earth can ever have
Only our spirits can mend its deep wounds.
Each gesture of kindness,
A bandage placed on a bloody scrape.
Only we can stop the hurting,
The Earth is only ours to treat.
We are all human beings,
Each one of us created equal.
Peace must be spread,
Violence must be eliminated.

Jenna Moldaver, Grade 7
Cedar Drive Middle School, NJ

Heart on Fire

My fire burns with all its might,
My fire gleams with its delight.
This fire is buried deep within my soul,
And exerts from my heart which is black as coal.
This black heart of mine,
Is a structured design.
Where love is lost, and sorrow is found,
Something by which you are not bound.
I go to sleep with my hair soakin',
And my dark brown eyes wide open.
I dream of a place far away,
And long for it each day.
But you have made this place I call home,
Somewhere I am no longer alone.
My ice-cold heart starts to crack,
And shades to red instead of black.
Where love is found and sorrow is lost,
This time it has no cost.
My fire burns with all its might,
My fire gleams so very very bright

Erin Foster, Grade 9
Oakcrest High School, NJ

Fall

Fall is the time of year where everyone is happy.
It is when Halloween and Thanksgiving take place.
Fall is where the leaves change color getting ready for winter.
It is the time when you get to harvest apples and pumpkins.
School is starting and you get to meet new friends.
Fall is a great season of the year.

Dorothy Shi, Grade 7
All Saints Catholic Academy, NY

Regret

I knew it was there, but I kept on walking away from it.
It slowly crept behind me, but I pretended
That I hadn't noticed. I couldn't stand it,
So I ran.
It began to chase me, but I was far ahead.
I saw a rope, and quickly held onto it.
I suddenly let go and dropped into
The water below me. I had known it all along.
Why? Why had I done it?
I swam farther and farther,
But the sea was endless.
Suddenly, the water beneath me disappeared.
I was in control of a plane, soaring above the clouds.
I descended towards the Meadow of Sorrow.
I saw her there, sitting over
A wilted rose, the rose of our friendship.
She continued to sit, just hoping.
Having almost drowned in the Sea of Ignorance,
I said what I should have said before my journey started. I said:
"I'm sorry."
Because Regret had caught me.

Sarah Alaeddin, Grade 7
Noble Leadership Academy, NJ

Hip-Hop Is on My Mind

Hip-Hop is something.
R&B is something too.
Hip-Hop is my thing; it can be your thing too.
I think about it every day like it's a life rule.
Saturday thru Sunday, Monday.
Monday thru Friday too.

Pick up a pen and a notepad and write what's
True. You know what happens.
The mic calls your name.
My mind goes, "Hmmm."
Hip-Hop says, "Yes."
The clock goes tick, tock, tick, tock as I think.

The mic mocks me as I choose.
I picked Hip-Hop because Hip-Hop will never lose.
It makes me want to skip.
It makes me jolly too.
Hip-Hop makes me happy.
It makes me feel smooth.

Camron Burse, Grade 8
St Clare School, NY

A Door

A door, the essence of life
When opened it unleashes answers and curiosity
However,
when closed it is a boundary
to all who cannot touch it.

Aaron Boos, Grade 7
Mill Middle School, NY

There's No Place Like (Grandma's) Home

My life starts
With my grandma's house: sneaking
Cookies, making crowns from flowers and creating
Fictional characters to play: pretending to be
Wizards, orphans, animals, et cetera,
The plastic
Christmas tree my grandma makes
Us build and decorate, me insisting
On putting the star on,
Our game,
Firehouse rummy,
For every Christmas,
Her dreadful, disgusting
Lasagna for every holiday,
My grandma teaching me how to neatly solve
Math problems and how to be
Right-handed,
Sewing clothes with her cloth, so we can be
Super heroes
And making odd
Ice-cream sodas

Eileen Brian, Grade 9
The Bronx High School of Science, NY

Stuck Between Seasons

The sun's warmth does not quite reach my cool skin
The winter's chill will not soften its bite
Leaving me in disappointed chagrin
This stage between seasons is growing trite
I become restless, exasperated
Watching snow turn to rain and back again
What's this season nature has created?
Being on the brink is such a big pain
I yearn for an end to the evil frost
That freezes everything in its place
Without you, Spring, I am utterly lost
Please stop teasing and show your pretty face
Stop winter and its unbearable strife
Melt away the cold and bring back all life

Shamilah Faria, Grade 9
Townsend Harris High School, NY

Life

I hear it moving faster and faster.
I see it moving faster and faster.
Life's legs crush the ground.
Life's legs jump up and down.
Now life starts to slow down.
Life then goes slower, and slower, and slower,
Until a complete stop.
Life starts to turn to stone.
Life feels nothing.
Life takes its last breath until
Death.

Jabahri James Taylor, Grade 8
St Clare School, NY

Fishing Is Great

Fishing is great but you'll need some bait
With some line, you can wait for a time
flip flop as the fish hop
the lake is great, try not to be late
no electronics allowed and you don't want to hear a sound
don't scare the fish so you give a big shh…
time to hit the hay so you pack up and drive away
I told you fishing is great but you still need more…bait

Matthew Schlenger, Grade 7
Ocean Academy, NJ

War

There lay the remains of war
Where hopes and dreams lay shattered
Where many people suffer, because of war
Where death haunts everyone
Where the angel of death remains
Reaping each and every soul, because of war
War welcomes death and death welcomes the angel
Where the angel lay the only soul survivor of them all

Aisha Salman, Grade 7
Al Ghazaly School, NJ

Gentle Beauty

Gliding so effortlessly,
She bolts to and fro
When the coast is clear.
Streaked with colors,
Her floating wings are coated with its insignia.
Bursting with happiness, singing so quietly, moving yet so shyly,
The butterfly is strikingly delicate.
Beauty is in every move!

Tim Sienko, Grade 8
New Providence Middle School, NJ

The Stars in the Midnight Blue Sky

Shining brightly in the sky,
The stars are as beautiful as the sun.
Standing out from the rest,
The largest star of them all in the midnight blue sky.
Glistening, sparkling, and sprinkling in the light,
The sky glows.
How beautiful are the stars in the midnight blue sky.

Samantha Caggiano, Grade 8
New Providence Middle School, NJ

The Snow Beast

Walking across the icy barren wasteland,
The Arctic white polar bear scavenges for a morsel of food.
Scanning constantly for any signs of life,
The predator looks for the prey.
Growling at a wolf, clawing at the ice, and begging for a meal,
He is never satisfied and always needs more.
What a majestic animal!

Josh Ornovitz, Grade 8
New Providence Middle School, NJ

Clouds

I am white and fluffy.
I can ruin your day or make it better
Depending on my pressure.
My color turns to dark gray.
Then, I'll choose to rain on you.
You can imagine me as any object.
I can be as big as a mile
Or as small as a couple of feet.
I will always be in the sky
As long as there's moisture.
You can just lay down and
Watch me
Become whatever your imagination sees.

Camilo Patino, Grade 7
Terence C Reilly School #7, NJ

Rubbish

My great work
Whispers without ease
Egging me to continue
Drawing and dreaming.

She tells me that
It is trash, but
Those doodles
Are no trash.

That little piece of work
Is like a flower, growing, wilting, and
Dancing.

Ben Lee, Grade 7
Fox Lane Middle School, NY

Kaleidoscope Request

Write and script again
Tales of infinite wisdom.
Carve out for me
A segment of a story.
Embellish pieces lost in ruins;
May literature rise again.
Drink in words of voices forgotten.
May literature rise again;
Embellish pieces lost in ruins.
A segment of a story
Carve out for me.
Tales of infinite wisdom
Write and script again.

Julia Allen, Grade 9
Susquehanna Valley Sr High School, NY

Life

Don't ever be sad
Because life is a journey
Go and adventure!!

Sherri Perez, Grade 9
Raritan High School, NJ

Fearless

Living with the things that scare me to death,
I realize that being fearless is not the absence of fear, but having courage to face it.
Learning to let go of something or someone I care about,
I know it's not about being completely unafraid.
Falling in love again, even though you have been hurt before,
Speaking out, and not letting the moment pass me by without saying something important,
Chasing after my dreams no matter how hard it is to achieve it,
I understand I must try hard to believe things will get better.
Being fearless is not the absents of fear; but having fears and doubts,
And lots of them.

Rose Flanagan, Grade 8
New Providence Middle School, NJ

The Toddler

Standing for the first time,
she boasts a wholesome grin
as she looks around.
Giggling at every moment,
her cheery smile lights up the atmosphere.
Waddling towards her mother, waving her tiny arms around furiously for balance,
and mumbling nonsense, she reaches her mother's loving hands.
Such precious moments are those of a baby's first steps.

Natalie Morse, Grade 8
New Providence Middle School, NJ

Ancient Master

Croaking in a voice like sandpaper,
The elderly frog stares into the pond's depths
As he ponders his next meal.
Bending his rear legs,
He prepares for an enormous leap.
Thrusting his powerful legs, flying through the air, and landing with a wet thud,
The elder dives into the pond.
Look how quickly his tongue flickers out!

Lloyd Goldstein, Grade 8
New Providence Middle School, NJ

Teddy Bear

My soft and cuddly friend, sent to lend me a hand in childhood,
I remember hugging the life out of you, as you guarded me from nightmares,
And scary monsters, and the creepy noises in my closet,
You promised me comfort through your warm fur,
I can concur, you transferred me love through your soft, soft fur,
Sadly I'm older now, my soft and cuddly friend, therefore our comradeship ends,
Even though I'm older, I'll never forget my guard, my supporter,
Thank you, my soft and cuddly friend.

Keyana Smith, Grade 8
Holy Family School, NY

Winter

Warm gloves and mittens
Sitting by the fireplace
Sipping hot cocoa

Emily McKenna, Grade 9
Raritan High School, NJ

The Future Dream

My future is bright
It's filled with creative stories
Writing is my life

Charu Arya, Grade 7
Iselin Middle School, NJ

2012

They say it's the end,
But we're never sure.
An infection will spread,
With an unknown cure.

Buildings will tumble,
Houses will crumble.
What we would be a fantasy,
Soon became a reality.

The Mayan calendar marks the end,
Of this world's life.
People everywhere will die,
Like a stab with a knife.

The world is at an end,
Not a single soul will live.
The day of resurrection will come,
Except with God's permission, no one shall be forgiven.

Ryaane Fadel, Omar Saleh, and Youssef Elshenawy, Grade 7
Al Ghazaly School, NJ

Art

I take out a sketchbook and my head fills with ideas
I see the drawing come alive with different shades
I hear the smooth pencil across the paper
As I watch the eraser move as the picture fades

I mold the clay into many different pieces of art
I watch as the kiln heats up and the fire rises
I carefully move the clay to the kiln
As I watch the clay harden into objects of different sizes

I take out paints of different shades
I look at the painting with my own eyes
I make short brush strokes across the canvas
As I wait until the painting dries

Art is everywhere
Art is intricate and designed
No need for skills like Picasso
You just need a creative mind

Karla Cordero, Grade 7
Little Falls School #1, NJ

Winter

Every single winter
It's always just the same
Snowing all the time
I think it's really lame

It's not that I hate winter
There are some things I like
Like my favorite drink: hot chocolate
And a good snowball fight

Then there is Christmas
I guess it's really cool
But then I do remember,
In a few days, I have school

Personally, I prefer summer
I really don't like the cold
But besides Christmas,
Winter is predictable and old

Ashley Bomar, Grade 9
Bishop Ford Central Catholic High School, NY

Ballroom Dancing

I walk onto the floor, ready for warm-ups
I stretch then start with the salsa
My shoes do a click-clack on the shiny floor
I am a ballroom dancer

Next I do the cha-cha
I pump the music loud and listen for the beat
My skirt twirls as I spin round and round
I am a ballroom dancer

To get energized, I start the swing
Bouncing up and down to the rhythm as I dance
Doing high kicks and small steps
I am a ballroom dancer

To finish up and slow things down I do the waltz
Swaying like a flower as I move in a box step
Moving gracefully and quietly, my feet can hardly be heard
I am a ballroom dancer

Yelena Stuberck, Grade 7
Little Falls School #1, NJ

July 4th Fireworks

Firing bolts of sparks
Fireworks shoot through the clear, summer air.
Cheering, joyous people
clap and point at the colorful sky.
Screaming little infants, petrified animals,
and enthralled teenagers
are the spectators at the wonderful event.
This is the nicest moment of the year!

Brett Caminiti, Grade 8
New Providence Middle School, NJ

A Winter's Day

Sprinkling from the sky,
Snowflakes gently hit the ground as I gaze outside my window.
Scorching my tongue with every sip,
Hot chocolate is a delicious treat.
Zipping on my ski suit, tugging on my boots,
And swooping my scarf around my neck,
I get ready for a day of excitement.
Winter is the best!

Lauren Lee, Grade 8
New Providence Middle School, NJ

To Abdou
Your death was so sudden,
I would've never thought.
Your funeral was on Friday,
Beautiful flowers I should've brought.
You were an inspiration, a true fighter,
But most importantly my friend.
Just because you're gone,
Is not a reason that our friendship will end.
The figure of your face,
Still stapled on my mind.
The words you've told me,
Will never be left behind.
Before I let you rest,
I would like to say something.
It's very quite short,
No need to be crying.
My name starts with a T,
And ends with an A.
If you ever need me by your side,
With you I will stay.
Threxia Macalde, Grade 8
Intermediate School 381, NY

Never Let Go
With her I sense a feeling
None quite like this before
I hug her once and say goodbye
Still wishing I had more
Seeing her every day
Such beauty and such grace
No one can imagine
The joy upon my face
Some say this love is fate
Some say it's just a phase
But when I look into her sunset eyes
I know we can't part ways
This love is just too valuable
Such a feeling so unfathomable
All I can give is a hug
Standing happy
Caressed in her love
Hopeful and peaceful in her warmth
Forever in her tender arms
Please never let me go
Alfonso Roque, Grade 7
William Davies Middle School, NJ

Autumn Days
Cool autumn weather
Heralds the start of harvests.
See the golden fields,
The singing sparrow that flies,
The burst of colors on leaves.
Patricia Luk, Grade 7
William R Satz Middle School, NJ

Narcissus' View
Who is she?
That girl that follows me
through the woods
while I hunt.

Who is she?
That girl that follows me.
Always repeating,
never speaking her own words.

Who is she?
That girl that follows me
wanting love
from me?

Who is she?
That girl that follows me
go away
and never return
Robert Shannon, Grade 9
West Morris Central High School, NJ

Music
Music is love.
Music is life.
Music can make you smile.
Music can make you thrive.

Music is a word from my mouth.
Music is a thought to my soul.
Music is effective.
Music is air in the lungs.

Music is the beat that moves you.
Music is the melody that grooves you.
Music makes you feel lively…woo-hoo!
Music makes you bold and confident.

Music is love.
Music is life.
Music is me.
Music is you.

Marho Bobson, Grade 8
St Clare School, NY

Sisters
I love you more than anything
And you mean so much to me
I will always be here for you
When you need me
We are all the best of friends
We will always stick by each other's sides
I will be here with you through everything
Now it's time for you to fly.
Kyleigh Norris, Grade 8
Holy Innocents School, NJ

Staying Drug Free
Drugs can do a lot of things
Impair my thoughts
And
Vision
Which leads to bad
Choices
Limiting my
Options
Kurt Kobain
And
Keith Moon
Two stars that died young
Taking drugs that messed them up
And didn't know what to
Do
Kobain killed
Himself
And Moon died from
Overdose
No matter how they are looked at
Drugs win in the end
William Tompkins, Grade 8
St Stephen's School, NY

Silently It Hovered
Silently, it hovered
Above the rainfalls, the wind roaring
A lion's wail

It brought joy
Thoughts of hope, thoughts of future
Thoughts of sorrow

Without life, without mercy
It struck down, pattering, pattering
Until dust was no more

Until dusk turned to night
Twilight to bewitching
The hour hand slowly turning

Time slipping by, ever slowly,
Ever silently
And as the rainfall began to cease,
As the clouds drowsily separated,
The paradox upturned
Sharon Lin, Grade 7
William R Satz Middle School, NJ

Kids in the Lunchroom
Kids in the lunchroom
Screaming and yelling wildly
Devouring food
At school's very own zoo
Kaitlyn Gearst, Grade 7
Schuyler School, NJ

Alone

Being alone does not mean you have nothing with you, for when you are alone, darkness is always with you.
Having nothing would be a release from the solitary feeling that comes with that dark cloud of solitude
that looms over the single individual.

Being alone does not mean there is no one to listen or talk to you.
The black fog of being alone constantly harasses you, tugging at you with a steadfast grip.

And it will listen to your pleas but will not answer, for if it did, you would not be alone.
And if loneliness is not with you, then loneliness becomes lonely itself, for it too, is afraid of being alone.

Nick Friedland, Grade 8
Hommocks Middle School, NY

Running

Running. I am running. I hear the barking of dogs close on my heels. Crack! The flash of lightning blinds me as a loud thud of a fallen tree echoes. The gooey mud is being kicked up by my bare feet as I sprint for a safe haven. I notice my friend beside me. Running. We are running. The trees are thrashing at us with long fingers, trying to slow us down. It begins to rain. The icy cold water trickles down my back and sets my spine on edge. While I am distracted by the cold, I do not realize the change in the texture of the ground. I try yelling out to my friend to stop, but the thunder drowns me out. Then it happens. He triggers the explosive underneath the recently dug mud. The explosion is deafening. I am being thrown about like a leaf in a hurricane, and soon I cross paths with a tree. The rough bark shreds my skin away as it digs into my bare flesh. I black out… Miraculously, I awaken within my nightmare unscathed. The rain is still falling, but there is no longer the bark of dogs in the distance. I look for my friend, but he is nowhere to be found. Walking. I am walking.

John DiNofrio, Grade 8
Belhaven Avenue Middle School, NJ

Soccer

As I kick the ball I feel the adrenaline in my body flowing.
Teammates on the bench cheer us on to get us pumped up.
When the ball goes in the net we all run down the field cheering joyfully.
The game gets serious when there are five minutes left and the score is tied.
When I hear parents cheering it fills me with intensity to get the ball and score.
I love the feel of the wind blowing through my hair as I rush down the field and pass all of the other players.
The ref is going to blow the loud whistle soon, which means the game is over.
The pressure builds up and I score the winning goal.
Soccer is a game for most but a passion for me.

Jacob Sanchez, Grade 7
Cinnaminson Middle School, NJ

Lost in the Moment

Have you ever frozen inside but only in your mind?
When I see him, talk to him, even think about him…
I freeze.
My heart sinks lower and lower into my body as he talks to me.
I could only hear him and another person inside my head telling me he's the one.
When he's around I'm clumsy but I know inside my head he loves me anyways.
I can't get him out of my mind even if I try, he's stuck in my mind forever.
My heart skips a beat telling me I'm about to freeze inside my mind again from him…I'm frozen.

Caitlin Altmann, Grade 8
Public School 66 North Park Academy, NY

Did You Hear That?

What did you hear?
The farmers heard the cries
The farmers heard the screams
The farmers heard the gun shots
What did you hear?
The neighbors heard the windows breaking
The neighbors heard the doors breaking
The neighbors heard the children screaming
What did you hear?
The Nazis heard cries
The Nazis heard whispers
The Nazis heard the sizzling
What did you hear?
The Jews heard the trains coming
The Jews heard the fires starting
The Jews heard the hatch opening
What did you hear?
The world heard cries for help
The world heard everything
The world chose to hear no more
So tell me, what did you hear?

Joshua Bostwick, Grade 9
Lenape Valley Regional High School, NJ

Love

Love
It's an interesting emotion when you think about it
You can't see it
Can't touch it
But you know it's there
Feeling the spontaneous outcome when it first happens
When you experience it you feel like a changed person
It's like being born for the first time
You just want to jump in the sky and show your true colors
As if you were a courageous rainbow
Then you hear the fireworks go off
No one can define what love really is
That's what makes it so special
It can be mistaken for something else
Or surely recognized
Love really shows who a person is
You can create it into something great you can't explain
Or cut it out your life and miss something worthwhile
So what can you say what love really is
I say love is a miracle that was given for us to feel
Love is love

Virginia Alalouf, Grade 8
Westampton Middle School, NJ

The Haunted House

Nightmares coming alive…
Seeing everything you don't want to see
Chills running down your back
Screams piercing your ears
Your hearing noises, feeling terrified
Rushing through the house
Your legs cramping up
You're getting dizzy
Not sure what's going to pop up next
Not wanting to see anything come alive
Time is standing still
They're waiting for you
All that's left is you, them, and the total darkness

Jordan Pinto, Grade 8
Keyport High School, NJ

Family Barbecue

My flawless summer day is a family barbecue.
The sun is shinning right on me like a spotlight.
The flowers smile in the spectacular sun,
And everyone's face glows.
The kids are playing, running, and chasing each other.
They hear the music and they dance.
The smell of the hot dogs and hamburgers on the grill,
Makes my mouth water.
I grab a plate to eat my food and the plates dance across the table.
The music roars,
And later we will play manhunt,
The perfect way to end,
My summer day.

Brendan Di Rago, Grade 7
Fox Lane Middle School, NY

Days Go By

At midnight,
the wind blows
the moon shines
it is cold.
We wait for morning to come,
when it's warm
and see the sun.
Then it's noon,
the sun is up high
and the sky is blue.
It's midnight again.
The days go by…

Amanda Cheng, Grade 7
Nathaniel Hawthorne Middle School 74, NY

The Girl

The girl you see is not really who she appears to be
The smile upon her face is sometimes out of place
The twinkle in her eye, doesn't always shine
She's not as perfect as she seems
She has her flaws; hidden behind her makeup and glitter
The girl you see is as sweet as can be
No matter what she goes through; she keeps herself together
It's what she was raised to do
Her heart, bigger than the moon has been shattered beyond repair
But she will never let it show
She is fragile; please handle with care
The girl you see is so much more than she appears to be

Tara Engelhardt, Grade 8
Keyport High School, NJ

Confused

Confused is white like a blank page and also like a drained out brain
Its annoyances quickly rush through my discombobulated mind
It reminds me of the time when I had to write a poem about the mixed up feelings I have inside
Each with their different opinions
Who is WRONG? Who is RIGHT?
It makes me feel A LITTLE strange
Or Out of place
Like how one minute I am Up And the other minute I am Down
I'm DIFFERENT
(!)
Strange
Or maybe even the same, I'm wild then tamed
So many questions and yet none seem answered
It makes me want to burst out and cry
Which path do I take? Which way do I go?
Two choices to make, two paths to take
Is everyone killing the dove? I will still stand strong no matter how long
And then I come to realize that everyone has left and now is all gone
I don't know what to do "I don't know where to go"
(?)
I'm confused

Amani Alnababteh, Grade 7
Hammarskjold Middle School, NJ

Dear Kimi

You are as beautiful as the North Star on a clear summer's night, brighter and more vibrant than all the rest.

When I am lost, you help me find my way, and when I am found, it's your arms I find my way into.
You lead me to freedom as I follow you blindly throughout the dark.
Your warmth radiates out to me, enclosing me in a calming and comforting embrace, never to let go again.
When I am with you, I am invincible, your strength, your courage, protecting me from reality.
Our love is surreal, bending and twisting outside the realm of possibility, breaking all boundaries, physical and mental.
My love for you grows with each waking breath. It defies logic and number, only stopping at my capacity for love.
Then my capacity grows, and my love for you grows with it, out of what I thought I was capable of.
I love you more than words can describe, and this will always be so.

Joey Tornatore, Grade 9
Odyssey Academy, NY

Alex C.

Alexander
Smart, funny, athletic, and weird
Brother of Emily
Lover of animals, sports, and games
Who feels bored when there's no friends around, excited when at a sport game, and sad when a family member dies
Who needs food, water, and a home to survive
Who gives presents to friends and family on birthdays and holidays,
help people who need it, and respect to the environment by picking up litter
Who fears getting bad grades, getting injured in a way that can change my daily life, and not going to college
Who would like to make over 20 points in a basketball game,
play for East Brunswick Bears football or basketball team, and to keep making new friends
Resident of East Brunswick
Clark

Alexander Clark, Grade 7
Hammarskjold Middle School, NJ

An Ode to Valentine's Day

An ode to Valentine's Day when you see a couple share a kiss
An ode to Valentine's Day when chocolate hearts are given to girls around the world
An ode to Valentine's Day when love is shared to one another
An ode to Valentine's Day because we share what we love about each other
An ode to Valentine's Day and what it really means to everyone
An ode to Valentine's Day and what life means on this one day
An ode to Valentine's Day and couples around the world
An ode to Valentine's Day and how many smiles are put on faces around the world
An ode to Valentine's Day and roses that are given out on this very special day
An ode to Valentine's Day and how many chocolates and love is given on this one day
An ode to Valentine's Day a day that everyone may not love, but a day that represents how love is shared to one another
An ode to Valentine's Day and the truth behind it
An ode to Valentine's Day when you hear a couple say they love each other
An ode to Valentine's Day when a new couple gets married
An ode to Valentine's Day when a guy serenades for his love
An ode to Valentine's Day when love can't be described
An ode to Valentine's Day and the kisses that are shared each day
An ode to Valentine's Day when a couple shares their first kiss
An ode to Valentine's Day when a new couple begins on this very day
An ode to Valentine's Day when a couple says their vows for each other
An ode to Valentine's Day when a couple stays together forever and ever

Zuber Ibrahim, Grade 8
Public School 232 The Walter Ward School, NY

All About Me!

Jennifer
Crazy, funny, awesome, and epic!
Lover of chocolate, candy, and TV
Who feels delighted when I'm home, irritated when the bus doesn't come, and thrilled on Christmas morning.
Who needs more time to watch TV, more time to sleep, and less homework.
Who gives hugs to my friends, jokes to my friends, and memories to my family.
Who fears needles, snakes, and spiders.
Who would like to swim in Bora Bora, see the northern lights, and skydive.
Resident of East Brunswick.
Perez

Jennifer Perez, Grade 7
Hammarskjold Middle School, NJ

Frigid

Inside the room my eyes opened; I was wonder struck staring at the hazy dawn.
Beneath my windowsill laid a blanket of ice and powder.
Toward the window's lock my fingers crept; was it all just a dream?
Regarding the chill seeping through my nails, yet I still opened the window up.
Across the open air I reached into the frigid cold, as snow fell onto my arms with rapid speed.
Down the stairs I rushed to unlock the door; I walked into the silent world.
Between the world and my body was a canvas of white snow standing completely untouched.
Underneath my feet as I walked, the snow fell away like early morning fog.
In the freezing snow, between my toes, were a hundred icicles going through me.
Past the snow-covered steps a wonderland of white waited like a newborn baby seal.
At the moment, nothing mattered, but the snow that was dancing around me.
During the realization that I was standing outside in the snow, I remembered something; yet, I didn't quite care.
For today was my birthday.

Erin Boutillier, Grade 8
Clinton Public School, NJ

All About Me

Richard
Happy, carefree, funny, open-minded
Brother of Edward, Alexander, and Hannah
Lover of pizza, cheese, and everything nice
Who feels sick when eating to much cheese, happy making people happy, and sad doing homework
Who needs a pet dragon, super powers, and new siblings
Who gives laughs to others, joy to some, and a cold shoulder to most
Who fears zombies, blood tests, and animal statues
Who would like to live in Europe in a castle with the world's most exotic cheese
Who lives in East Brunswick, New Jersey
Jang

Richard Jang, Grade 7
Hammarskjold Middle School, NJ

All About Me

Justin
Ambitious, Fun, Outgoing, Helpful
Brother of Caitlyn
Lover of music, art, and family
Who feels joy when I see paint, intimidated in the sight of a test, tormented when my family is hurt
Who gives care to my family, effort to school, and amusement to my family and friends
Who fears failing, standards, and losing opportunities
Who would like to be successful in school, to see the world, and enjoy life
Resident of East Brunswick
Valerio

Justin Valerio, Grade 7
Hammarskjold Middle School, NJ

The Day the World Cried

It was a warm beautiful morning, with the sun out until a plane crashed in the North Tower. People were shocked and scared. People who were inside must have been panicking and trying to get out. A lot of them were trapped and thought they were going to die. But, help is on the way and several people got out. After another few minutes…another plane went into the South Tower. People now know this was not an accident. People screaming, people crying, people panicking, people scared. Several people came outside. But, then the First Tower collapsed and then a big ash cloud came in.

HURRY UP, RUN!!! People ran like they never did before. Then, the Second Tower fell. Another ash cloud came in and people still ran. It looks like a sand storm in the desert. Another horrible tragedy happened in Washington D.C. when an airplane crashed into the Pentagon. Another airplane crashed in Shanksville and killed a lot of people.
10 years later, people come together and remember what happened. You cannot forget 9/11, that's The Day The World Cried.

Elizabeth Quinto, Grade 7
Public School 232 The Walter Ward School, NY

Holidays

Labor Day is a day we catch our breath, take a day off and rest,
School starts back up I'm happy to say "School I'm on my way,"
Next Halloween comes it's time to "trick or treat" and see how much candy we can eat,
Thanksgiving Day comes time to sit, eat, and watch the Macy's Parade "Oh the turkey is on its way,"
Christmas comes, Santa delivers the gifts so we can have fun,
It's a New Year, the countdown starts, when it hits 0 we cheer,
Valentine's Day comes we give out love to each other especially to our father and mother,
Easter has come with Easter baskets for all the kids,
Then Memorial Day has arrived as we remember all the soldiers who fought for us and risked their lives,
Finally the 4th of July is here as we celebrate and cheer as our country is here!

Julian McCrea, Grade 8
Ocean Academy, NJ

The Dark Days

The brisk air takes control,
It's time to layer, and layer, and layer!
Hats, coats, scarves, and mittens,
Insulate throughout the bitter, brutal days of winter.
Soon snow begins to fall,
Each flake individual and inimitable,
Each flake a diamond of the sky,
Transforming the surroundings to white from tip to tail.
Light fluffy ice falling, twirling, dancing down from the heavens,
Captivate throughout the bitter, brutal days of winter.
The holidays resume action,
Christmas, Hanukkah, Kwanzaa, and more.
Some thank through love,
Some thank through greed,
Some do not thank at all,
Some mourn.
Special days of bliss yet bleakness,
Enthrall us throughout the bitter, brutal days of winter.
Throughout the cold, and the snow, and all the holidays,
No matter how difficult times can be,
Embrace those bitter, brutal days of winter.

Sarah Pallay, Grade 8
Hillsborough Middle School, NJ

Fall Park Fun

Different colored leaves cover the ground
As you walk you hear leaves crackle under your feet
The cool crisp air whirls around
A regular place with new people to meet

As you walk you hear leaves crackle under your feet
Children playing and having a ball
A regular place with new people to meet
Just walking around the park in the beginning of fall

Children playing and having a ball
The cool crisp air whirls around
Just walking around the park in the beginning of fall
Different colored leaves cover the ground

Casey Hendrickson, Grade 8
New Egypt Middle School, NJ

A Perfect Day

Autumn leaves descend to the ground
Only for the independent wind to lift them up again
Leaves dance as the wind sings the melody, carrying the whole song
Orange, red, yellow, and brown leaves surround me…
A light breeze brushes my hair back and chills my body
Making me receive goose bumps
Collapsing into a soft crunchy pile of leaves, that act as a cousin
I stare at the best masterpiece…the sky
I am a painting
A perfect corsage
All this comes together to form a ideal day

Samantha Haley, Grade 7
William Davies Middle School, NJ

Dear Friend

This time of year reminds me of dear friends
I always think of you when I remember people
I care about
Our friendship grows year after year and we have
millions of memories already
By the time we are old we will have shared a
billion good and bad times
When times are hard, you lift my spirits up
In the good times, we share so many laughs
When we play sports together, we are so in sync
We always know the play the other one will make
Sometimes I just need a quiet friend, and you are her
There are times I need you to pick up the pieces,
and you always do
We never have to worry about peer pressure between
each other
We each love and respect the other
I am the best person I can be when I am with you
I know you have been sent by God to walk
down the path with me
I call you my best friend

Emily Meyer, Grade 7
St William the Abbot School, NY

I Love Fall

Cool crisp and colorful,
Fall is Lovable.
From the brown, red, orange and gold leaves that shimmer,
to the delicious smell of Thanksgiving dinner.
I love fall,
for all the sports games I play.
I also like watching the Jets and Yankees
on a lazy day.
Oh, I love fall from all the food I eat,
from pumpkins and apples.
What a treat?
Now you know why…
I love fall because it is such a ball!

Jason Kessler, Grade 7
St Mary School, NJ

Christmas!

The time of joy when the seasons change,
Near the glowing warmth of the fireplace.
Cuddling with family that you dearly love,
Is this all I could want?
Presents by the oh so glorious and beautiful Christmas Tree,
My heart so suddenly fills with joy!
But, Christmas is not so much of the presents,
But of the birth of Christ!
"Rejoice!" Said the kingdom, "The king has been born!"
The carolers sing with glee,
And they are so powerful with the song,
I sing in harmony!

Erynn Heggan, Grade 7
William Davies Middle School, NJ

Clouds

They mock me.
Sitting up there in the crystal blue wave.
They can do whatever they want.
Throw a mammoth tantrum with bolts of furry.
Cry a river of clear drops.
Or get angry and blow gigantic gusts of wind
And throw liquid knives at your back.
No one stops them.
No one punishes them.
No one sends them up to their rooms.
Nothing.
Spoiled brats.
My parents take away dessert for two weeks
If I take a bit of my brother's treat without asking.
But no, they give the cotton balls a break.
I like the enormous blazing candle much better.

Samantha Orndorff, Grade 7
New Egypt Middle School, NJ

The Lake

The lake that draws me to it,
because it washes away all of my troubles.
The lake that invites the sun in the morning,
because it celebrates the sun
in a million glistening moments.
It tempts the bunnies to go in it,
by looking as clear as a glass.
It attracts the ducks after breakfast,
so they can cleanse their mouth.
It bewitches the baby deer
to stray from their mom out of curiosity.
The turtle that attracts the fish
by its strange movements.
The lake that brings everything to it.
The mysteries about the lake
No one will ever find out.

Kyairaa LeRose-Almeida, Grade 7
Terence C Reilly School #7, NJ

When You're Not Here

Life is so different now that you're not near,
I can't handle knowing you'll never be here.
Most people think they know what I've been through,
But they don't understand I'll never have you.
This feeling I know will never go away,
And I'll keep on missing you each and every day.
In my life you didn't last very long,
But I know you were here and you tried to stay strong.
You don't know what it's like to live my life,
Every day is such a strife.
You suffered so much just to be here,
I'll always miss you so much oh father dear.
But in the end I can still hear your voice and see your face,
Even though all heaven and space.
I love you so much you'll never know,
Until we meet up again when they see me go.

Sara Kanopka, Grade 7
St William the Abbot School, NY

No Matter What Color

Whether tan, peach, black, or white,
We are all created in God's sight.
I don't understand why others can't see,
People aren't based on color, but quality.
We all deserve a chance to become what we wish,
Not be ordered around, no longer human but rubbish
Why do we even think to discourage someone because of the color,
It is an insult more hurtful than any other.
Imagine a world where we all looked the same,
To look for difference would be our aim.
White is like the feathers of the birds that sing,
Black is like the night, pondering what tomorrow will bring.
The two can become very great friends,
Segregation must soon find its end.
Maybe someday, we'll all act as one,
This horrible division will be all done.

Shannon Kennedy, Grade 7
St William the Abbot School, NY

My Sister

A vicious 14 year-old monster,
Always telling me what to do.
She might make me mad,
She bothers me when she has nothing better to do,
Yet, she has her good moments too.
She can make me smile,
When I'm feeling down.
My sister has a soft side when she's playing the guitar,
Or when I compliment her on her talents.
And, at the end of the day,
I'm glad I can call her my sister.

Pamela Becher, Grade 7
Terence C Reilly School #7, NJ

No Longer

No longer will you feel the harmful rays of the sun
Or the horrid wind that can knock you over
Nor the ground under your feet
Or look over thousands of miles of beautiful country
For you are dead
I am sorry, but is there anything I could do
Life is a gift don't waste it
Before the present inside is gone
Because once it is gone it will never come back
Just like how your presence is gone
And the worst part is there is no receipt to report it stolen

Sean Jacobus, Grade 7
New Egypt Middle School, NJ

Memories

Every day I sit in front of an open window
Feeling the breeze move my hair
I usually sit here until the sun fades away
I sit here with the dread of old memories
My eyes start to tear
As I remember your beautiful stories
Sometimes I even laugh
Then I remember you're not here
That's when I feel lonely
But in the end I remember you'll be back
In the stories I will tell
You will never be forgotten
My old friends
Amanda Bliss, Grade 7
Holy Innocents School, NJ

Be Drug Free

If you make a wrong choice,
You can't go back,
You will get hooked,
Just like that.
If your best friend says,
"its okay!"
Just say "no!"
and walk away.
You will live a good life
If you listen to what they say,
"Taking drugs will
Throw your life away."
Lindsey Lepenven, Grade 8
St Stephen's School, NY

No Excuse

There is no excuse for doing drugs,
You chose to do it.
There is no exception,
And it's hard to quit.
You have to be smart,
And not even start.
Your friends might think it's so cool,
But they are all just fools.
Don't do drugs,
Or even consider it.
Because if you try it,
You might not quit.
Laura Bierbrauer, Grade 8
St Stephen's School, NY

Algebra

Algebra makes me queasy
The terms are weird and cheesy
With variable like y
And numbers like pi
It's nowhere close to easy
Blain Liang, Grade 8
William R Satz Middle School, NJ

The Day America Cried

The saddest day in America.
In silence we ponder, the grief and pain came over.
People who sacrificed their life for
Their loved ones.
For that we are grateful, but in pain.
We the people now must be strong. We are now the guardians of our legacy.
Together we stand strong. So let us remember

The people who sacrificed their life for the life of their
Loved ones. The written memories forever
Written in our hearts.
May the fallen stand tall. May our loved ones who died
On 9/11 always be in our hearts.
Years fail to wash away the memories of yesterday.
Memories of such heroic acts shall
Not perish but will always remain.
In our hearts. An ordinary day that started out to be
Soon their lives were given to you and me.
As we watched the anger, and hatred unfold. People in disbelief,
We never though this day would come. So may our loved ones who sacrificed
Their life, live on in our hearts.
Natalie Hernandez, Grade 7
Public School 232 The Walter Ward School, NY

Water Skiing

About 7:00 in the morning, from my bed I arise.
Down the stairs I go.
With slalom ski in hand, I head for the lake.
Below me awaits glass as I put my ski on.
Into the water I jump.
After yelling, "Go," I slice through the water like a knife through a tomato.
Beside me when I carve, water sprays up in the shape of an arc.
Behind the boat, I am a race car speeding across the wake.
Past the two-mile marker, I'm still not tired, and so I continue on.
Before I reach four miles, I turn around, cutting the corner as sharp as barbed wire.
Near shore, with water spraying up, my ski is a fire hose.
Michael White, Grade 8
Clinton Public School, NJ

Fall

The cold, breezy air surrounds you,
You take a second and breathe in the refreshing air,
Your cheeks start to burn as you run and jump into the pile of leaves,

"Breathtaking," people say as the leaves start to change,
Happiness surrounds your every move,
The sky just sparkling as it shines,
The rush of wind,
Birds singing,

The sun shining brightly on you,
This reminds you about the fall,
Take your time and listen to the earth,
The season is changing.
Farren Cardinale, Grade 7
St Mary School, NJ

Sometimes

Sometimes I want to cry but can't find the tears,
Sometimes I want to hide instead of chasing my fears,
Sometimes I want to speak but can't find the words,
Sometimes I want to be free just like the birds,
Sometimes I feel restricted and all alone,
Sometimes I feel weak with no backbone,
Sometimes I feel hurt and embrace the pain,
Sometimes I hold on for my personal gain,
Sometimes I cry and let it all out,
Sometimes I face my fears without a doubt,
Sometimes I soar like an eagle in flight,
Sometimes I know in my soul it's right,
Sometimes I feel invincible and strong,
Sometimes in my heart I know I belong,
Sometimes I feel joy and love,
Sometimes I ascend high above,
Sometimes my life is filled with sometimes,
But that is life with all of its climbs.

Marina Aweeda, Grade 7
Louis Pasteur Middle School 67, NY

9-11-01

They came and they left in the blink of an eye.
But, they'll never realize that they ruined our lives.
The smoke filled the city.
As the building crashed down.
People ran in panic to try to get out.

Then the police and the fire department came.
They saved who they could.
But things will never be the same.
When everything was over.
The damage had been done.
The people who suffered varied.
Some were old but some were still young.

Now it's been ten years.
But people still have fears.
What could still happen.
What might have been.

Amanda Kane, Grade 7
St William the Abbot School, NY

May

The snow has vanished.
Hibernating animals have come out famished.
The flowers start to bloom,
Summer will be here soon!
School is almost done.
Now we can get some sun!
Kids running all around,
Oh how I love all of these spring sounds!
All of these summer things,
Guess that's what spring brings.

Alexis Fredricks, Grade 8
St Stephen's School, NY

The Mask

This white blank page
This unfinished thought
This continuous battle
I have recently fought

My mind is in motion only settles for the best
Do I stay true to my heart or conform like the rest?
I'm screaming in silence yet no one can hear
I'm looking for guidance yet no one is near

I stare at the page
Confused and in thought
I tried to write a story
Of a life I had once sought

But living with what we're given
Is such a difficult task
And that's why every person
Is living with a mask

Isabelle Eisenberg, Grade 7
Holy Innocents School, NJ

Souls of the Wind

There is a soothing wind blowing through the night
That feels like many souls surrounding me
They whisper loudly in my ear calling me to take flight
Though their open path I cannot see

I wish my soul could fly their way
Oh how I dearly wish
I can hear them dancing on the waves
Above the tiny fish

They teach me how to send my spirit
Into the starlit gleaming sky
I would love to finally go there
Or even just pass on by

Oh this feeling that I feel
Oh I cannot explain
For now the souls take off to the sky
And I shall do the same

Lucia Petruccelli, Grade 8
Our Lady Queen of Apostles School, NY

Goodbye Summer

Goodbye summer, hello fall
Hello school buildings that are big and tall
Goodbye to swimming in the pools
Hello to autumn, you're nice and cool
Goodbye to late nights, hanging with friends
Hello to new fall fashion trends
Goodbye to being lazy and having a ball…
Goodbye summer, hello fall!

Aly Maguire, Grade 8
Keyport High School, NJ

Drug Free for a Reason

I want to be drug free
Because
Just the thought of
Wasting money to
Ruin my life
Doesn't make sense
People think it's funny
To do Drugs
But is it funny
When the Cops
Catch You
No
What a
Pity.
Brian Smith, Grade 7
St Stephen's School, NY

They Say

They say write and I wrote
They say run and I ran
They say sit and I sat
They say steal and I stole
They say speak and I said "No!"

They say bite and I bit
They say spin and I spun
They say sing and I sung
They say dig and I dug
They wonder why and I said "So?"

What more could they say?
I ask this because I can no longer obey.
Francesco LaTorre, Grade 7
New Egypt Middle School, NJ

My Grandpa

My Grandpa can't really hear,
I wonder if he is in fear.
My Grandpa can't really walk,
Thank you God that he can talk.

I wish I could go there,
This is not even fair.
He is really kind,
He always has an ambitious mind.

He is coming to live with us,
I think that is a plus.
He can always rest in bed,
So my Mom and Dad said.
Jamie Ryan, Grade 7
Holy Innocents School, NJ

Clouds

I watch you from below.
And even above when I'm in a plane.
My head fills with variable thoughts when I hear your name.
So soft and cushiony almost like cotton candy
However you rain on occasions and other days block the sun.
But you can be fun as I watch all of your different shapes go by.
You're a cloud up so far in a world of great imagination.
In my dreams, I walk upon you.
In my wake, I gaze up at you.
Full of mysteries and wondering yet when you will rain on my parade.
Do you feel like cotton fluff?
Who knows, maybe like marshmallow stuff.
You are a cloud up so far causing one to use their imagination.
Here I go again,
Thinking of all the possibilities you share with me.
Jeslie Ortiz, Grade 7
Terence C Reilly School #7, NJ

Why Is This?

Why do people have to put others down?
Is it fun? Is it amusing?
What kind of people are they?
Innocent people ask questions to themselves every day.
Why are they doing this to me? When is it going to end?
Why is this?
Why are there people in this world who bully others?
Is it cool? Is it fun to watch smiles turn into frowns?
Why is this?
There are mean people in this world. They think it is funny.
Bullying is a reason why people kill themselves.
Is it funny now, after people kill themselves because of this behavior?
If only the bully could walk a mile in the victim's point of view.
No one would forget what they did to innocent people.
Their lives will be changed forever.
Tina DeLuna, Grade 8
St. Mary's Prep, NJ

Birth of Jesus

Christmas is the day when Jesus was born.
Christmas is the day when you put up the tree.
We make popcorn streamers and gingerbread men.
We put up the ornaments and sing all day long.
Put up the stockings, if you have a chimney.
So little elf men may fill them with joy.
When you fall asleep, a special one will come,
With little eight reindeer pulling his sled.
The one who rides this sled wears a red hat and coat.
This man calls himself Santa, a jolly old fellow.
He goes down the chimney puts presents under your tree and eats all of the cookies.
He flies to each house and does the same thing.

He says, "Have a merry, merry Christmas, and to all a good night!"
Ariana Foster, Grade 7
St Mary's Prep School, NJ

The Land I Call Home

Our stars say we are 50 in 1,
Our stripes say we started out small.
But the fact that we still stand at all
means we are strong says our flag.

Just because we are scared, sad and lost
does not mean we are alone.
As the world turned dark
our hearts did as well.
As the last bell had rung
the battle finally begun.

Our flag still stands, our voices are still heard,
and Lady Liberty still awaits.
With the world atop her head,
With shackles crushed and torch in hand,
She shines over our land.
Not just the land of the free and the brave,
But the land I call home.

Ashley Torrenti, Grade 8
Holy Family School, NY

Pencil Less

I walk into school and open my locker,
As I put my backpack on one of the hooks;
I talk to some of my friends that play soccer,
When I'm done I gather up all of my books.

I hurry into class with my thinking cap on,
But I notice that my pencil is gone;
I looked all around and it wasn't there,
So I asked my friend if he saw it, but he didn't care.

I tried to look some more but there was no pencil,
So it seemed today I had no writing utensil;
I decided to ask a friend if he had one to borrow,
And he said, "Sure, just give it back tomorrow."

I said "Thank you, I will do,"
And I took the pencil without further ado;
I never found that pencil today,
And it is gone and I have nothing to say.

Dylan Manuguerra, Grade 7
New Egypt Middle School, NJ

Hypnotized

Every time I look into your eyes I'm hypnotized
I'm put into a daze with no way to get out
But it's okay
When you're around me I'm breathless
When you talk to me I'm speechless
My heart beats so loud, it's like I just ran a race
It's like you take me out of this world
Somewhere into outer space

Brooke Gardner, Grade 9
W Tresper Clarke High School, NY

Recover, Rebuild, and Remember

At the age of two, I really didn't have a clue.
The sky was so blue, and people were on the rescue.
Many people had perished that day,
Now 9-11 will always be a day that we pray.
9-11 will always be a day to remember,
Just like that cold, 25th day in December
The World Trade Center and the Pentagon have been terrorized,
Which means there's much more people to be recognized.
The people of flight 93 were patriots,
And they succeeded with excellence.
They flew to heaven from Shanksville, Pennsylvania.
This day, really has drained us.
Now the World Trade Center is being rebuilt,
Our hearts could now be fulfilled.
The people who have survived this day,
Now have stories to say.
These three tragedies, will be known for many centuries.
We had many heroes, that came to ground zero.
Now we mourn our lost loved ones,
And pray that someday we'll rejoice with them one day.
Let's enjoy the company of the ones that are here with us today.

Carla Burbano, Grade 7
Public School 232 The Walter Ward School, NY

9/11

Gigantic planes float over the clouds
Loud screams were being heard
Large plans disappearing into the World Trade Center
Smoke covering up the whole New York sky
The smoke is being seen from New Jersey
People all over felt horrified
Loud sirens blaring all throughout New York City
Electric wires going out
Lights out
What's going on, everyone is wondering
Our country is still moving on
We are still healing 10 years later
Now finally bin Laden is gone

Zack Smith, Grade 8
Keyport High School, NJ

Thrill of Fall

From green to orange, red, and brown
The leaves change color, then fall to the ground
Children frolic in the crisp air
Knowing that winter is just waiting there
Picking out pumpkins, harvest is here
It's the most wonderful time of the year
Halloween's coming, prepare for a scare
The smell of the season filling the air
Costumes, candy, knock on the door
Ghouls, ghosts, goblins galore
The frost, the chill — the season of fall
The most wonderful season of all!

Julia Kudrick, Grade 7
New Egypt Middle School, NJ

We the People, of Earth

We the people, of Earth
Stand together as Pangea
Broken up, into floating lands
Connected together as a picture
One nation molded and collaged
Held together with liberty
We were born with —
Mixed like colors of a rainbow
Each color representing a land
We, a nation, are that rainbow that shines together across from the sky
But only after a rainy day —
Each flag from each land represents many different things
But, for a nation as a rainbow, our flag is that rainbow that shines up in the sky on that same rainy day —
For centuries as people
We think our color is better than the other; making a problem for our color line.
Some believe the color white is rich, and the richest color of all is us as a rainbow —
Color cannot determine faith and strength; only you and your brain.
Color cannot determine power and fame; only you and your intelligence —
Power isn't everything; love, friendship and freedom are priceless.
And together we can make that happen.
We are one. We are Pangea. We are…One Tribe.

Gabrielle Taylor, Grade 9
Bayside High School, NY

Stephanie
Stephanie,
Nice, bright, shy, artistic
Daughter of Yvonne and Richard
Lover of pets, Disney, and dancing
Who feels nervous on the first day of school, thrilled when I'm with my family, and happy when going on trips
Who needs to do good in school, watch less TV, and study more
Who gives love to my family, food to pets, and gifts to friends
Who fears spiders, rats, and the dark
Who would like to go on more trips, do good in school, and meet more friends
Resident of East Brunswick
Pi

Stephanie Pi, Grade 7
Hammarskjold Middle School, NJ

Swish
Filled with excitement,
I finally obtained the basketball.
Because we thought alike, the ball and I both knew where it belonged.
As I dribbled the basketball, I stared at its natural objective, the hoop.
Surveying the court,
Processing all of this in a split second,
Dribbling the ball like the Tasmanian devil,
I ran downhill ready to send that basketball to where the ball and I wanted it to go.
Feeling my path was complete, I took a jump stop.
Shooting that ball with form and purpose, I tried to send him where he belonged.
"Swish"
Showing off its backspin and beauty, the basketball sunk through the hoop, touching nothing but the net.
Cheering with excitement, the crowd roared my name.
There is nothing more beautiful than scoring that point for my team.

Jordan Price, Grade 8
New Providence Middle School, NJ

A Day in the City
I step off the subway
Walk up to street level
Stop and stare
Thousands of colors are in front of my face
It is Times Square

Mom screams in the background of my daydream
We are going to miss our matinee
We scurry down the street
Taxi horns blowing and people hollering
The smell of pretzels and roasted chestnuts fill the air

We make it to the theater on time
Find our seats and await the start
The excitement of seeing a play kicks in

The curtain falls
We applaud

Across the street we go
My favorite part of the day, Carmine's
We dine until satisfied

To the 49th Street subway we go
Homeward bound we are
I thank my parents for the day
Joseph LaManna, Grade 7
St William the Abbot School, NY

Mother Nature and Father Time
Mother Nature and Father Time
Both have forces that can shine.
The sunset, the ocean, how wondrously they glisten,
Birthdays, holidays, anniversaries for which we listen.

The two give people a renewed spirit each day.
Between nature and time, there is beauty in every way.
Yet, at times they trap people in a cage,
They unleash immense power in fits of rage.

The winds tackle the achievements of society.
They toss up and shatter towns in their entirety.
Rains descends and slowly they rise,
Uprooting homes, leaving faces of surprise.

Oh but not just nature has wind.
The winds of time affect those from within.
Those winds take our memories and throw them out.
They force our loved ones to scream and shout.

Mother Nature and Father Time
Both have forces that can shine.
Don't forget though, their winds of despair.
They can be invoked by the slightest flair.
Joshua Speck, Grade 8
Westwood Jr/Sr High School, NJ

Leaving Footprints in the Sand Until We Travel Inland
A year of school, a year of tests
The beach is my only escape from hours of stress.
Strolling down the path as I reach the sand,
Anxious to work on my newest tan.
A summer of fun, a summer of sun,
I just don't want the day to be done.

I commence my mornings with a rove on the beach
If I stand still and silent, you can hear my heart beat.
I watch out in the distance as waves pounce ashore,
And wonder if the new memories will total more.

The days rush past in seconds as the surfers' big wave,
But the memories remain for a majority of days.
The sandcastles reprieve until the next water battle,
And the seashells will remain until their last rattle.

The final days come when I have to depart,
So I'll make it my best and leave my mark.
A carve on the boardwalk, final step in the sand,
The beach will be missed, you must understand.
Rhiannon Accetta, Grade 8
Hillsborough Middle School, NJ

You Don't See What I See
You don't see what I see.
A girl crying because people say she is not pretty.
A child going home, fearing a beating.
You don't see what I see.
A widow desperate to find good for her daughter.
A boy drinking because his parents don't see him.
You don't see what I see.
A homeless boy cuddling up with only a coat while it's snowing.
A baby being left on the side of the road.
Now you see what I see.
Why aren't you doing something?
Jessica Onorati, Grade 8
St Mary's Prep School, NJ

Autumn Leaves
Watching leaves fall
Before Christmas calls
Autumn colors start to glow
While the wind starts to blow
Making everyone slow
Pumpkins start to show
While it starts to snow
McKayla Rizzo, Grade 9
Delaware Valley Regional High School, NJ

Eyes
Beautiful eyes
The brown blows me away but
She doesn't love me
Patrick Kenny, Grade 9
Raritan High School, NJ

Where I'm From

I'm from pretty pink flowers and sweet smelling perfume.
I'm from hip hop, tap and jazz recitals and glittery black costumes.
I'm from getting the best part in Beauty and the Beast.
I'm from straightening irons, blow dryers, and mousse galore!
I'm from Abercrombie jean shorts, skirts, and dresses.
I'm from diamond necklaces.
I'm from late nights at camp making s'mores.
I'm from jumping off the zip line with my camp friends.
I'm from green grassy yards as wide as the ocean.
I'm from swimming at 4th of July parties with family and friends.
I'm from family road trips to Maine and day trips to Manhattan.
I'm from visits to my loving Pop-Pop and Nana and holiday dinners with my cousins.
Growing up through the years made the person I am today.

Jessica Rothrock, Grade 7
Cedar Drive Middle School, NJ

Love

Living for the things you care
ab **O** ut. Being open to
V arious ways of living and hoping
for the b **E** st in everything I do.

P **L** aying sports with my friends is something I
will always have time f **O** r. Simple acts of
lo **V** e is all the world needs, and I
wish could happ **E** n.

L ove isn't just about hearts and flowers,
it's about respect and h **O** nesty. My friends and I are different, but
that's what makes us **V** ery unique. This is what love is all
about: fri **E** ndship.

Giovanna Scrimo, Grade 7
Schuyler School, NJ

Clouds

They float in the sky
Sculpted like cute animals
Clouds solve my problems
Matthew Mason, Grade 8
Hommocks Middle School, NY

The Beach

Evening sun sets
Erased footprints in the sand
What a peaceful place
Colby Jones, Grade 9
Raritan High School, NJ

The Goal

Running up the field
Sweat on my face
Ball in my net
Never-ending race

Cradle and dodge
Digging deep in my soul
I find an open lane
I shoot for the goal
Michael J. Guarino IV, Grade 7
Great Meadows Middle School, NJ

My Mom

She's in my mind, in my heart
When I mostly need her
She's always there
Never gone
I love my mom
With all my heart
Very supportive with what I do
Really strong bond
That can't be broken.

Nicholas Corte-Real, Grade 7
Terence C Reilly School #7, NJ

Fall

The leaves are changing,
Falling from the trees.
A sign that winter is near,
And summer is no longer here.

I love to see the colors,
Of the leaves as they change.
So many different hues,
Why aren't they all the same?
Taylour Praga, Grade 8
All Saints Catholic Academy, NY

Fall

Leaves are falling on the ground,
The breeze is blowing them around.
The children have their jackets on,
Ready to go have some fun.

In the leaves they play outside,
Having fun as time goes by.
When it's time to go back home,
They get their things and on they go.
Gia Rotundo, Grade 8
All Saints Catholic Academy, NY

Nature

Spring morning
The air is fresh and crisp
Dew sparkles
Everything beginning to sprout and grow
Earliest flowers blooming
Trees growing its leaves
Everything turning green
Take a breathe of fresh air
And take a walk through nature
Catherine Figueiredo, Grade 7
Terence C Reilly School #7, NJ

Starlight

Staring down at me
Through the night
Always there shining
Right up in the sky.
Lighting your way
Inside you,
Guiding you,
Helping you find your way
The stars are there to stay.
Cassidy Fleming, Grade 7
Sts Peter & Paul School, NY

Memories

I remember the splendid old days
When I had a tremendous amount of imagination
When I was a kid
Playing with my brother
I was a faithful knight
A tin bowl as a helmet
And a wooden plank as a sword

My brother was a dragon
A bed sheet as leathery wings
Slaying a dragon with my brother was enjoyable
When I won the combat
My brother carried me running down the halls
And then I got crowned as king
I still can't imagine anything better than that

Mohamed Elsaid, Grade 7
Fox Lane Middle School, NY

Untitled

Insecure with you.
Second guessing all the time,
If you are worth it.

Wishing you were them.
Jealous of what you don't have.
Feeling empty inside.

Maxwell Barrett, Grade 9
Raritan High School, NJ

Grades 4-5-6
Top Ten Winners

List of Top Ten Winners for Grades 4-6; listed alphabetically

AbdurRahman Bhatti, Grade 5
Cambridge Friends School, MA

Katie Dominguez, Grade 4
St Joseph School, PA

Avery Fletcher, Grade 5
Balmoral Hall School, MB

Foxx Hart, Grade 4
F L Olmsted School, MA

Maximiliana Heller, Grade 5
Stanley Clark School, IN

Sarah Kim, Grade 5
Avery Coonley School, IL

Grace Lemersal, Grade 6
Meadowbrook Middle School, CA

Julia Peters, Grade 4
Toll Gate Grammar School, NJ

Lucas Tong, Grade 6
Chinese American International School, CA

Mallory S. Wolfe, Grade 5
North Knox West Intermediate/Elementary School, IN

All Top Ten Poems can be read at www.poeticpower.com

Note: The Top Ten poems were finalized through an online voting system. Creative Communication's judges first picked out the top poems. These poems were then posted online. The final step involved thousands of students and teachers who registered as the online judges and voted for the Top Ten poems. We hope you enjoy these selections.

Help the World

Let's stop everyone from littering.
Instead, plant beautiful flowers and trees.

Give a gift to our soldiers.
Bring them home for the holidays.

Provide shelter and food for the homeless.
There are homeless and hungry people in Africa and everywhere.

Build more hospitals.
Hospitals help the sick and the needy in Haiti.

Stop the shootings in my neighborhood.
We need to increase our population, not make it smaller.

Bring peace to my family.
There should be peace for all mankind.

Joshua Elgandy, Grade 6
New York Institute for Special Education, NY

The Apple

Apple apple round and shiny, red and very fat,
Inviting you to come and take a really huge bite.
It's really very crunchy and has a great taste, so I eat it all up.

My hands are now sticky, my face is too.
But I just ate a yummy apple, what does it matter to you?

Now I want another, and another after that,
Yummy, yummy,
crunch, crunch,
Now the apples are gone.

My tummy begins to ache,
and now I wish that I didn't eat so many apples.

Apple, apple round and fat,
you are very yummy.

Olivia Jager, Grade 5
Bartle Elementary School, NJ

Keep It Clean, Keep It Healthy

Drugs are poison
Our bodies are fragile temples
Keep them clean
Keep them healthy
Dealers get the money
And junkies ruin their lives
Don't get sucked into that Miserable black hole
Of harsh dependence
Keep it clean
Keep it healthy
Exercise, Fight to be free
And don't get sucked into the tempting peer pressure

Priya Bommaraju, Grade 6
St Stephen's School, NY

Unfinished Day

"Whoosh, whoosh"
The wind blows in the fall night
As the night sky darkens I see the stars shining
Their light bouncing off the handle of the slick black rake

I can smell the crisp, cold fall air above me
The bark of the wood smells like fall
The tall, barren tree stands its guard
Protecting the leaves from the rake
Ready to puncture them right through their heart
The leaves felt lonely just like the tree
Until they met up

As the big, fresh, orange pumpkin sits there waiting to be harvested
The pumpkin almost smells like a pumpkin pie waiting to be baked
The grass is slowly growing day by day
As the night ends
Work is left unfinished
Until morning rises

Gabrielle Hanlon, Grade 6
Harold D Fayette Elementary School, NY

I Am a Waterfall

So beautiful and bright
But as the night comes, I become dark, and filled with fright
When the morning comes again,
I now start to glow
My stream moves quickly as the cool air starts to blow
No one gets me,
I am so alone
My true colors will never be shown
My stream will not stop flowing
But I also will not stop glowing
The light will shine down on me
As people come around, I am full of glee
I wish I could see the world
I begin to feel sad I see that little girl
I see many people passing by me
Why can't they just see who I really am?
I'm just like you
I'm telling you, I really am!
I am a waterfall!

Rachelle Rivard, Grade 6
Holy Innocents School, NJ

Yellow Mellow

On the outside, you look like an oval-shaped bright sun.
You feel like a hard rock, and a thick tree.
When I peel you, you sound like I'm zipping a zipper.
When I slice you, you sound like I'm digging in the sand.
Inside you look like a dark yellow eclipse.
You feel like a smushy snail.
You taste like a sweet ice tea.
Tell me, why are you sweet and yellow?

Jalen Bateman, Grade 5
Roosevelt Elementary School, NJ

Fall Night

A darkening day coming to an end
As the calm pink sky dominates the trees,
Leaves and grass like a giant
As the sky becomes sleepy it whispers, "Good night."
And goes to sleep.
As the sky fades away the small yellow stiff grass becomes freezing and tastes ice
From the day becoming cooler and the leaves
Proudly protect the grass
By going on top to see if something is there.
The leaves changing different colors as they rip off the tree like paper
Start flying with the wind to hear nature until they softly land on the ground with a small thump.
The day is almost done as the big soft orange sun loses its brightness like a fire.
It silently slides down into the dark sky
And patiently waits until tomorrow morning,
To bring happiness to the trees, grass and leaves.

Michael Hoefenkrieg, Grade 6
Harold D Fayette Elementary School, NY

Outstanding Autumn

Amber, golden and brown leaves fall to the ground as Mr. Softy takes his last route around town
Jack-o-lanterns glow like the harvest moon in the middle of October
The gooey insides of a pumpkin are like a great big ball of mud after a rainy day
Picking crisp apples from a beautiful tree makes me eager for a warm apple pie
On Halloween night trick-or-treaters ring my doorbell; anxious and hyper from sweet sugar in candy
The crinkle and crunch of leaves under my feel as I walk home from the bus
Fairs and festivals hop into town and people pour in
Eager to have a drink of apple cider and have fun on hay rides
An abundant amount of children running throughout the streets can't be mistaken on Halloween!
A bird's cheerful chirp blossoms like a morning glory in the late summer
The bonfire's golden glow embraces the light on a mourning evening

Fall is here, I love it!

Alexia Trotta, Grade 6
Oakdale-Bohemia Middle School, NY

Fall

Every year when autumn or fall comes around. In the days of it you see the leaves change color to yellow, orange, and brown mostly, a lot of leaves fall down at that time of the year. A lot of kids start jumping into different color leaves. All the hard work you do to make your yard clean of leaves and dead branches, but the leaves just keep on falling in your yard. In fall it gets very cold because in a couple weeks it's going to be winter. So usually you would be wearing a big fat jacket to keep you warm. A lot of people get allergies in the fall. It takes a while to rake all of the leaves. Plus it is Halloween time when people come to your house and ask for candy. That's why I like fall!

Matt Dickson, Grade 4
Eugene Auer Memorial School, NY

Fire Heroes

Fire fighters are people who help make the world safe.
Our world is a better place because we have them to save others from fires.
They risk their lives to save others and run into buildings to save fathers and mothers.
On September 11, 2001 our firefighters were our heroes.
They lent a helping hand to help people stand.
When you see a fireman show respect and kindness since they go into burning buildings with blindness.

Preston McCutcheon, Grade 5
New York Institute for Special Education, NY

Why I Love Halloween

When I hear the word Halloween
Monsters come to mind.
So, me and my cousin go trick-or-treating and hide.
We get lots of candy.
And scare our friend, Mandy.
Then, we go to a haunted house,
And we see a scary mouse.
Then, Peter and Patricia pick a pumpkin out of a pumpkin patch.
Brandon bought a book bag to bag more bubble gum.
The pumpkin we got was as big as the sky.
That is why I love Halloween.

Brittany Jackson, Grade 5
Buffalo United Charter School, NY

Dreams

They come alive when you believe.
you must believe and then you'll see.
Don't let doubts turn your attitude,
Upside down.
Reach for the stars,
And get rid of that frown.
Right now they're just in your head,
But give it some time and they'll be real instead.
Don't let darkness take over you,
one day, your dream will,
COME TRUE.

Jennifer Lynn Galvet, Grade 6
Holy Family School, NY

Welcoming Fall

The tall brown tree is guarding the fluffy squirrels
Stands in the crisp air
Like a wooden soldier.
The hot orange egg-yolk sun melts into he light green rolling hills
It goes into another dimension.
The colorful leaves flip and twirl
They land on the stiff hard ground.
The wind whipping and branches swaying.
The leaves go swimming to the ground like a sky of color
The country hills, a rolling ocean wave in the back.
The bare, barren tree like an abandoned island welcomes fall.

Daniel Marcello, Grade 6
Harold D Fayette Elementary School, NY

Soccer

Rubber soccer balls fly quickly through the air.
Hard shin guards protectively shield player's shins.
Loud fans cheer continuously in the metal stands.
Fierce goalies block viciously in front of the giant goal.
Rough fouls eliminate players quickly on the grassy field.
Aggressive players frequently run across the turf.
Frustrating refs yell hopelessly in the stadium.
Soft shorts cover bodies easily in the locker room, and
Sweaty exhausted players are relieved that the game is over.

Winter Favre, Grade 4
Maud Abrams Elementary School, NJ

Flying

Swoosh!
Through the sky on a purple colored night.
The warm air flows,
As a gentle breeze whips through my hair,
And I land on the torch of our statue.
I look all around and I find my dear friends,
And I pull them up into the sky with me.
I find my parents,
And we float on a cloud.
I pick up a piece of cloud,
And it's cotton candy!
This is the life of a traveler,
And I am honored to live it,
So come soar with me,
Because…
I can FLY!!!

Mina Gurkan, Grade 6
MS 167 Robert F Wagner (SP), NY

Basketball Rules

Basketball rules
Basketball is my favorite sport
I've always wanted to be king of the court
Watching the pros makes me go out and grab a ball
I always try to give my all
I venture out to play with my friends
Hoping the game would never end
Playing basketball is like having a paintbrush in my hand
Because I am a basketball artist
I always want to play my hardest
It is a part of my life and I want to play forever
Basketball is the best sport ever
The drills might be tedious but I love it anyway
It is a sport that I always want to play
My goal is to take the ball all the way
And to hopefully make it to the pros someday.

Xavier Foushee, Grade 6
Westampton Middle School, NJ

Zombies

Zombies are people sort of like us,
Except they are dead and make a big fuss.

Their favorite supper is brain stew
Even if it is hard to chew.

And for dessert the worst meal of all
On top of ice cream they put an eyeball.

They come out of the ground on Halloween night,
And give tons of children a very big fright.

So next time you see one be sure to run away,
And you just might live to see another day!

Shayne Davies, Grade 5
Liberty School, NJ

Picture Poetry

I see the beautiful bright sun, blazing in the sky showing that there is a beautiful world down there shining.
I hear the winds blowing through the tall, brown leafy tree.
I see the beautiful flying birds chirping and singing tunefully.
I smell the wet ground as people walk over it all muddy.

Danielle Evans, Grade 6
Harold D Fayette Elementary School, NY

Who I Am

If you had a paper
With different labels written all over it
Where would you put my name?

If I were to write it, I wouldn't
I would rip, rip, rip that meaningless paper
And throw it away forever

It would be gone, gone, gone
And not a soul would miss it
It's unfair, immature, unreasonable

I am what I am, and what I am is who I am,

And who I am, is who I want to be, so don't judge me
So don't try to tell me who I am through YOUR eyes,

Maybe it's wrong, maybe I already know
Maybe I will figure it out another day
I can read between the lines
Don't do it for me

I am what I am, and what I am is who I am,

And who I am is who I want to be,
So don't label me

Kathy Griffin, Grade 5
Toll Gate Grammar School, NJ

My Name Means…

In the dictionary
my name means crown
or crowned.
That could be true, but not yet.
Stephanie means bookworm
a dog lover and a dreamer.
Someone who is trusting
and caring.
My name means
someone who loves to swim
in big blue oceans.
Someone who is amazing
at gymnastics
and dance.
I love all the different
things I know about me.

Stephanie Walsh, Grade 4
John G Dinkelmeyer Elementary School, NY

Seasons

Seasons, oh, seasons
I love seasons.
Here are some reasons
Why I love these seasons:

In winter it's mostly cold,
You have to bundle up.
If you don't, then you're bold
To be out with nothing warm in that very cold, cold.

Now there's a season when birds come out to sing,
When flowers sprout and trees come out.
This season is called spring.
This is when the weather gets warm.

Summer is never a real bummer,
You can go out under the sun.
Summer is never a newcomer,
That's because it's a beautiful summer.

This next season involves trees that stand high and tall.
There are two names for this season,
Some people call it autumn, some people call it fall.
That's because at this season, leaves fall, fall and fall.

Then, we go back to winter.

Olivia Idzikowski, Grade 5
Tecler Arts in Education Magnet School, NY

A Season to Remember

The leaves rustling
Like a small earthquake
The colorful floor covered with leaves
Like a blanket on a cold child.
Children shivering
Like a dog that has no fur.
Birds flying south for the sunny world
Like a hungry shark searching for food
A chilly breeze sends the children squealing
Like yelping dogs in the dark
Houses with dim lights but outside is dark
Like the midnight sky
Fathers raking leaves
Like a busy bee collecting honey
Seeing families giving thanks for being together
Like a baby duckling reuniting with its mother

Austin Reid, Grade 6
Ridgeway Elementary School, NJ

The Ocean
Sand in my toes
Ocean smells…in my nose.

The ocean breeze hits my face,
It makes me feel like I'm in a special place.

I never felt so happy before,
It makes me feel like I'm much more.

I love the waves and the breezes' motion,
I never want to ever leave the ocean.

Angel Williams, Grade 5
Tecler Arts in Education Magnet School, NY

Blue
Blue is the color of the bike I love to ride
It's the color of the walls in my room
And the covers I snuggle under at night
Blue is the color of my summer sandals
That I like to wear at the beach
And the color of my jeans
That I wear every day
Blue is the color of my toy cars
As well as the sky over my head
Blue raspberry ice cream is one of my favorite flavors
I could eat it every day.

Javen Cabral, Grade 4
Roosevelt Elementary School, NJ

Starry Night*
Starry night
Oh, you shine so bright
So many colors, too many to name
No other painting will ever be the same
Silent, mysterious, beautiful it is
Twinkle, twinkle, goes eleven stars
Whoosh! The wind may blow as it may
Silent the houses lay
Even though the painting is old
So many secrets it will hold

Rowena Songcuan, Grade 5
Roosevelt Elementary School, NJ
*Inspired by "Starry Night" by Vincent Van Gogh

Miracle Bird
Flying stealthily through the dull night
Soaring as fast as the night's cold gust
With a colorful trail of vivid painted feathers
The flying feat is a wonderful sight
Makes Earth an abstract, not gray as dust
Bringing the world color, it's not much absurd
The path of the creature is cleared for the "rainbow"
The world is its canvas
The brush is the Miracle Bird

Andrey Morales, Grade 6
Holy Innocents School, NJ

A Synonym for Life
A synonym for life
Itself
Like a cat who lost it's stealth
The wind beneath my wings
Are not that strong
to carry me
And now,
I'm on the ground
Nothing else to do
but
Sulk and frown.

Amber-Nicole Walker, Grade 6
Graham Elementary and Middle School, NY

Red
Red is the color of a sweet, juicy apple
It's the color of the stripes on the American flag
Red is also the color of fall leaves
Mostly red is the color of a beautiful rose
and the color of stop lights
There are nutritious foods that are red
Like tomatoes, ripe strawberries,
and sweet, juicy, delicious cherries
But the thing I like most about the color red
is that it is part of a
rainbow.

Samuel Dorielan, Grade 4
Roosevelt Elementary School, NJ

I Can Teach You How to Make a Better Universe
If you want to make this universe a better place
you better get up and bring your best
and put a smile on your face.

You should help old people cross the street
and say hello to the people you meet.

Say thank you to the people that help you,
and give food to the homeless people.

This is how you can make a better universe.

Anthony Alverio, Grade 4
New York Institute for Special Education, NY

Divine Dancing
Knowledgeable teacher kindly instructs in small rooms
Heart-touching music sweetly entertains the dancers while
Stiff hair spray strongly holds hard hair
Pink point shoes gracefully rise on hardwood floors
Beautiful makeup softly creates new looks backstage
Remarkable costumes constantly shine
Gold glitter beautifully creates clouds in the air
Dancing divinely at dance school, for
Big performances on one special weekend

Desiree Matthews, Grade 4
Maud Abrams Elementary School, NJ

Flying with Tina

Big, brown, and spunky, Tina's silly like a monkey
Small hooves, big heart, a pretty girl who's really smart

Let's go, Tina, It's time to tack up
Our class goes next, I need a leg up

In the ring, Tina's eager to ride
Watch the corner, she gets spooked on that side

Soft ears pinned back, scared of a squirrel who won't attack
Don't breathe heavy, Tina, I'm not going to leave you

Keep going, top speed, a few more jumps is all we need
First the red fence, then the blue, come on girl, there's more to do

Now she's soaring over fences and we're flying around the course
Up in the air is my favorite place on my very favorite horse!

Nikolette Sarna, Grade 5
Buckley Country Day School, NY

The Harmful Effect of Drugs

Drug free is the way I want to be
Even when I am under peer pressure,
I will refuse
If that is what I do,
I will never lose
People make wrong choices,
And their life is gone
If I make the right choices,
My life will be long
I want to stay fresh and clean
My reputation and friends mean so much to me
People get addicted and die every day
I'm telling you truthfully,
Drugs is not the way
I hope you trust me
Drug free is the way
We should be

Lauren Curtin, Grade 6
St Stephen's School, NY

Thanksgiving

T urkey legs are delicious
H appy guests means we all have fun
A ll guests enjoy the food
N o person goes hungry
K ittens get extras of the turkey
S oon everyone leaves
G reat, it's time for the wish bone
I t's fun to eat all the tasty food
V isitors play games together
I n the house, it smells good
N ot one part of the house is without a smell
G reat, it's time to eat!

Seth Babbitt, Grade 5
St Aloysius Regional School, NY

Chained for Life*

I am a slave.
My life is a never-ending nightmare.
I can never wake up from this.
I wake to a cruel life, and slave away at a loom all day.
Abused and downtrodden, no one cares about me.
To them I'm the same
As their sock or their dog.
I'm a product, not a human.

I miss my family.
Every day I long to be home, living my old life.
At home, I am cared for, and treated well.
I don't belong in this horror of a world.

My life as a modern day slave
Is a living nightmare.
I'm trapped, and unable to move.
This is my fate.
I have no liberty or freedom.
I'm chained,
And bound for life.

Stephanie Tom, Grade 6
Roslyn Middle School, NY
*Written in the view of a modern-day slave.

Lime — The Green Thing

On the outside, you look like the Grinch
who stole Limeville!
You feel like a big, heavy, asteroid from space.
When I peel you, you sound like a zipper going
up and down a jacket.
When I slice you, you sound like rubber trying to
be cut into a million pieces.
Inside you look like a rotten old orange gone wrong!
You feel like something slimy, squishy, and gushy.
You smell sweet and sour and tropical-like.
You taste sour and bitter and stingy in my mouth.
Tell me, why are you the way you are?

Alexis Carter, Grade 5
Roosevelt Elementary School, NJ

Thanksgiving Fun

T ogether we gather around the table to say our
H appy prayers. We know that God is listening,
A bove the sky he hears us pray.
N ow we sit around the table
K nowing that we are going to eat Grandma's
S weet and juicy ham.
G randma serves us gracefully, but
I soon indicate that I am full.
V igorously that ham stuffs everyone, but it's so
I rresistible, because it is
N ice and juicy. I love the meal because after all,
G randma made it.

Carman Bishop, Grade 6
Riverside Middle School, NJ

Imagination in Drawing

As I scratch the paper with shining black graphite,
A glowing door appears to me in the moonlit night.
I see it very often, but it's very rich today.
I get my pad and pencil, and start to draw away.
The light is imagination, and it's flowing through my hand.
I feel at home, yet in a faraway land.
My drawing is almost finished, as I sketch the last line.
A newborn drawing is like the freshness of a pine.
Then, my drawing begins to glow as the door fades away.
The light of imagination brightens up the new day.

Vinayak Sharma, Grade 6
St Mary's Prep School, NJ

Basketball

Up and down the court the players run
It looks like a great deal of fun
Every ten seconds there is a lot of scoring
If you are into the game it's not boring
Players running sometimes they trip
Often some players sliding after they slip
My awesome dad took me to a real game as a gift
Many of the players were very, very swift
Waiting for an autograph on my lucky ball
While I quietly lean against the big wall.

Chad Ghee, Grade 5
Bartle Elementary School, NJ

World Peace

I hope one day
I see a shooting star
My wish will be
World Peace.
If my wish comes true,
There will be no more
WARS or
SEGREGATION anywhere.
I'd feel safe,
Knowing that everyone else is safe.

Kelsey Lora, Grade 6
New York Institute for Special Education, NY

My Drug-Free Future

I don't want to die young
When I'm drug-free I won't harm my body
Good people never do drugs
I want to be successful and not be a bad person who does drugs
I won't do any drugs
I hope all people are drug-free
I don't want to end up six feet under
Being struck by thunder
I won't fail my life
I won't be a druggy

Dominic Nappo, Grade 6
St Stephen's School, NY

A Drop

Comes down from the white pillows above,
And plops onto the tree
Then rolls down the green silky carpets,
And into a water-slide
Sending me down to all my friends,
Who wait
For the fireball in the sky,
To some day,
Bring us back up,
Where a drop belongs.

Joseph Gashinsky, Grade 5
John G Dinkelmeyer Elementary School, NY

Walking Across an Ocean

They say she runs across the oceans —
Walking planks of light.
Running away,
looking for someone.
They say she sleeps on the clouds —
making flowers bloom.
Even when there is no shining star in the day,
She'll ask a light in the sky for a kiss
of sun-swept love.
Walking across an ocean.

Katia McGreal, Grade 6
Mountain View Middle School, NJ

Blue Monster

I see a blue thing in the dark,
I'm scared and stranded in the park,
I'm alone in a tent,
And I don't want it to get bent,
I see it coming closer to me,
It looks like he's eating a blue cookie,
But when it came up as close as it could,
I said "Hey I know you better than I should!"
I am a person that likes to eat,
He is Cookie Monster from Sesame Street!

Caitlin Checca, Grade 5
Hillside Elementary School, NJ

Simple Smiles

Of all the things that make me smile
there's nothing quite like running a mile
Of all the things that make me laugh
there's something so silly about a giraffe
Of all the things that make me happy
there's nothing quite like eating taffy
Of all the things I love the most
There's nothing better than cinnamon toast
These are just a few things that brings out a smile
simple things really, but oh so worth the while

Alivia Brill, Grade 6
Westampton Middle School, NJ

Death

Death can be sad
But when you are ready, it can be peaceful
When you die because of loyalty for your country,
protection of your family, and because of age,
Death greets you with open arms and kindness.
But when you die because of irresponsible choices like suicide,
drugs, or heart attacks from smoking.
Death's disappointment is with you forever.
Death has reasons that no human will understand.
You must be ready for death and not fear it.
Be careful with your life and only die for true reasons and love.
Death is no joke.
You must understand its reasons and purposes.

Jessica Ritchie, Grade 5
St Aloysius Regional School, NY

Fall Football

F all is the best time of year
A ll of the leaves fall from the trees
L eaves cover the ground
L ots of noise, blowing leaves

F ootball season starts
O versized monsters take over the field
O ver-talented players astonish the fans
T he main event, the Super Bowl is life
B ut players play for the heart of the game
A ll players are tested to see their abilities
L oud fans roar in the stadium
L ots of comments also roar through the stadium

David Andreu, Grade 6
Slocum Skewes School, NJ

Overcoming Loss

When you lose something or someone dear to you
You feel an everlasting pain
You think your world is going to end
Lost in a land of confusion and depression and pure melancholy
But don't worry, light and happiness will come your way
Plant a seed and take a small step towards happiness
Because your lost one is watching over you
Goodness will come to you
And your depression will eventually come to an end

Chloe Chamberlin, Grade 5
St Aloysius Regional School, NY

Leaves

The leaves on the trees float through the air
and onto the ground.
Many colors from red to orange.
As kids dash across them they say crunch, crunch.
Being raked for jumping piles.
They sleep through the rest of the seasons,
waiting for fall to come again.

Chloe Foga, Grade 5
Bartle Elementary School, NJ

By the Sea

Have you ever had a dream by the seashore?
You see the birds soar and soar.
You feel the sand in between your toes.
You feel the wind blow through your nose.
The dream never goes away.
But you like it that way.

You can collect seashells or just lay down in the sand.
You can look up at the sky and see the clouds pass the land.
You don't have to leave, no, you can stay.
You can live here, sand just drift away.
By the sea.
With me.

James W. Lyon, Grade 6
Sts Peter & Paul School, NY

She

a friend is a part of your world
she's a rose in a patch of daisies
losing her would be like losing a piece of your heart
she's a bank filled with trust and secrets
she is there to catch you when you fall
she believes in you even when you've lost hope in yourself
she is a song you know all the lyrics to
she is a key to yourself
she brings out the best in you
and you bring out the best in her
she's your shoulder to lean on
she's the sun on a cloudy day
friendship is like a circle, it will never end.

Rachel Chang and Marissa LoCurto, Grade 6
Shelter Rock Elementary School, NY

Christmas

C ookies are bitten…carrots are gone
H appy children everywhere
R ip open the wrapping paper
I dream about the presents
S now outside is drifting down
T ime for joy and time for play
M assive piles of snow outside
A present is sitting on the end of the bed
S urprise, surprise…I got underwear!

Jade Martino, Grade 5
Tecler Arts in Education Magnet School, NY

Mt. Vanilla

The caramel syrup rivers flowing golden brown
Oreo boulders rolling down the mountain
The chocolate syrup canals were everywhere
The Kit-Kat cliffs were still and proud
The ground was vanilla
It was great
Trust me, this is what I ate!

Nicholas Hoy, Grade 6
Harold D Fayette Elementary School, NY

Sky
Clouds drifting, lonely
Sprawling forests
Cold, brittle air
Maybe, just maybe
Heaven is above

The sun is harsh and unfiltered
Except for the occasional cloud
Covering the sun
I am completely under its unexplainable control

The only sound
Is the roar of the wind
Accompanied by rocks falling

Is the lord really up there?
Will I touch the sky?
Will the valley swallow me whole?

I am awed by the sky.
I am small to the valley.
I am beaten by the sun.

Small,
Small,
Small.

Derek Brown, Grade 6
Bay Shore Middle School, NY

Horses
Horses are the wind
Flowing, galloping
Free in the wild world.
Carrying you far,
Far away in a dream made of love.

Horses are music
Unique more than anything.
Beauty singing from every millimeter.
Notes dancing in a glorious neigh
Worshipped joy never to end.

Horses are rockets
Skimming over the ground
Hooves not seeming to prick the dirt.
Flying, gliding
Fast as fire with ease.

Horses are soldiers
Loyal to the end.
No matter what happens
There is space in their heart for you
At day's end.
They are the soldiers riding off into the sunset.

Andrea Sickels, Grade 6
Great Meadows Middle School, NJ

The Season of Winter!
Winter is the season of beautiful snowfall
I have fun sliding, gliding and playing football

With winter comes cold weather
I wear gloves made of leather

In winter we turn on the heat
Drink hot chocolate and bake cookies to eat

Winter is like a monster of snow and lights
And children having crazy snowball fights

Danial Hameed, Grade 4
James A Dever School, NY

Winter Is Back
The children had red faces
Like fire

There were so many children fighting with snow balls it was
Like the civil war

The snow was so cold it was
Like a freezer

There were so many people shoveling snow it was
Like a gold mine

Ari Swanson, Grade 5
Ridgeway Elementary School, NJ

Football
I love football and I play it in the fall.
You play it with an oval shaped ball.

Offense tries to score a touchdown
while defense tries to get the carrier down.

The team who wins will feel very great.
There's nothing about football you would ever hate.

I think football is a lot of fun.
It is a sport for everyone.

Chase McGill, Grade 5
Dickinson Avenue Elementary School, NY

9/11/2001
All this sweat and tears.
Remembering our losses
For all these years.
Our loved ones weren't supposed to die.
As we remember this day we all still cry.
We let the days pass by.
Wondering who bombed the towers and why.
We must say that we hate vengeance.
This day is a day for all of our remembrance.

Moises Rodriguez, Grade 6
Myles J McManus Middle School, NJ

Laura Valentine

L is for lollipops that taste very sweet.
A is for apple which is a nice healthy treat.
U is for unicorn, a magic horn on the head.
R is for rabbits that sleep so well.
A is for angels that watch me every day.

V for a valentine that I always keep
A for Alyssa who is my best friend
L for love that will never end
E for everyone who is kind to me
N is for night and all the stars I can see.
T is for Tuesday and we go to gym
I for idea about singing a pretty hymn
N is for never, I'll never forget about you
E for everything you do.
    That is the meaning of my name.

Laura Valentine McEwan, Grade 4
Good Shepherd Regional Catholic School, NJ

Purple

Purple is the best
I don't settle for the rest
I have a lot of things, shirts, pants, and ties
If I ran out of purple things I think that I would die
I have a purple sweater and hat
I even have a purple mat
I have a purple hairdo
I also have a huge purple tattoo
I don't like orange or green
Honestly I think black looks mean
Purple is my favorite I am set
I even have a purple jet
The color purple is quite a dream
If you've seen purple you know I mean
Purple is officially my favorite
I am thankful to whoever made it

Devon Antinoro, Grade 5
Hillside Elementary School, NJ

Family Time

Sunlight and joy pours through me
Like honey into tea
Family sinks into pink couch, gobbling them up
Boom! Bang! Boom!
Pots, pans fly
Turkey
Seeps into my nose

"Out!" voices shout playing running bases
"Touchdown" "Yeah!" dad screams from the kitchen
Football flies from my hand to my uncle Rob's hand
Happiness and love float into my heart
The excited sun sleeps
While the moon awakens

Melissa Saporito, Grade 6
Harold D Fayette Elementary School, NY

I Want to Be Drug-Free

When I am older I want to be...
A teacher,
A veterinarian,
And I definitely want to be drug-free
I want to be drug free because...
Drugs are bad for me,
And could kill me,
They cause diseases that would cause me to die young,
I could get arrested and be put in jail if I took illegal drugs.
I wouldn't look healthy
And more importantly I wouldn't be,
My friends wouldn't want to be around me,
Addicted I would be,
Peer pressure wouldn't influence me.
Friends who want me to take drugs aren't real friends,
Trust me as I follow my dreams

Shannon Klein, Grade 6
St Stephen's School, NY

Beautiful Autumn

B lowing winds shoot all around me.
E very leaf falls off the dark brown maple tree.
A utumn is here and everyone knows it.
U nique little animals start storing food.
T he wonderful smell is pumpkin pie cooking.
I n a warm little home, animals eat.
F east of food on Thanksgiving.
U nforgettable celebrations occur.
L ife outside starts to die down.

A ll the leaves are beautiful colors.
U navailing personalities from everyone.
T ree branches sway from side to side.
U nstoppable laughter everywhere I go.
M any things to learn about nature.
N urture and care from animal moms.

Hannah Beckett, Grade 5
St. Rose of Lima Academy, NJ

The Changes in Fall

Colorful leaves gently float away
With the breeze of the autumn wind
Towering trees sway side to side in the wind
As if they are waving hello
The smell of freshly mown grass
Fills your nose with a pungent smell
The world is quiet
As if everything was asleep
The only thing you hear is the sound of cars
The weather gets colder
As if mother nature has a cold
Children wait for winter
And for winter and for white and fluffy frozen pieces
Of rain to fall from the sky

Yohan Yun, Grade 6
Slocum Skewes School, NJ

Friends

The friends we have made this year,
will last through every year.

They were there when you were sad,
they were there when you were glad.

As the years go by,
they must all eventually say their goodbyes,
and carry on…with amazing memories.

Annamaria Fazio, Grade 5
Buckley Country Day School, NY

My Grandparents Rule

My grandparents rule,
they came to my school!
with bingo and more,
we had fun galore!

We had muffins and pie,
and there were new things to try,
my grandparents rule,
they came to my school.

Kali Burres, Grade 5
Hawthorne Christian Academy, NJ

Without Poetry

Without poetry
A mind without thoughts
A song with no sound
A zig with no zag
I can't imagine a world without poetry
Poetry is
The beauty within a sunset
The imagination of a child
The mystery of a murder

Nicole Farina, Grade 5
Newbridge Road Elementary School, NY

I Am Sorry

As I grow from a seed
Everything to, I disagree
Now I feel so heartbroken
I feel so bad, that I've even misspoken
I feel mistook, I need to be shook
I need to advance
Just give me a chance
I feel, just feel, so sorry!

Anshyka Dhanda, Grade 4
Stony Brook Elementary School, NJ

Pineapples

I like pineapple.
It's my favorite because
It is so so juicy.

Hannah Morris, Grade 4
Cortland Christian Academy, NY

Mystery Sweet

Candy is sweet
I just want to find
my one special treat

Will it be
Snickers
Skittles
or Starburst
galore

Oh I know
I have the perfect one
but its not a type of candy

It's a Honey-Bun

Q-Tiye Clarke, Grade 6
The Urban Assembly Institute of Math & Science for Young Women, NY

Determination

Determination is a beast snapping a metal bar in half,
Determination is an athlete training rather than complaining,
Determination is scoring a triple double in one game,
Determination is placing a winning trophy on the top shelf.

Determination is a boxer never giving up,
Determination is practicing for six hours every day,
Determination is running two miles a day,
Determination is a quarterback watching the opposing team's tape all day.

Determination is winning over 900 games in a career,
Determination is scoring a game-winning buzzer-beater,
Determination is shooting hoops outside for five hours,
Determination is shooting one hundred lacrosse balls a day.

Ryan O'Hara, Grade 6
Great Meadows Middle School, NJ

When I Play Soccer

When I play soccer it feels like it is my territory.
My team is The Spartans of Hainesport and we are in first place.

When I play soccer I like to intimidate my opponents.
So when I dribble the ball they get out of my face.

When I play soccer I try to emulate my favorite player.
He plays for Argentina and is their striker, Lionel Messi.

When I play soccer I run, pass, dribble, and shoot.
I am positively sure I am the best.

When I play soccer and get ready to score I make the ball fly like a rocket into the net.
The more I play soccer the better I get.

Harrison Parker, Grade 6
Westampton Middle School, NJ

Last Leaf
One last leaf,
That's on the tree,
Just doesn't want to let go.
It was there all spring and summer,
And changed its colors.
It doesn't want to leave its branch,
And take a chance.
As the weeks go by,
Time seems to fly.
As the wind blows,
The leaves will no longer grow.
And then one cold November day,
The leaf had to go away.
The leaf fell down, down, down
All the way to the ground.
The leaf will come again,
When winter comes to an end.
Michaela Flynn, Grade 6
Regina Coeli School, NY

Hello Fall
On a new fall day,
we go outside and play ball all day.
Let's listen to the birds call
and not go to the mall.
We pull up our sleeves
and rake these leaves.
When we're all done,
we can have some fun.
Here comes school as it gets cool.
Look at the trees so high,
and the leaves that fall from the sky,
As they change from color to color.
The sun starts to set, we sit and eat pie.
We say bye, to the old summer way.

Hello fall!
Lilly Elizabeth Michaels, Grade 5
St Rose of Lima Academy, NJ

The Fireplace
Warmness of the fire,
You keep me as warm as the sun.
You glow ever so bright,
warm, glittering, and comforting you are.
You make me feel safe,
I hope Santa
doesn't come down
the chimney tonight.

You need the wood of nature,
and a lit match to start you.
You keep yourself so sparkling.
Darn, Santa extinguished you.
Lachlan Witt, Grade 6
St Mary's Prep School, NJ

At Bay
Hot sand
on my feet
Cold water on my toes
Not bothered by the heat
Humid air
In my hair
And nose
I'm at bay
Kids running places
Fun places to play
They're at bay
It's the place to be
When you've got the blues
You come, too, but you're looking sad
I ask you why, but you then turn mad
You look at the shore
A smile spreads across your face
You then realize
The bay's a happy place
Everyone gathers and we all say,
"We are all at bay."
Aaron DeCourte, Grade 5
Public School 114 Ryder Elementary, NY

I Want to Be Drug Free
Drug Free
A horrible thing
I might die
young
It will waste my
life
It makes me
sick
Harms my
body
It annihilates me from the outside world
Could get me
arrested
It makes me disobey my
parents
People won't want to spend
time with me
I will let down everyone
I know and love
Will be an
addict
Spencer Mitchell, Grade 6
St Stephen's School, NY

Car
Red, black
Stays, drives, moves
Faster than a jet on its flight!
Vehicle
Brandon Parker, Grade 4
Ethel M Burke Elementary School, NJ

My Name
In the dictionary
Noah means
Rest, peace
That is true
But there is more
I am one

Who loves
Soccer
Who likes
Homework
But not all the time
One who is
Kind and happy

Noah also
Means get excited
Have fun with
My dogs and friends
Noah Lashin, Grade 4
Saw Mill Road Elementary School, NY

Winter
Winter, winter
Snow everywhere
Christmas is coming
And New Year's Day!

Winter, Winter
Can it be?
Delayed plane flights and arrivals
'cuz of the snow

Winter, cold season
It's when
Frosty the snowman lives

Winter, winter
Is it already?
Just wait…
'till spring is comin'
Daniel Ribeiro, Grade 5
Roosevelt Elementary School, NJ

Listen
When winter comes I will look outside
And see the beauty of God's creation
I will watch the silent snow fall softly
My heart will fill with concentration

Because people talk too much these days
Instead of listening to what God says
Listen, quietly, and watch the snow
And he will show you, yes, I know.
Rachel Rypkema, Grade 5
Hawthorne Christian Academy, NJ

Thoughts

My thoughts are like a windmill spinning round and round
The thoughts I have cobbled and encountered
Sometimes I want them to hush
They overpower my mind
Thoughts create my passions which create my life
My thoughts are chockablock in my mind
My thoughts are pulsing just like my heart
When I slumber my thoughts perform solos
Then in harmony they shimmer and shine
With gusto they dance around
My thoughts are telling me how to live my life
They say please please show me around
I will guide you but think of me

Haley Bernstein, Grade 6
Saw Mill Road School, NY

The Way of Life

When you are young
Nobody thinks you can do
The things an adult can.
When you are older
Nobody thinks you can do
Things as well as older people.
You can be young for a while,
But you will grow up
And make sure you smile
You keep getting older,
You always change;
You may not like what you have to arrange.
You do not get to choose the way of life for you.

Diana Nelson, Grade 5
St Mary's Prep School, NJ

Christmas

C ookies
H oliday
R eindeer
M **I** lk
S anta
T ree
M erry
A ntlers
S now

Harmony Carpenter, Grade 5
Tecler Arts in Education Magnet School, NY

War

War is peacemaking
In war I made peace
Against our enemies we fight
War helps to achieve freedom
I made peace
Against our enemies we fight
War is peacemaking

Michael Harris, Grade 6
New York Institute for Special Education, NY

Purple

Purple is the color of juicy, tender, delicious grapes
Purple is the color of smelly violets that bloom in the spring
Purple is the color of the colorful autumn leaves
Purple is one of the amazing colors in a rainbow
There are purple crayons, markers, paint, and chalk
There is also purple fabric
Purple is the color of the sky right after sunset
Purple is the color that can be made by mixing red and blue
Purple can be the color of a tissue box
Purple is a color that a lot of girls like
And a little bit of boys like
But it is still
A wonderful color.

Devin Echavarria, Grade 4
Roosevelt Elementary School, NJ

The Moment

If you had one luscious moment what would you do
Would you control it like a hypnotist controlling your subconscious
Or would you let it slip out of your hand like pollen
Being dispersed throughout the universe
If you didn't control it, you would miss the splendor
It would be like you fell asleep and missed all the excitement
If you let it control you like a genie
You would be solo, swirling lifelessly in his world
Like the arms on a windmill

It is "The Moment"

Tantalizing, Inspiring

Matt Serpe, Grade 6
Saw Mill Elementary School, NY

Fall

Leaves crunch when you step on them
I see curled up leaves
I see red, tangy orange, and coffee brown colored leaves
I smell fresh winter air
It smells like dirt and dead leaves
The leaves feel bumpy and dry
The air tastes like Halloween
I see leaves falling from the trees when the wind blows
The air is frosty and I know winter is coming

Michelle Wang, Grade 6
Slocum Skewes School, NJ

The Headless Man

A boy and his friends went walking one Halloween night.
They saw a man who was a sight.
They thought something wasn't quite right.
He had no head which gave them a fright.
It wasn't a goblin or a ghoul.
It was his little sister trying to fool,
All of us!

Gavin McMahon, Grade 5
Liberty School, NJ

Seasons

Raindrops fall on glistening leaves,
Robins chirp in forest trees.
Bluebirds zigzag the endless skies,
As flowers bloom, time quickly flies.
About the flowers buzz the bees,
As birds retreat to the shade of trees.
Each morning the sun burns ever so bright;
But the moon still dominates the blackness of night.
The wizened leaves of the grandmother tree,
Fall to the earth wherever they please.
The chirps of birds each one of a kind,
Fill the cool air, so wonderful and divine.
Tiny ice crystals blanket the landscape,
As birds fly south; a hasty escape.
The snowcapped mountains rise ever so high,
Reaching no limits; touching the sky.
How Mother Earth makes such a touching difference,
I do not know, for I can only make an inference.

Vanessa Zhang, Grade 6
Shelter Rock Elementary School, NY

Poppi*

I knew a man who was big and strong,
Who I thought could do nothing wrong.
To me he seemed to stand six feet tall,
And he taught me how to play basketball.

When I would fall and skin my knee,
He always had a special hug for me.
He came to our home one special eve,
And told us all that he must leave.

We cried and begged for just one more day,
But he smiled and said he would be gone by May.
May came and went and we thought he had a chance,
But then June came and God took Poppi to his big sky ranch.

Mommy and Nana tell me I have the most special angel in the sky,
But I wish he was still by my side.

Austin Arndt, Grade 5
Tecler Arts in Education Magnet School, NY
*In loving memory of Poppi: February 21, 1957-June 19, 2011

A Fall Day and Its Leaves

The crisp air was like an alarm clock blaring
A wake up call for all the birds.
I was raking and raking all of the leaves.
My hands were as busy as a nest of bees.
Out from the sky from the heavens above,
A walnut fell on me about as heavy as a dove.
I searched around franticly,
And heard a chuckling from the tree.
I shook a fist at the tiny squirrel
But soon forgot because I had work to be done.

Anthony Kim, Grade 6
Slocum Skewes School, NJ

Bahamas

Busy airport constantly transports to islands.
Comfortable hotels always open by the beach.
Hard coconuts fall quickly from palm trees.
Refreshing pool slowly cools your feet.
Noisy dolphins playfully splash near the rocks.
Huge boats carefully float in the harbor.
Thrilling water slides dangerously drop into giant pools.
Fast river rides wildly flow around bends.
Big fish happily swim in humongous fish tanks.
Gentle waves quietly crash on the soft sand.
Fun cousins slowly swim in the ocean.
Stinging jellyfish carelessly drift with the current.
Soft towels quickly dry with clothes.
Small stingrays warily hide under flat rocks.
Silly shows loudly entertain at a stage.
Colorful coral slowly grows under the ocean.
Hot sun quickly warms the ground in the Bahamas, and
Interesting souvenirs helpfully remind about exciting trips.

Dakota Black, Grade 4
Maud Abrams Elementary School, NJ

Moose

Moose you crazy goose.
Buddy you're always on the loose.
Running at my side.
Chasing animals outside.
Smelly ears at my surprise
Puppy eyes get me every time.
Love the way you chew your food.
Now quit howling at the moon!
My friend forever
Never brings me down.
Makes me laugh when I am down.
Pals 'til we die
Sadly taken by surprise.
When I awake I run to seek him in his crate.
Lying deathly still
I fall and cry
Years later by his grave.
When I think of him I'm always lonely.

Olivia Havens, Grade 6
Holy Innocents School, NJ

Fall

My grandma is baking
I watch the leaves fall
My mom and I are raking
My brother is playing football
My friends are roasting a turkey
We are jumping into leaves
In the fall we are raking
My brother prefers beef jerky
The wind is shaking the leaves
What a beautiful season

Jayleen Medina, Grade 4
R.J. McNulty Academy for International Studies and Literacy, NY

Puppies

Puppies are cute, puppies are fun,
I think they're great for everyone!
They play all day, and they bark the night away.
Then they'll lay on your lap and take a nice, long nap.

Leah's my Shih Tzu,
She'll play with, and kiss you,
She loves meeting new people and friends.
She's cute and she's cuddly,
She's furry and funny,
And I'll love her from beginning to end.

Ashleigh Requijo, Grade 4
Holy Family School, NY

Snow

Cold, glittery and bright
Shining in your eyes all day and night

Fun to play in with your friend
Snowball fights that never end

Swirling, swirling over your head
It isn't scary it's fun instead

Silently the world turns crystal white
Bright sun beams it's rays now it's out of sight

Elizabeth Telysheva, Grade 5
Bartle Elementary School, NJ

Blob

The morning was sweet and full of cinnamon
The leaves fall
And crunch on the floor
As the calm wind blows through the air the cats meow
Around you there are brown, yellow, red, orange, and crunchy leaves
When you pick up a dried, silky, crunchy leaf
It feels like a sharp, rough, pointy grass
Rubbing against your skin
The rough, cold dirt smells like earthly air
As you rub your hand through the grass
It feels slimy and wet like blob

Antonio Gil, Grade 6
Slocum Skewes School, NJ

Colorful Leaves

The small leaves were green at first
then it started changing color.
They then started turning orange
four weeks it changed red.
I saw them changing dark brown
then they started falling down.
They fell and fell until they touched the ground
and the kids jumped into a pile of
orange, red, dark brown leaves.

Alice Lou, Grade 5
Bartle Elementary School, NJ

Hide and Seek with Words

My words are missing!
Where are they?!
So I went outside and hollered,
"Words, come out from play!"
No answer.
I went to the bushes and the words jumped!
They ran into the house, faster than wind.
I fell into my bed out of breath!
No words can run faster than that!
I went downstairs to look at my words I should have known,
It was just my dog.

Ana van Goodman, Grade 4
St Mark School, NY

An Autumn Day

The orange pumpkin tumbled in the wooden wagon
The metal wheels screech as they bring the wagon to the field
In the wind
The thin grass dances
Red, orange, yellow leaves fall to the ground
From the large tree
The branch is bare now
Like a plain piece of paper
It's a beautiful scene
Until the pale, strong hand pulls away the wagon
With the perfect pumpkin inside of it

Paige Sfiroudis, Grade 6
Harold D Fayette Elementary School, NY

The Night's Unknown

As night returns, so does the unknown.
It flies, glides, hovers, weeps, cries, and wails.
It drives empty cabs around the town.
It boards trains.
It sings out when the sky is lightless,
But not lifeless.
It lets out strange pets for some air.
It haunts and tortures.
But when morning dawns,
It does not disappear, but hides.
Hides in the shadows until night returns.

Jessica Nikaj, Grade 5
Martin Avenue Elementary School, NY

Our Friendship

The meaning of friendship too important to explain.
The power of friendship too powerful to bring.
The value of our friendship so bright just like you.
The tightness of our friendship is like two unbroken chains.
The awesomeness of our friendship could rule the world.
The sweetness of our friendship is way sweeter than many things.
The happiness of our friendship is rated 100 on the scale of 1-10.
The talent of our friendship can go beyond infinity.
But the worth of our friendship it is too much to count.

Christina Chan, Grade 6
Holy Family School, NY

The Gaze

A comforting view
All the blackness
With some twinkling lights
Shining through

The splashes of color
Almost
Painted into the sky

I am lying here
Imagining all the stories
She would tell
If only she could speak

Stories about
People
Places
And
Evolving time

The greatest dream
In reality

Inspiring
The only word that comes close
To her beauty
Julia Caponi, Grade 5
Saw Mill Road Elementary School, NY

What Is the Answer?

The last question is so hard
I don't know what to do
All I can think about
Is the rock that's in my shoe

I look around
I see the clock
In its mocking tone
It says tick-tock, tick-tock

I stare at the paper
My mind is blank
I heard the bell ring
My heart just sank

What is the answer
I've got to know
My teacher said
"It's time to go!"

"Hey, I know the answer,
Can I write it in?"
I think I've got it
I wonder where it has been
Ysabel Tullis, Grade 6
Little Falls School #1, NJ

Drug Free

I want to be drug free
Because
I will have no friends
It'll make me feel
Bad
I could get hurt or hurt a lot of
People
I will go to
Jail
I will die
Young
But most of all
I do not want to
Make my parents
Feel bad
And
Make them feel
Like they did a bad job!
Nick Falbo, Grade 6
St Stephen's School, NY

Autumn

P umpkin picking is fun.
U p early in the morning.
M ashed potatoes and gravy.
P ilgrims were the first to celebrate
K indness is the way to go.
I enjoy playing in the leaves.
N ature is amazing!

P umpkin pie is delicious!
A pple picking is fun!
R iding a tractor going out to the orchard.
T urkey is a wild animal.
I enjoy carving pumpkins and
E ating pumpkin pie and
S weet cranberry sauce.

Thanksgiving is amazing and
Pumpkin picking is fun.
Lailah Watson, Grade 5
St Rose of Lima Academy, NJ

I Know What Fall Is Bringing

I feel a chilly breeze,
I hear birds singing.
I see colorful leaves,
I know what fall is bringing.
I smell nature,
I see a squirrel.
I hear the laughter of boys and girls.
I can't taste fall but I will tell you all…
After Thanksgiving,
I will know what fall is bringing!
Amanda Silva, Grade 6
Slocum Skewes School, NJ

The Never Ending Road

Silently my footsteps fall
Not making any sound at all
Leaving footprints in my wake
Wondering how long this will take

Kicking pebbles at my feet
Waiting for sunshine that will never greet
Knowing I might not make it through
Knowing there's nothing I can do

Silently my footsteps fall
Continuing to make no sound at all
Feeling the silence in the air
Thinking life is so unfair

Walking along a road that never ends
Walking along the twists and bends
And suddenly I stop my pace
Feeling tears trickle down my face
Chloe Bugat, Grade 5
Hillside Elementary School, NJ

I Am…

I am brave and pretty
I am smart and daring
I am funny and caring
If I fail once, I will try until I get
Where I need to be
I am the greatest mountain
The young Harriet Tubman is me
I am a leader and giver
A fighter and survivor
I am one of God's creatures
I am the Statue of Liberty
Standing tall and never coming down
I am a skyscraper
I am the young Sojourner Truth
Fighting for women's freedom
I am unstoppable
I am proud to be me
I am free
I represent my generation
Brianna Gardere, Grade 5
Public School 114 Ryder Elementary, NY

9-11-01

Although their smiles are gone forever
Their hands we cannot touch
Still, so many memories of the
Ones we loved so much
They gave their lives for us to have
A stronger country, we are so proud
We still hear the cries of Flight 93
As their bravery screams, so very loud!
Amanda Reynolds, Grade 5
Helen B Duffield Elementary School, NY

At the Lake

Last week I went to the lake,
A long boat ride I did take.
We skied, we tubed, and we swam
We even saw a beaver dam!

We roasted marshmallows over a fire
And sang songs just like a choir!
"It is time for bed!" said Mother dear.
"We won't be back until next year!"

The next morning we did wake,
And said goodbye to the lake.
Then Mother said, "It is time to go.
We will be back next year, I hope so!"

Claire McCarty, Grade 4
The Holy Name of Jesus Academy, NY

Extreme Fishing

I got in the boat.
I put the line in the water
And wait for a fish to come by.
I sleep for 20 minutes,
But I wake up with a fright.
My line was tugging like crazy.
I tugged back,
But it tugged again so hard,
That I almost fell in the water.
I tugged harder and harder,
Until I finally got it
It was a huge bluefish.
I went home
With a big smile on my face.

Angel Castaneda Jr., Grade 4
Lincoln Park Elementary School, NJ

That Robin

Every week
I see that robin
perched on my fence
it reminds me of my grandfather
how he loved the birds
and how the birds loved him
then, the bird takes off
soaring through the wind
flying as high as his wings will take him
getting stronger
and maybe someday
he will be strong enough
to fly high
as high as my grandfather lies

Ailish Egan, Grade 6
Saw Mill Road Elementary School, NY

Rock Climbing

Please hold me tighter
I don't want to fall
My foot keeps slipping
I grasp onto the wall

Don't take me down
I could do this
I'll try and grab the rock
But what if I miss

I'm sweating bullets
My hands really sting
I try and hold the rock
But I fall down and swing

I try with my might
And I grasp the last rock
I slowly fly down
With my face filled with shock

Sweat drips down my face
I'm so happy I'm done
I had a hard day
But I still had lots of fun

Christina Folan, Grade 5
Little Falls School #1, NJ

School on Saturday?

Why today, out of all these days
I rush to go to school
I throw on clothes in different ways
So my friends will think I'm cool

I put on non-matching socks
And try to brush my teeth
I pour cereal out of the box
Into my bowl with a banana beneath

I ran out the door
To catch the school bus,
I saw my neighbor
Who asked, "What's all the fuss?"

"I'm late for school!"
I reply
He said that I'm a fool
But I don't know why

Then he whispered in my ear
And I wanted to shout "Yay!"
Down my cheek fell a joyful tear
I have no school, it's Saturday!

Nell Grabowski, Grade 5
Little Falls School #1, NJ

Thank You Veterans

Thank you
For serving our country.

Thank you
For being in the Army,
Marines, Navy, Air Force,
And Coast Guard.

Thank you
For protecting us.

Thank you
For making the
World a better place.

Thank you!

Hanna Tufano, Grade 4
Raynor Country Day School, NY

My Name

The dictionary says
I am a tile maker
But it is wrong
Tyler means unselfish
An inventor
A sword fighter

Tyler means
To swim
In the bright blue ocean
To lay on a sandy beach

Tyler means
To soar above the clouds

Tyler is my name

Tyler Douglas, Grade 4
Saw Mill Road Elementary School, NY

Fall Fun

The sun is bright
The sky is blue
The kids are having fun
They're climbing trees
Collecting apples
And jumping into leaves
Some kids do other things
Like catch with a football
The other side of the field
Is full of soccer players
Other children just run around
Or sit and watch the sky
Others sit and feel the breeze
With the autumn's leaves

Daniel Kim, Grade 6
Slocum Skewes School, NJ

My Mom

My mom makes my world a better place
because she picks me up when I am down
and spins me all around.

She teaches me wrong from right,
And tells me I should never fight.

My mom makes my world a better place
because she works hard and keeps a roof over my head
and lets me sleep in a nice warm bed.

If more people were like my mom,
The world would be better.

Isaiah Bracero, Grade 5
New York Institute for Special Education, NY

Earth Gave Us

E arth gave us…
A ardvarks
R ivers that roar
T rees made for shade
H umongous hayfields

G argantuan storms
A ir to breathe in
V egetables to eat
E arthquakes for fearing

U nripe seeds for growing
S o never take what Earth gave us for granted

Emily Berkow, Grade 4
Deerfield Elementary School, NJ

New Years

N ew you
E ngaging conversation
W iser than ever

Y es! We all come together
E xciting moments
A pple cider
R esolutions
S urprises

Zoe-Alexandra Hall, Grade 6
Graham Elementary and Middle School, NY

My Heart

My heart is where I love
Where I appreciate the things I get
My friends and family mean the world to me
My heart sings to me
Like my mom singing a lullaby to me
My heart is the center of me
My heart is love

Joseph Cucinella, Grade 6
John G Dinkelmeyer Elementary School, NY

New York City

It cost twenty five dollars to buy a fork,
and that's how you know that you're in New York.

The lights, shows, and buildings ablaze,
you look up, there are no stars in your gaze.
Pollution, terrible as it may be,
does not stop this city from looking so pretty.

Home of the Yankees, Mets, Giants, and Jets,
and don't forget about the Knicks, Rangers, and the Nets.
Don't even get me started on Broadway,
I'd go there, any time, any day.

So many stores, clothing, and nails,
You've got all the women buying out the sales,
Rockerfeller Center, malls, and Times Square,
Yes, in New York, you've got everything there.

Avi Braun, Grade 6
Yeshiva At The Jersey Shore, NJ

Stronger

I am stronger than I have ever been
I have a vision problem
At times I feel like I am different from everyone else
It makes me feel like I am alone
But I am not!
I am stronger because of my vision problem,
I feel like I have to try everything
Even things I would do without a vision problem!
Now that I am stronger, I can play my favorite games,
Baseball,
Ice Skating!
Some people said I couldn't do it,
But look at me,
I am stronger!
I can conquer anything and you can too.
I am strong

Lunique Agostini, Grade 5
New York Institute for Special Education, NY

Abstract

When you think of the word abstract what do you see?
I see a mist of colors forming a collage
Blending into perfect symmetrical columns
Creating art
I see the sun setting
Making the sky purple and orange
The ocean making a reflection
Causing the sky to be wondrous blue
I see the impossible
Becoming possible with a quick line of a brush
That to me
Is
Abstract

Michael Laupheimer, Grade 6
John G Dinkelmeyer Elementary School, NY

The World's Masterpiece

Long grass, getting caught in the wind.
Sparkling blue water, like crystals, catching the rhythm of the river.
Land with adventures all around.
Concentrated sunlight on the trees, the hint of life.
Birds singing, making music that takes my breath away.
I can't believe my eyes.
The world is a story that is waiting to be told.
As I drink in the world around me,
I realize I am in The World's Masterpiece.

Nicole Weber, Grade 5
Lee Road School, NY

The Pumpkin and the Little Munchkin

One morning I was crunching
and munching on my food.
I found a seed and planted it
on the moon.
It turned into a pumpkin
And there was a munchkin
inside my pumpkin.
So I went to the moon
And I ate them both with a spoon.

Aidan Ortega, Grade 4
R.J. McNulty Academy for International Studies and Literacy, NY

Waiting

They are the people
Waiting
Waiting to continue their lives
Waiting to step out of the darkness
And face the world waiting for them
The time is now
No more hiding
No more
Waiting

Cassidy Soloff, Grade 6
The Trevor Day School – Upper Campus, NY

Squirrels

Squirrels are funny little creatures.
They always make me laugh.
You can hear them chattering to each other all day long.
They are always busy; they never really rest.
But that is what squirrels do, they run around all day.
The world would be silent without squirrels.
So be glad that they are here.

Rachel Eelman, Grade 5
Hawthorne Christian Academy, NJ

Destroy All Weapons

I want to get rid of all weapons that can hurt people.
No wars or fights.
People would stop killing each other.
The world would be such a better place!

Benjamin Cobarrubia, Grade 4
New York Institute for Special Education, NY

Pink

Pink is the color of my favorite shirt.
Pink is the color of tasty strawberry ice cream.
Pink is the color of my favorite jacket.
Pink is the color of the Breast Cancer Awareness ribbon.
Pink is the color of my doll's dress.
Pink is the color that I wear the most.
Pink is the color of some delicious raspberries.
Pink is the color of Aaliyah's barrettes.
Pink is the color of sweet lollipops.
Pink is the color of yummy cotton candy.
Pink is the color
That no boy in the world likes.

Alaysha Waugh, Grade 4
Roosevelt Elementary School, NJ

September 11, 2001

Remember
September?
The greatness that died?
The day that we let our anxiety fly?
The lies that were told on the day of despair?
Still leaving our memories to lives lost there?
Yet through sadness and woe,
We should still let that life go!
So, remember
September;
Our memories left,
And meant to be stolen away like a theft?

Abigail Fridman, Grade 6
Holy Family School, NY

I Love Drawing

When I'm alone or by myself,
I pick up a pencil from my shelf.
There's a pad of paper in my drawer.
Drawing for me is never a bore.
I sketch people real and pretend.
I draw creatures or even my friend.
I'd rather be doodling than watching TV,
I don't always know what they'll turn out to be.
When I draw something special, I feel very proud.
I might have a talent. My head's in the clouds.
Designing cartoons or billboards on streets
Is a job for adults that just cannot be beat.

Spencer Flint, Grade 5
Tecler Arts in Education Magnet School, NY

The Leaves

The leaves fall from high trees, slower than lazy bees.
The leaves lay like sleepy lions, quiet and peaceful.
They get piled up and make themselves into snow angels.
The kids jump into them and get themselves dirty.
The leaves decay into the ground until next year,
When they change and fall again.

Zeyue Li, Grade 5
Bartle Elementary School, NJ

Christmas Cookies

Tasty treats,
Nice and sweet,
There isn't ever enough to eat.
So many shapes,
On cookies and cakes,
The best of all,
Is not cookies in fall.
It's the Christmas cookies,
Even for the rookies.
They're so easy to make,
And your taste buds will quake,
In anticipation,
For the sweet sensation,
Of those delicious Christmas cookies.
Veronica Gray, Grade 6
Sts Peter & Paul School, NY

Bicycle

When I ride
I feel unstoppable
Wind carries me away
As the ground makes my
Bike glide to Neverland

My hair pushes through the wind
As if it needs to be somewhere

My bike screeches and squeaks to a stop
As my pants get stuck in the wheel
But the voice in my head
Tells me to keep going
And to never stop.
Zoe Weissbach, Grade 4
Norman J Levy Lakeside School, NY

The Puppy

Look at that puppy
So fat and so small
Its fur is brown like mud
And has a nose as small as a button
Small as a bird
Fast like the wind
Fluffy as a cloud
Has spots black as night
Eyes blue as the day sky
Playful like a child
A tongue pink like a flower
With teeth white as snow
Waiting for me to take him inside
It's time to take a nap
Hannah Tullis, Grade 4
Little Falls School #3, NJ

Oh! Alaska

Oh Alaska, how beautiful you are,
With your beautiful glaciers.
Oh Alaska, how beautiful your wildlife is.
Oh Alaska, your nights are peaceful,
Like heaven and earth.
Oh Alaska, you're so cold, yet so warm.
Oh Alaska, have a peaceful night.
Oh Alaska, you have so many animals.
Oh Alaska, you have so many icebergs.
Oh Alaska, you have a lot of history.
Oh Alaska, you're the best.
Gavin Coelho, Grade 6
St Mary's Prep School, NJ

5 Senses

With our noses
We smell pretty roses.
With our eyes
We bake pies.
With our mouth
We say we are going out.
With our ears
We hear everything near,
And with our hands
We feel and
Touch the world.
Margeaux Dase, Grade 6
Sts Peter & Paul School, NY

Fireplace

There's a cold, empty pit
That we just lit

The crackling sparks in the air
Will leave a pain that you can't bare

Warmth that makes you feel toasted
With marshmallows that are roasted

The flames are bees that are swarming
We sit quietly watching them performing
Emily Berman, Grade 5
Bartle Elementary School, NJ

A Sport of Fun

Soccer is a sport of fun
You dash and sprint in the beaming sun.
Scoring a goal is when you run
In an hour the game will be done.

We pass and kick with that soccer ball
We'll play until the next referee call.
This happens in the season of fall
When the ball is loved by one and all!
Cierra Page, Grade 5
Liberty School, NJ

Different

People are different...
Shapes, sizes, looks
Blonde hair, brown hair, red heads

People are different...
Blue eyes, brown eyes, green eyes,
Light skin, dark skin

People are different...
Curly hair, straight hair,
Glasses or contact lenses

People are different...
Shy, mean, nice,
generous, caring, nervous

People are different...
One world, different actions.
Gabrielle Schoenberg, Grade 4
Norman J Levy Lakeside School, NY

Glistening Day

Sun was bright
Hot
Fiery
Sight
Beautiful rays glaring at me
The tree staring at me with an empty site
Thinking, why, why
Did all the leaves leave me?
But the leaves are saying to themselves
We don't need that tree
There's so much we could do
Skydive, climb
But one very small leaf
Says
I miss that tree.
He was the only thing I had
The rake came by and cheered him up
And he made a new friend
Katie Goodman, Grade 6
Harold D Fayette Elementary School, NY

Space

As dark as a black magic marker
As weird as a half man, half horse
As beautiful as a tropical flower
As extraordinary as the world
Planets are rotating while space
looks...
dark, weird, beautiful
AND
most of all
extraordinary
Danielle Raffa, Grade 5
Dickinson Avenue Elementary School, NY

Boo! Says You

Boo! says you on Halloween,
Whoever scares you is very mean!
Boo! says you on Halloween,
If you cry you'll make a scene!
Boo! says you on Halloween,
While you munch on your ice cream!
Boo! says you on Halloween,
I'll haunt you in your dreams!
Boo! says you on Halloween,
Try not to scream!
BWA-HA-HA!

Giavonna Bovino, Grade 5
Eastplain School, NY

The Sea

The sea
Never ending
A wide span
Of untouched
Life
The fish's
Way of life
Beyond
Our imagination
And our way of
LIFE

Tyler Dunat, Grade 5
Dickinson Avenue Elementary School, NY

Summer and Winter

It is mid summer
I walk outside
I hear the wind rushing
I see the birds glide
Two squirrels go running
And it's hot outside

Oh, winter — when will you arrive?
If it was winter, I could play in
the snow
Oh winter — please never go!

Dean Fricke, Grade 5
Dickinson Avenue Elementary School, NY

Sweets

I love sweets they are so good
I always eat them in my childhood
I love gummies, chocolates and sours
I could eat them all for hours

Sometimes I can't help myself to sweets
I don't even hunger for meats
I usually wear sweets as bling
How can I stop? it's my thing

Lydia Jackson, Grade 5
Hawthorne Christian Academy, NJ

Shoe Heaven

I wake up at midnight,
On a fluffy cloud.
I see some nice shoes,
And they're perfectly proud.
A sparkly shoe hops over to me.
It says…
Welcome to Shoe Heaven,
A great place to be.
Do you like sparkly slippers?
Or red rubber boots?
We have one million shoes,
So you have nothing to lose.
Wait a second…
Where are we going?
Right to Shoe Heaven,
Look! The mall's sign is showing.

Samantha Gottlieb, Grade 4
Concord Road Elementary School, NY

Spring Is Coming

Nature falls
off the tree
so gracefully,
Nature springs
up from the ground
without a sound,
Nature flows
through the stream
with a gleam,
Nature blows
all around
with a peaceful sound,
Nature rains
filling lakes
animals begin to wake,
All because spring is coming!

Courtney Wright, Grade 4
Nellie F Bennett Elementary School, NJ

Spotted Striped and Wrinkled

Tall and spotted
Delicate yet muscular
Shading themselves under trees
While they enjoy green juicy leaves

Small and striped
Brave and bold
Hiding in their herd
From the lion waiting to pounce

Big and broad
Gray with wrinkles
Showering themselves
With every step

Emma Curtis, Grade 5
Toll Gate Grammar School, NJ

Soldier

No toes
To feel the dirt
Moist and warm
Squishing in between —
Making you smile.

No feet
To feel the
Cold crisp floors
Underneath your heels —
Making you almost cry.

No legs
To run across fields.
Your warm hand in your son's tiny one
Wishing it would never stop.
Never ever stop.

But you grin.
With the tattoo on your arm
An eagle proud and bold
And say,
"I'd do it all again, miss."

Cassy James, Grade 5
Forrestdale School, NJ

Homesick

Where are the red brick buildings?
Where are the taxi cars?
Where is New York City?
I'd rather be on Mars.

Where are the advertisements?
The big suitcases and suits?
The sound of the subway?
The squeaks of heels and boots?

I am sick of being homesick.
Being the sickest of the sick.
If you are going to cure me,
You better make it quick.

I might have pneumonia,
Or a mighty flu,
Or even chicken pox.
My nose might turn blue!

So I called up my doctor,
On my same old gray phone.
And you know what he said?
That I should go home.

Elena Sapelyuk, Grade 5
Public School 195 Manhattan Beach, NY

Great Oak

Down a leaf flutters from the Great Oak,
It flutters down so beautifully, you dare not poke

And it lands on soft, green grass — so nice
You'd think it had been practicing to make its landing so precise

Tall, straight, and proud stands this magnificent tree,
If you tried to cut it down, you'd have to pay a fee

Gold-brown is the trunk, orange-red are the leaves,
It's a glorious sight, I guarantee

So, today and forever the Great Oak stands,
Let us ring around it in awe, hand in hand

Emma Fisher, Grade 5
Dickinson Avenue Elementary School, NY

A Question of Love

Trees are dancing in the wind
I hear a soft note
Mockingbirds sing their song
I am dead to the world
A golden light shines softly over me
I am standing in the air
But I am not falling
Is this love?
I always wondered if I would be swept off my feet
Now I have
Is this Love?
Would you hold me when I cry
Yes you would
This is love

Shama Vaidya, Grade 6
Crossroads South Middle School, NJ

I Live Near a School

I live near a school.
It's so big and so bright.
Even when it's dark,
It shines at night.

When I go to this school,
I feel so proud,
To be a Catholic student,
To spread my love around.

I leave school at quarter of three.
I want to stay for the whole day
Even though I have come home to rest,
I'd really rather stay!

Camille Chomiczewski, Grade 4
Good Shepherd Regional Catholic School, NJ

Nature's Birthday

When I think of fall,
I think of it as nature's birthday.
The brightly colored leaves are the decor,
and the animals are the guests.
The sounds of fall are the music,
and the nuts and berries are the food.
The cool air is the candlelight on nature's cake,
and all the bird's nests make up her cake.
The rustle of the wind is nature's first shake of her rattle,
and the heavy rain is her first sip of milk.
Finally, the sunset brings the end of nature's birth,
and on to a new reenactment of nature's birth again.
So when the first snowflake falls,
remember the joy you had on the days of nature's birthday.

Taylor Anne Hughes, Grade 4
Holy Family School, NY

Fall Leaves

Crinkle,
Crackle,
Crunch,
Is the sound beneath my feet,
When I walk upon the leaves fallen throughout the street.

The leaves twist, turn, and dance to the ground,
Like snowflakes falling softly,
Without a sound.

Leaves are changing color,
To purple, red, and brown.
Leaves are changing colors,
Not a green one to be found.

Jessica Tsu, Grade 4
James A Dever School, NY

Starry Night*

The stars
are as bright as the sun.
The sky is
swirling, going into circles.
The mountains are
as rough as an ocean.
The town is
as quiet as an ant.
The statue in the
front of the picture is
as still as a tree trunk.
Tell me Vincent what is that object in
the front of this magnificent picture?

Ti'Anna Lee, Grade 5
Roosevelt Elementary School, NJ
*Inspired by "Starry Night" by Vincent Van Gogh

Poppy

Poppy, you lie in Flanders Field
bringing death and sleep
to the meaning of the poppy.

Poppy, you lie there peacefully
on the grass after World War 1.
How do you do that?

Poppy, how do you lie in Flanders Field
in-between the crosses
when we honor the soldiers still alive?

Poppy, when you lie there
do you feel sadness or death coming to you?

Poppy, when you are asleep,
do you dream about the soldiers who died and are sill alive?

Poppy, we love you and remember you
a symbol of death and sleep, and life.
Thank you, Poppy, for bringing yourself to Earth.

Ethan Aube, Grade 4
Raynor Country Day School, NY

My Name

There are many interesting things about me
But being a god is not one of them
And that's where the dictionary is wrong
It says my name means
Grace of God
But I a not a god
True I might be one someday
And I might be the elegance that God beholds
But that is just the beginning

Grace means
To Irish Step dance
And win many medals and ribbons
To be a fabulous singer and dancer
To wake up early
And to go to bed late
To play lacrosse in the summer and in the winter
Whether to be a writer or a poet I do not know
So I might as well for now be both
When I am older I might change
But for now I am just me.

Grace Cutler, Grade 4
Park Avenue Elementary School, NY

The Dancing Snake

There once was a snake from France,
Who was gifted in the field of dance.
He'd shake and he'd twist, he'd do that, he'd do this,
But he simply could not do jazz hands.

Aidan Champeau, Grade 5
Hillside Elementary School, NJ

A Day at the Beach

You look at the water,
Hear the noise of the waves,
As you lay on a towel,
You watch the birds fly in the sky,
You get up and run into the water,
Feeling it as it splashes your body,
Then when you run out, feeling the sand between your toes,
As you play in the sand,
You feel the sand going through your fingers,
Little kids run happily together,
You hear them laughing and screaming,
Then you lay down to look at the sunset,
You see all the pretty colors in the sky,
It makes you think of the great times you had this summer,
You think of all the times with your friends and family,
In the sky you see seagulls passing by,
They land close to you, so you go to chase them,
They all fly away into the sunset together,
As you pack up and dump the sand out of your shoes,
You are happy from your great day at the beach,
At last you go home and think about your wonderful day.

Courtney Balcerzak, Grade 6
Sts Peter & Paul School, NY

Time

Tick…tock! Tick…tock! Take a glance on the clock!
Time is passing on and on…
Like a melting ice-cream cone
If you ever miss it, never try to catch it
Because you never will!

Days are passing. Weeks are gone!
You may think today is over!
But tomorrow may not come!
Finish your work now! And do it properly
Because, you may not get the chance to do it twice
So get it done, before you shall be gone.

A liar said: You can always try tomorrow.
But in life, it's not guaranteed; today will be over, no harm done.
Now look what you've done!
You've already wasted enough!
You don't know how long you're going live
But, you know you haven't got that much time left!
Now get started, but careful with the clock!
Because it never goes backwards or never stops…

Alyaa Elkhafif, Grade 6
Al Ghazaly School, NJ

Money Can't Buy Everything!

Money is very fun to have and can buy a lot of stuff.
But time and time again it can't buy love.
It is impossible to buy happiness.
And it certainly can't buy lots of success.

Jack Ryan, Grade 5
Bartle Elementary School, NJ

Autumn

Autumn, autumn, autumn is here
Apple and pumpkin picking is near
Juicy apples oh so sweet
Lots of pumpkins at your feet
Colorful leaves falling everywhere
Even falling in your hair
Hear them crinkle under your feet
As you go for a trick-or-treat!
Brianna Gaudio, Grade 6
Slocum Skewes School, NJ

Presents

P resents and candy are on there way,
R eady for tomorrow Christmas day.
E njoy the anxiousness and the wait,
S anta can't be late!
E xcited for presents and toys,
N ow my body is filled with joy.
T oday he's coming from the North Pole,
S anta accidentally gave me coal!
Dean Dridi, Grade 6
Riverside Middle School, NJ

Winter

Winter
Colds, storms
Sledding, snowing, coughing
Wind, white, beach, pool
Swimming, playing, relaxing
Sunny, warm
Summer
Fabiana Morales, Grade 5
Bartle Elementary School, NJ

Fall

Red, orange, yellow
Leaves are changing colors now
The air is chilly

Leaves crunch beneath feet
Leaves are falling off the trees
Red, orange, yellow
Hannah Amber Lefkowitz, Grade 5
Catherine A Dwyer Elementary School, NJ

Wiggle and Wobble

I pull on my skates.
I step on the ice,
But I slip and fall.
This time I hold onto the wall.
I take it step by step,
But I always wiggle and wobble,
And fall to the ice.
Eun Bi Hahm, Grade 4
Lincoln Park Elementary School, NJ

The Fall Train Is Coming

Baseball fields are emptying

Now the sound of hockey pucks banging against the boards is coming
Packing away the shorts and letting out the trapped winter gear

The delicious taste of turkey that melts in my mouth
Will soon be replaced by warm tomato soup

Instead of leaves, having paint-ball fights the color of white will take over the land
The sound of birds chirping will fade away
Like the colors of the American Flag fade in the sun at the farm

Instead of buying bails of hay
The astonishing color of white will be falling the entire day
Brian Paris, Grade 5
Helen B Duffield Elementary School, NY

The Multiplication Machine

I have been building a multiplication machine for the last five weeks.
It was hard, brutal work.
I got some homework
It was about math facts.
I went out of my house
I brought my homework home and
I put it in the machine and hit the big, red button.
It went to work.
It started to do my homework
My homework was done in 3 minutes.
My homework started to come out of the machine
It was all wrong
Then the machine got up on two legs
and started to run away

Kenneth Smith, Grade 5
St Aloysius Regional School, NY

Give to Your Family This Thanksgiving!

T urkeys are cooking in the oven, and we are waiting for people to come.
H aving relatives over for our Thanksgiving dinner.
A lso, family and friends gather in the living room while having conversations.
N ever eat too much food on Thanksgiving.
K eep the food all to yourself.
S ave leftovers for later.
" **G** ive me some mashed potatoes," I say to my mom.
I nvite everybody for a huge Thanksgiving feast.
V ery delicious desserts for after our meal.
I n between meals, we take a break so we don't get overstuffed.
N o one can resist having delicious apple pie fresh from the oven.
G ive to your family and be very thankful about what you have.
Sheridan Campbell, Grade 6
Riverside Middle School, NJ

The Terrific Thanksgiving

T urkey from the woods got cooked to perfection.
H arvested crops that have been deliciously cook spread the table.
A s family arrives, dinner is simmering and cooking in the kitchen.
N earing the steamy kitchen, I smell food and hear the sizzle of a pan.
K ettle corn in a clear glass bowl is perched on the snack table.
S oon, the delicious feast will begin.
G reens stretch down the table and tons of food from Thanksgiving cover the counter.
I place my spoon in a bowl of creamy soup and my brother laughs at a funny joke.
V egetables are fresh from the harvest and steam comes pouring from them all.
I n the kitchen, my grandmom is taking the turkey out of the oven and hot air is coming from it!
N ext to me, my family converses, as blazes of the evening sun shine in.
G iving thanks to God on this day is very important.

Juliana Rudzinski, Grade 6
Riverside Middle School, NJ

Fabulous Fall

When fall arrives, I know it's here
The crisp, cold air blows across my face and summer clothes are packed into the attic

The squishy, gooey insides of a pumpkin cover the dining room table
Trick-or-treaters knock on the door as terrified as a six-year-old lost in New York City
The aromas of pumpkin pie and turkey roasting fills the kitchen like a big balloon pumped with helium

Leaves are scrunching outside
A bonfire is cracking and warm, chewy s'mores are roasting

Fall is slowly fading, but winter is quickly approaching…

Jodi Cochrane, Grade 6
Oakdale-Bohemia Middle School, NY

Making the World a Better Place

To make the world a better place, this is what I would do.
I would help animals and their habitats.
I would help animals such as dolphins, whales, and bats.
I would put up signs saying to not cut trees from rain forests.
I would tell people to hunt whales at certain times a year.
I would tell people to not hunt whales and dolphins that are almost extinct.
Another thing I would do is put signs that say "No Littering," also I would want people to live in peace.
Last, I would want people to live in harmony and to not hit or hurt anyone.
It would be nice to make the world a better place. I think it would make people feel happy and thankful.

Misael Gonzalez, Grade 4
New York Institute for Special Education, NY

Coffee in the Fall

As the wrath of Fall has arrived we go and get warmth.
We get blankets, jackets, and…coffee for shelter from these horrid cold temperatures.
We wait in line for mocha lattes and such to get our healthy bodies warm.
It is humankind's most delicious way to keep happy during this annoying season.
These magnificent hot beverages will keep us warm and will let us last through the fall days of our lives.
These coffees are heaven in a drink that won't let us sink in the terrible autumn sea.

Lazaro Conde, Grade 6
Slocum Skewes School, NJ

I Know

I know I can trust her.
I know she can keep all of my secrets.
I know she can calm me down.
I know she has my back whenever I need her.
I know what makes her tick.
I know I can tell her anything.
I know she accepts me for who I am.
I know I can be myself around her.
I know how to cheer her up when she's upset.
I know when something is bothering her.
I know she will always support me.
I know she believes in me.
I know she's my best friend.

Katie Barnes, Grade 6
Shelter Rock Elementary School, NY

My Name Means…

The dictionary says
Christian means
Follower of Christ
That is true but
There is more to my name
Christian means
Someone who likes sports
Someone who can go crazy any second
Someone who likes to wake up early
And plan the day ahead
Christian means one who loves his family
One who has a lot of friends
One who just wants to get some air in the open backyard

Christian Murcia, Grade 4
John G Dinkelmeyer Elementary School, NY

Band Is Music

Band is…

M aking music with a family lifelong friend
U nderstanding how commitment and dedication lead to success
S haring joy and rewards of working together
I ndividuals who develop self — confidence
C reativity expressing yourself in a universal language

Band is music!

Marina Rivas, Grade 5
Tecler Arts in Education Magnet School, NY

Money

Money can't do everything
It can't buy my dreams, my friendship or hope
It can't buy my feelings, my family or friends
It can't love my pets or play or dance
That's what I can say money can't do
And it can't buy me
And it can't buy you!!!

Isabella Godish, Grade 5
Bartle Elementary School, NJ

Holiday Joy

I walk outside
In a land of snow
In every window
And outside every house
There are lights
Lights of joy
Lights of hope
Lights of peace
Happiness fills the air
And everyone has their own reason
To be excited
They get ready
For a week
Of new surprises
In every box
Not wrapped in paper
Wrapped in curiosity
And love.

Lindsey Pollack, Grade 5
John G Dinkelmeyer Elementary School, NY

Pink

Pink is the color of yummy cotton candy
That I eat on the boardwalk
Pink is the color that ballerinas wear,
For tutus
Pink is the color of pretty sunsets,
Pink is the color of delicious strawberry ice cream,
Pink is the color ribbon for Breast Cancer month,
Pink is the color of babies' onesies,
Pink is a color that all girls loveee,
Pink is the color that is in everybody's barrettes,
Pink is a color that stands for love,
Pink is a color that every girl wears,
Pink is a color that no boys like,
Pink is a color my sister Claryssa likes,
Pink is the color that is on a birthstone,
Pink is a color that really stands out,
Pink is a very popular color
And it's my favorite color.

Tattyanna Vega, Grade 4
Roosevelt Elementary School, NJ

Friends

My friends are always there for me
They will do all I need
They make me laugh, they make me sing
They hug me and say "You can do anything"
They pick me up when I am down
They will never let me frown
They mean the world to me
If I cry, they cry
If I smile, they smile
I will never lose my friends

Ella Miller, Grade 5
Hillside Elementary School, NJ

It's Jesus' Time on Christmas

Christmas is time for joy,
for every single girl and boy.
It is time for all the toys.
It's Jesus' time on Christmas.

Celebrate Jesus on this day,
on his birthday we put on a play.
To your relatives say, "Come and stay."
It's Jesus' time on Christmas.

Christmas joy brings snowman kits,
it's very hard to make them sit.
Christmas lights will make them melt.
It's Jesus' time on Christmas.

Megan Wilson, Grade 4
Holy Family School, NY

Happy Halloween

Happy Halloween
Don't make a scene
Give someone a fright
But don't stay up all night

Happy Halloween
Look at the mummy
Don't eat too much candy
Or it will hurt your tummy

Happy Halloween
Frankenstein is green
Brutal monsters drool
Watch out for that scary Halloween ghoul

Dakota Jones, Grade 5
Eastplain School, NY

Monarch

High in the bright blue sea
Above
Aflutter
As high as it's small
Beat-up wings will take it

Above the ocean
With
No land ahead
No one to guide him
No family left

One small monarch
Two small wings

Sydney Rubin, Grade 5
Saw Mill Elementary School, NY

The Silent Crowd

Beep!
The whistle echoed in my ears
The other team had the ball.
Suddenly,
My teammate steals the soccer ball.
He zips through everybody
With no sweat.
He makes it all the way
To the cornerkick area.
Boom!
The ball bursts into the air.
While running into the 18yd box
I do a bicycle kick
Into the goal
The sideline is dead silent.
After a few seconds,
Everyone bursts out
Cheering.

Alexandra Vucenovic, Grade 4
Lincoln Park Elementary School, NJ

A Homerun Hit

The other team is up at bat.
They swing once,
They swing twice,
They are out.
I was so happy.
It was our turn now.
My team was winning by five.
It was my turn.
I swing once,
Twice,
And I hit the ball.
The crowd went wild.
I ran to first,
To second,
Third,
I hit a homerun.
Everyone was screaming.
We won the game.

Alexis O'Shall, Grade 4
Lincoln Park Elementary School, NJ

Snow

Snowflakes fall quickly to the ground
And makes a big mound.
The snow falls silently to the ground
Without making a sound.
The snow is shiny and bright
And sure is a beautiful sight.
The sunlight causes the temperature to rise
And our mound is decreasing in size.
The snow is finally gone
And now all that's left is our lawn.

Mary-Kate Sweet, Grade 6
Regina Coeli School, NY

Autumn

A ir is cool and crisp;
U nlimited assortment of leaves
T rees decorated with many different colors;
U ndeniably a wonderful season!
M any pumpkin picking filled days.
N ature's most beautiful time of the year!

I nteresting transition into winter.
S oon it will be winter!

F un to jump into piles of leaves.
U ndergoing change of weather.
N ice chilly nights.

Nicolas Almonte, Grade 5
St Rose of Lima Academy, NJ

Dr. Martin Luther King

When the driver told
Rosa go to the back
Of the bus!
When the waiter told the kids
They don't serve your
Kind!
When the mayor told the voters
"Your vote doesn't count!"

The King stood strong
He stood proud
He stood tall
He spoke of peace

Hadia Bah, Grade 6
Public School 138, NY

Autumn

Autumn is so much fun,
But you can't bake in the sun!
You can rake the leaves,
and no more bees!
You can go apple and pumpkin picking,
But, hurry up, time is ticking.
You can play soccer,
But, don't be a mocker!
The weather gets colder,
As you get older.
Autumn is so much fun,
But, you can't bake in the sun!
That's why I Love Fall!

Matthew DiCaro, Grade 6
St Rose of Lima Academy, NJ

Nature

Nature comes and goes.
Trees turn yellow, red, and brown.
Leaves blow up and down.

Joy Mydlenski, Grade 4
Cortland Christian Academy, NY

Leaves

I look outside the car window
I see many pretty colors
It reminds me of summer veggies
Squash, beans and corn
I love the sight of trees changing colors
Red, orange, yellow
I love the sight so much
I feel like I can grab it
But just staring and thinking
Is all the fun of it.
Taylor Carter, Grade 5
Hawthorne Christian Academy, NJ

Snow

Snow, snow falling here and there
Jumping and glittering everywhere
You're white as a cloud
And so freezing cold
You fall down from the sky
And you land on the ground
Winter is almost over
And the snow is almost gone
Please don't go away
I want to play in snow all year round
Elizabeth Joseph, Grade 5
Hawthorne Christian Academy, NJ

Sisters

Sisters are described in many ways,
Some are bad and some superior.
I have many words of praise,
For my only sister, Aria.

A true friend,
R eally understands me and I value her.
I love her because she is an
A wesome sister.
Gabriella Lugo, Grade 4
Holy Family School, NY

Baseball

I hit the ball,
I ran for the base,
The coach said steal
And that's what I did.
I'm on the base,
I'm about to win,
I'm running down the baseline,
…will I make it?
That's a run for our team!
Donovan Mierlak, Grade 5
Hillside Elementary School, NJ

A Winter Holiday

Snowflakes dancing,
Reindeer prancing.

Winter holiday is here!

Gingerbread cookies baking,
Children in bed are waking.

Winter holiday is here!

Cookies and cocoa for Kris Kringle.
Sparkling Christmas lights
Like twinkling stars in the night.

Winter holiday is here!
Sophia Inshanally, Grade 4
James A Dever School, NY

New Year's Eve

At midnight I'm ready to celebrate,
in the favorite month of the best date.

December thirty-first, everyone is ready.
people are waiting like uncooked spaghetti.

When I look at the clock,
more people start to knock.

The music is playing,
and everyone is saying,

Have no fear,
cause the new year is here.
Alexa Xiomara Patino Nieves, Grade 5
Bartle Elementary School, NJ

Fireworks

Boom,
Crash,
Crackling around,
Colorful lights in the sky.

Wow,
Cool,
Just amazing,
How they beauteously glide to the ground.

Clap,
Cheer,
Applaud for the night,
Then fall asleep, dreaming of the lights.
Cynthia Billovits, Grade 5
Long Island School for the Gifted, NY

Drug Free Me

Drugs can't help me
They will only hurt me
Addicting, controlling, keeping me from
Being me
Unhealthy, dangerous, and deadly
That's why I won't take them
They can mess up my
Mind
Body
And my life
I won't let that happen
Drugs can't help me
They will only hurt me
Addicting, controlling
Keeping me from being me
I will never let that be
Nicole Finn, Grade 6
St Stephen's School, NY

Winter

Snowy floors
Smiling snowmen standing out
Cold sheet covers plants
Hiding ants
Sliding sleds down slopes
Hibernating bears
Animals growing hairs
Bells jingling
Blizzards
Angels singing
Christmas
Unwrapping gifts
Cookies for Santa
Fall gone
Squirrels with nuts
Don't forget joy to all!
Evan Burke, Grade 4
James A Dever School, NY

Riding Free

My favorite thing to do
Is to ride my horse.
Sometimes I gallop in the meadow,
And sometimes I jump a course.

When I'm in a horse show
Jumping is my favorite thing.
It feels like I'm flying,
On a bird's wing.

Riding free isn't just what I say,
It's how I live,
It's how I pray,
It's how I survive.
Gracie Klimas, Grade 5
Liberty School, NJ

Winter

Lose a snowball fight
It's hard
To make a snowman
No school
On snowdays
Anthony Giraldo, Grade 4
Catherine A Dwyer Elementary School, NJ

Winter

Winter,
What a thrill
Penguins waddle
Pass my door
It's Christmas Day
Liam Gregor, Grade 4
Catherine A Dwyer Elementary School, NJ

October

October
Colorful, cold
Tricking, hopping, skipping
Bag filled with candy
Halloween
Kayla Issurdatt, Grade 6
Caroline G Atkinson School, NY

Friends

Friends
Awesome, trustworthy
Caring, laughing, playing
I really love them!
Buddy
Jessica Pinzon, Grade 6
Caroline G Atkinson School, NY

Summer with the Fish

Whoosh!
There goes the fish
Trying to catch that fishy
Yeah!
I caught the fish
Matthew Kritz, Grade 4
Catherine A Dwyer Elementary School, NJ

Alvin

A mazingly well behaved, my little friend
L oving and sweet, best pals till the end
V ery small, but just enough
I s as furry as a cotton puff
N o one loves my dog as much as I do!
Michael Besosa, Grade 5
Dickinson Avenue Elementary School, NY

Autumn

I can taste autumn in the air!
The warmth of the orangish, yellowish sun,
Welcoming nature into a whole new world. The big shiny star protecting the tree
giving it light to grow, watching over the land below.
I can touch the brown bark on the short tree in the distance.
It's so empty, so alone.
Guarding the colorful leaves that are flying through the sky.
I can see the leaves floating down to the ground.
It's raining leaves! The colorful leaves are dancing with the wind.
Red, orange, yellow, and brown leaves are shooting stars,
I hear the wind whistling in the air. The beautiful sky, wrapping it's blue blanket
around the world,
racing against the night.
Keeping and protecting the land below.
I can hear the buzzing of the bugs around the river.
The river is like an athlete running around the world.
It's long and blue, and always changing and moving from place to place.
The brown bridge, serving as the finish line for the running river.
it's planks stretching across the green grass,
Waiting to be walked across
to another place to watch the sun set.
Taylor Adler, Grade 6
Harold D Fayette Elementary School, NY

Open Your Eyes

In my head I think…
As I'm walking down the street, I want…I want…I want.
In the corner of my eye, I see the glimpse of a little girl.
Probably filled with sadness and doubt
She's filthy and heartbroken as others pass her with disgust.
I imagine how much anger, sadness, and fear she feels.
As others laugh and ignore her, thinking only about themselves.
They start thinking more about what they want.
Now I think…
What if I were that poor little girl, afraid and depressed?
I'd be full of fear, thinking I don't have a chance of happiness.
I would feel doubtful that anyone would ever reach out to me.
How enraged and cast down I would feel,
Thinking, that without food, I could die tomorrow.
I'm done thinking and I realize I want too much.
I go help the little girl.
I give the girl a hug and then I buy her some food…she smiles.
I feel happy, but stupid for always wanting things I don't need.
At least now I can rest knowing the child can live at least a day longer.
She made me realize what I needed most…to open my eyes.
Trisha Ortiz, Grade 6
Holy Innocents School, NJ

Fall

The leaves are changing color and the leaves are falling.
Everyone's raking and making a big pile of leaves so the kids can jump in them.
They're making a mess of leaves and it is cold outside.
It is a good time to ride scooters and bikes around your neighborhood.
Also, in October you can go trick-or-treating for Halloween for the entire day.
Tyler Losee, Grade 4
Eugene Auer Memorial School, NY

Earth Pledge

Death or life
Do you stand
To take this task of effect to all?

To become an animal's heart
Pressured by sorrow
To not murder one of yourself
To never have to be guilty?

Do you not join the useless
Ending with nothing
But to join the help?
Of all, we are earthlings!

Will you be the nature tribe
Of hope and blesses
Allowing to take in cries to mend?

The decisions are yours at your risk
To pass will award your name
Not only in fame but in bold green!

Mayowa Ayodele, Grade 5
Community Park School, NJ

Mountains

Mountains are so calm.
When I feel them it's like my palm.
Rough, yet satisfying.
When it is autumn,
I like to see the leaves change.
When it gets cold, it starts to snow.
I go snow boarding.
I shred the snowy, wet mountains.
By the time of April,
The snow melts away.
So I'm here.
In the mountains so rocky to stay
All alone in this house
Watching people walk by day by day.
But it's only May
Does this mean it is time?
The time of year that I grow happy...
Hikers come to my door
And ask to come in.
I always say "Yes."
Thank God for the mountains.

Geno Coppola, Grade 6
Regina Coeli School, NY

Birds

Red, yellow
Fly, eat, drink
All around us day and night
Parrots.

Marlen Castellanos, Grade 4
Ethel M Burke Elementary School, NJ

Winter

Winter is the coldest season.
People go out and start to sneeze.
The snow is as white as the clouds.
Kids go outside and scream out loud.
The snow stays white throughout the night.
In the morning, it's light.

People dress up warmly.
They go outside.
Play while the cars go by.
After all the playing they go inside.

Michael Lucas, Grade 6
Public School 138, NY

Relaxation

Relaxation
Peaceful and quiet
Open and free
I do not see how anyone could disagree
Catch it and do not let it go
Throughout your body let it flow
Just you and your mind
Keep it calm and kind
Your thoughts blissful and serene
Soon all of your stress will be clean
Relaxation.

Cameron T. McCullough, Grade 6
Westampton Middle School, NJ

Dreams

Dreams are a place to get away
you don't have to think
or work or try
all you have to do
is close your eyes
and wander through space
until you get lost
and don't know where you're going
or what to do
and you panic and worry
and finally wake up

Eliza Whipple, Grade 5
Hillside Elementary School, NJ

Max-a-Million

I love you and you love me
we were as happy as could be
I pushed you around
and you pulled me
but when it was time to say goodbye
I really did start to cry
but as long as I love you
and you love me
I'll be as happy as could possibly be

Allison Reda, Grade 5
Hawthorne Christian Academy, NJ

Ruby

It was a long day,
the sun was beating down on us.
We could see the water inside boiling,
we hoped she wouldn't leak.
She was getting redder by the moment,
at least we gave her life even though
she will probably face death soon.
Finally all of us get safely to the house,
sit down in the lawn,
and start to play.

We look over,
an army of boys is approaching.
They have their water balloon too,
but it's named Pupera.
Suddenly they launch Purpera into the air.
Then boom!
Pop!
Ruby is gone.

Samia Renzi, Grade 6
Harold T Wiley School, NY

Creativity

Creativity is an explosion
It erupts over paper
Many different colors surrounding
Creativity can blow your mind

Creativity is a blast of colors
It spreads through everywhere
Lots of different colors to see
Many dull and many vivid colors

Creativity is imagining
Colorful pictures in your minds
Wonderful colors pop in your brain
Imagining the colors

Creativity is anything
Everything you see
Something interesting
Creativity is everything

Amber Russo, Grade 6
Great Meadows Middle School, NJ

Peace

Bubble floating in the air,
Gently blowing everywhere,
Peace,
Delicate, and fragile,
Easy to break
Peace,
For nations everywhere
For children anywhere.

Ella Watts Gorman, Grade 6
Our Lady of Mercy Regional School, NY

Bicycle

Wind blowing in my face
Mopping my hair back
Whistling in my ears
Telling me to hold on tight

I feel in my heart that I'm unstoppable
Trees pass
Bushes pass
People pass

I squint as the wind blows into my face
I get a burn from holding onto the steering holders so tightly
Chains clang as I pedal
I don't look back
As I pump the pedals
One by one

When my mom calls me in
I stomp on the brakes
As my bike comes to a screeching halt
After awhile,
I get back on my bike and do it all over again!

Cassie Livingston, Grade 4
Norman J Levy Lakeside School, NY

Beautiful Blue

Blue is the color of the beach waves.
Blue is the color of sweet cotton candy.
Blue is the color of my favorite dress.
Blue is the color of my pretty birthstone.
Blue is the color of the border of my computers.
Blue is my favorite color out of everything else.
Blue is the color of blueberries.
Blue is the color of raspberries.
Blue is the color of my cousin's eyes.
Blue is the color of the aquamarine.
Blue is the color that will always be in my mind
Forever and ever and ever!

Najee Cuevas, Grade 4
Roosevelt Elementary School, NJ

My Thanksgiving Festivity

T urkeys roast on a toasty fire,
H aving a harvest is one of my desires.
A mazing food covers the table,
N ot including the apples with maple.
K itchen pots are all over the house,
S oon it was time to put on my blouse.
G etting ready for the feast was a lot of fun,
I couldn't wait for the food to be done!
V arious fragrances roamed through the room,
It was time for the food to be consumed.
N ot counting me, everyone ate a ton,
G iving food to my family was a lot fun!

Makayla Jack, Grade 6
Riverside Middle School, NJ

Thankful for Thanksgiving

T hanksgiving is a great time of year,
H ungry relatives are full of cheer.
A t last it's time to eat the turkey,
N obody wants the old and stale beef jerky.
K ids running around the delicious looking table,
S oon it was time to read a Thanksgiving fable.
G iving thanks in every possible way,
I can eat leftovers until Christmas Day.
V egetable soup and turkey wings,
I ncredibly thankful for everything.
N ow that Thanksgiving is coming to an end,
G obbling turkeys no longer have to defend.

Katie Wallace, Grade 6
Riverside Middle School, NJ

Winter Wonderland

In the dark of December
As long as I can remember
Gloves and scarves fill shelves
As we bake cookies for the elves

As I look out the window
It looks like a white winter wonderland
With snow carpeting the ground

Santa and his reindeer were prancing around
In the whirling winter wind
With tiny fragile gems of white snowflakes falling around

Muhammad Hydarali, Grade 4
James A Dever School, NY

The Thanksgiving Dinner

T ime goes fast when you go pumpkin picking.
H ats are what the Pilgrims wore.
A big turkey for the whole family to eat.
N icky stuffs his face with mashed potatoes.
K icking our feet until the turkey comes out.
S ick from all of the talking.
G etting ready for the dinner to begin.
I ce in our cocoas, yeah! Yum!
V ery hungry all day.
I love Thanksgiving.
N ever stop eating turkey.
G iving thanks that we are all together on Thanksgiving.

Adriana Centrone, Grade 5
St Rose of Lima Academy, NJ

Mothers

Mothers are the ones that teach you right from wrong
Mothers are the ones that sing you a goodnight song
Mothers are the ones who soothe you when you see a scary sight
Mothers are the ones who tuck you in at night
Mothers are the ones who love you very dear
Mothers are the ones that will always be here.

Malorie Rosa, Grade 5
Hawthorne Christian Academy, NJ

Creativity

Creativity is an ocean
Beautiful and peaceful
Filled with life and love
Dangerous and mysterious

Creativity is art
No limits to imagination
Use your heart more than mind
Love, happiness, sadness, all used as inspiration

Creativity is a best friend
Always there when you need them
Lifts you up never pushes you down
More understanding than words can describe

Creativity is a child
Your own creation so never wrong
The most beautiful thing in your eyes
The light in your window that keeps you going

Gabrielle Wogou, Grade 6
Great Meadows Middle School, NJ

My Father

My father
He works at a restaurant
He cooks,
He cleans,
He loves me,

He watches TV
He calls and texts,

He laughs,
He cries,
He screams,

He claps,
He mops,
He even plays games,

He is no ordinary man,
He is my father.

Clemika Edwards, Grade 6
Graham Elementary and Middle School, NY

I Want to Make the World Better!

I want to help people stop robberies
I want to help stop fighting and violence
I want to help feed people that don't have food
to make the world safe and
I want to make peace
I want to help others
when they can't help themselves.
That's what I want

Damion White, Grade 6
New York Institute for Special Education, NY

My Day at the Beach

I love the acute feeling of the grainy sand
as it scratches the skin on my hand.

The sand scorches the bottom of my feet
but as it goes between my toes it feels really neat.

As the water chills my toes and skin
I hasten to get my whole body in.

Part of the day I swim like a fish
as the pinnacle of the day, it is all I could wish.

Hostile seagulls ascend and decline high and low
I'm waiting to devour my food until they go.

Now I'm laying in the sun to get a tan
I dread riding home in the kid-packed van.

Ashley Lowe, Grade 6
Westampton Middle School, NJ

You're on Your Own!

I walk on stage in the dark.
Suddenly, the curtains rise,
The stage's lights turn on,
And the music starts slowly.
Then something strange happens.
I get nervous!
That never happens to ME!
Not when I'm dancing.
I finally convince myself to start,
But I forget what to do!
I look around,
I see no one except the audience.
Then I remember it's my solo,
So I do what every good dancer does,
Dance!
These aren't the dance moves I have practiced,
But I am the only one who knows that!

Kelly Doyle, Grade 4
Lincoln Park Elementary School, NJ

Special Relatives

T hanksgiving is so very fun,
H enry eats many biscuits and buns.
A unt Mary is already full,
N ina's Thanksgiving outfit is cool.
K ari doesn't eat at all,
S haron is extremely tall.
G ary always likes to share,
I van says Thanksgiving prayer.
V innie dances all around,
I an had to take Bob to the pound.
N ikki brought sweet potato pie with cheer,
G avin said Thanksgiving was the greatest this year.

Jada Gale, Grade 6
Riverside Middle School, NJ

Flight
Feel the wind through my hair,
as my arms stretch out,
I can see houses down below,
as I soar about,
I can touch a fluffy cloud
as an airplane passes by,
I can feel a ray of sun,
I can hear an eagle's cry,
Higher and higher
up I go,
I swim through the air,
I feel the breeze blow.
A wonderful way, to spend the day
give it a try and you'll see why
that I wish I could fly.
Aidan Joyce, Grade 5
Hillside Elementary School, NJ

Alpacas
they spit at me
they spit at you
they're in the mountains in Peru

he's soft and woolly
with light brown hair
we show him off at the county fair

we'll use the wool
to make a sweater
it makes me feel so much better

he's my pet
I love him so
I really hope he'll never go
Gabrielle Lee, Grade 5
Dickinson Avenue Elementary School, NY

Life
The river runs
The animals sleep
The trees sway side to side
And the weeping willows weep

Nature comes and it goes
As life stays life
I hear frogs and toads

We stay silent all the night
Not with one single fright
The bears snore
We hear the crickets' song

As life goes on and on.
Sydney Hay, Grade 6
Buckley Country Day School, NY

Martin Luther King Jr.
He was generous
Loyal, bold, and shinning.
He fought for his and
Other people's needs.
He wanted Blacks and
Whites to be together.
He wanted them
To reunite in one big
Bunch.
That man's name was
Martin Luther King Jr.
He was born 1-15-1929.
Seaniah Mcleod, Grade 6
Public School 138, NY

Candy Corn
Look! There in the bowl!
It's a beautiful sight!
Orange, yellow, and white!
It's candy corn!
Get it! Get it!
Go! Go!
Before the candy corn is all gone!
We need help! Call in our army!
We must get it! The beautiful sight!
The candy corn, the candy corn!
Orange, yellow, and white
Before it's all gone, that's my fright!
Maren Tamburri Saunders, Grade 5
St Rose of Lima Academy, NJ

I Always Do
Shoot and score.
I always do.
There's a guy in front of me,
So I pass it to the guy in jersey #2.
The other team gets the ball,
But Johns runs like there's no tomorrow.
He gets the ball.
I am wide open,
So John passes it to me.
I shoot with my powerful kick.
I shoot and score.
I always do.
Aleksandar Ruteski, Grade 4
Lincoln Park Elementary School, NJ

Shining Star
Bright
A yellow light
Marvelous
Wishing and hoping to come true
Shining
Big and beautiful
Harris Freeman, Grade 5
Park Avenue Elementary School, NY

Water
In the water
What do you see?
A big, gray fin coming at Dean
I jump in and scream.

Then I look back
and 1, 2, 3
my good friend Dean
is gone from
ME!
Nicole Steiger, Grade 5
Dickinson Avenue Elementary School, NY

Why I Am Drug-Free
Drugs can give me cancer,
And tear my family apart.
The dealers seem to be the worst of all,
But they are druggies too.
They can put my athletic career downhill,
And stomp on all my dreams.
If I can't pay the dealer back,
"Boom" there I go.
Everyone tells me to stay away from drugs,
And now I know why!
Joshua Costolnick, Grade 6
St Stephen's School, NY

Sassy in Jazz
Stretch with all your heart!
Batma kicks with your hands on your hips!
Shuffle ball cute!
Fan, split, side body roll!
Side, reverse, switch leap!
Turn around, touch the ground!
Terrific toe touch!
Swivel, swirl, sweet!
Perfect podaborays!
Sassy Shenays!
Samantha Scaltro, Grade 4
Lincoln Park Elementary School, NJ

Splash!
The swimmers dive in.
I kick like there's no tomorrow,
But I'm not in first.
With water seeping into my goggles,
And my bathing cap stuck to my head,
It might be over.
The flags are straight ahead.
My muscles are aching,
I can't feel them at all.
Then I realize I'm in first.
Erin Benson, Grade 4
Lincoln Park Elementary School, NJ

Leah

Leah means weary
But that is just not me
I am full of energy
Always running in the grass
Lover of trampolines
And swimming pools
Even when the day is done
I am still wide awake
Leah should mean
Flute player
Artist
And
Lover of cats
And many other things.
Leah Loetman, Grade 4
Newbridge Road Elementary School, NY

A Puppy

A puppy is soft,
a puppy is sweet,
A puppy will run
after your feet.

A puppy will trip,
a puppy will fall,
A puppy will stay
not-so-very-tall.

A puppy is loyal,
as cute as can be,
A puppy is a friend,
as you can see.
Catherine Tom, Grade 4
Harbor Hill School, NY

The Center of Winter

In the center
Of winter a snowman
Lays he
Controls the
Coldness when
He is gone his son
Will be the one who
Controls winter his son
Winter
Create colder clearer
Crunchier snow some people
Might not understand his ways

He is a wise guy people say.
Branden Pulido, Grade 4
James A Dever School, NY

My Pencil

My pencil and I,
Are the perfect pair.
You can find us together,
Almost anywhere!
You can find us in my house,
And you can find us in a tree.
But wherever we are,
We will be together, writing happily!
My pencil guides,
My hand to write.
It gives me ideas,
All day and all night.
It moves my hand,
From place to place.
It even picks it up,
When I need to make a space.
Together my pencil and I,
Fill my writing cravings.
But now all that is left of it,
Are some long and curly pencil shavings.
Sage Agatstein, Grade 6
Willow Grove Middle School, NY

My Cat Caramel

I have a orange pussy cat
He sleeps on a fluffy blue mat
His fur is so bright
It sparkles in the night.
His eyes are shiny green
They are the biggest you ever seen
He sometimes likes to snore all day
Specifically in April, June and May.
My cat Caramel is very sweet
He always asks if he can eat
When it was Halloween
I dressed him as a jelly bean.
He likes to play with little balls
Sometimes it's funny if he falls
He jumps in to my comfy lap
It's where he likes to take a nap.
My cat is very big and chubby
He won't fit in my gray cubby
I am done writing this poem
I hope you got to know him.
Elizabeth Shoykhet, Grade 6
Our Lady of Grace School, NY

The Mine Rap

The mine was a lot of fun,
I got a lot done,
but, the underground was the most fun.
I didn't know
there could be a 1,000 foot pool
but it was really, really cool.
Dezmond King, Grade 4
Roosevelt Elementary School, NJ

Halloween Night

Costumes, costumes here and there,
Costumes, costumes everywhere.

Ghosts and ghouls love to fright,
While fairies and pixies bring delight.

Witches and warlocks take flight.
All the children carry a flashlight.

The jack-o-lanterns are so bright.
Wrestlers and boxers love to fight.

Football players show their might.
Rock stars' clothes are too tight.

Watch out or Dracula will bite.
So much fun on Halloween night.
Jake D'Ambola, Grade 5
Liberty School, NJ

It is Fall

The tall, brown tree was shaky
Through the invisible gusty wind
Hugging the cold brisk air
Brown branches
Sticking out
Like arms on a person

Small red, purple, orange leaves
Gripping tightly on a branch
Or diving toward the ground
Like planes landing on an airfield

The short, green grass
Swaying, full with leaves
Short green stems
The cold brisk air
Means it is fall
Jack Caroddo, Grade 6
Harold D Fayette Elementary School, NY

Big Brother

He is nice
He is sweet
And I love him for loving me

He is tall
He is very strong
And he is still nice to me

I will love him forever
And I hope he loves me
Because he is my Big Brother
and he is Family.
Jen Cleary, Grade 5
Martin Avenue Elementary School, NY

Football

Pass, catch, tuck, and *go*
Run quickly to the *endzone*
Crowd cheering *touchdown*

FOOTBALL
Sean Nelson, Grade 5
Dickinson Avenue Elementary School, NY

Peace

Family
Togetherness, forever
Relaxing, welcoming, never-ending,
Family life,
Peace…
Liam Corbley, Grade 6
Our Lady of Mercy Regional School, NY

The Day

I am at the bus stop
And I go on the bus
I see my mom as she vanishes
As the bus goes down the twisty road
As day goes by
Natalie Bodycomb, Grade 4
Catherine A Dwyer Elementary School, NJ

Nature

Fun, cool
Classy, great, wild
Favorite free feeling!
Green.
Mary Ruggiero, Grade 4
Ethel M Burke Elementary School, NJ

Bubble Gum

Pink, sticky
Pops, dances, talks
The best discovery ever
Fun food!
Riya Patel, Grade 4
Ethel M Burke Elementary School, NJ

My Jacket

Purple, warm
Zips, opens, closes
My handy dandy thing in cold weather
Winter coat!
Roheena Saleem, Grade 4
Ethel M Burke Elementary School, NJ

My Dog

My dog is Lily.
Her hair is gold like the leaves
That fall off the trees.
Rachel O'Hearn, Grade 4
Cortland Christian Academy, NY

Gus Learns a Lesson

Running and jumping, skipping and hopping,
Lion and Tiger played without stopping.

With his nose in the air,
Tiger announced "Catch me if you dare."

The two of them laughed and had fun in the sun,
If they weren't interrupted, they'd never be done!

"Hey what are you doing together like that?" screamed Tiger's brother Gus,
"We're friends Gus, don't worry about us."

"Friends you can't be, it's easy to see,
He doesn't look a thing like you or me."

"What you look like doesn't matter,
Whether you are skinny or fatter.

You should learn to accept others for who they are,
If you do that you will go far!"

You can never have too many friends!

Sophie Weiss, Grade 5
Shelter Rock Elementary School, NY

Thanksgiving with the Webbs!

T he Turkey was fat! So fat you would think the table could break!
H aving no doubt, the plate added 10 more pounds.
A squeak and a crackle, I can picture it now.
N ever in my life could I have eaten so much food.
" **K** eep walking!" said my Uncle Joe whenever I looked at his plate.
" **S** omeone's hungry!" I replied.
G reat smells of stuffing were all throughout the house.
I inhaled heavily as well as everyone else.
V arieties of food barely fit on our plates!
I n minutes, my family was lined up for seconds.
N o one spoke until their plate was clean with crumbs resting upon their mouths!
" **G** reat food! Who made it all?" The voices grew on top of one another.
It was a true Thanksgiving with the Webbs!

Miranda Webb, Grade 6
Riverside Middle School, NJ

Stronger

The reason why I am stronger?
I am stronger because of my mom.
When I was younger my mom taught me how to tie my shoe.
It is because of my mom that I always try to stay calm even when people get me angry.
She has taught me how to be kindhearted and brave.
Even when I'd get scared, I still get scared,
But when I know she is near it makes me feel better.
My mom has taught me how to help others such as my family and my friends.
Everything I have told you is true and I hope you know.
When I grow I hope to be just like my mother.
The kind, sweet, helpful, smart, beautiful, and funny woman that she is.
Chelsie Reid, Grade 5
New York Institute for Special Education, NY

Horseback Riding
The horse in the field
trotting across the pasture
is so beautiful.

Put the saddle on,
put the bridle on her head,
roll the stirrups down.

I need a leg up
in order to mount my horse.
I am not that tall.

Walk, trot, and canter,
it is so much fun to do.
Let's do that again!
Cecelia Winn, Grade 4
Helderberg Christian School, NY

Patrick Henry
May 29, 1736,
Henry was born
Hanover County, VA
A Founding Father
Serving 1st and 6th Governor of Virginia
From 1776-1779, July 5th and June 1st
Anti-Federalist
Anti-Administration
Planter and lawyer
His speeches contains
"Give me liberty, or give me death!"
1799, June 6th
Henry lay there
Hopefully happy
Resting in peace.
Ayanna Agarrat, Grade 5
Public School 114 Ryder Elementary, NY

Cloud
There was a cloud in the sky
that looked pink when people
looked up at it
Every day it kept
floating away, to some other land,
country,
or place
making people smile
and point at it

Then one day it
grew bigger
and made
people smile
even more.

Emma Glick, Grade 5
Dickinson Avenue Elementary School, NY

I Wonder…
I'm sitting at my desk
Gazing outside
I wonder what it's like,
To go on a magic carpet ride.
Maybe I'll fly to Turkey
Or maybe even France,
Maybe to Hawaii
And do the hula dance!

Should I go to Neverland,
Where Peter Pan roams?
Or maybe Mount Olympus,
The gods' mighty home?

But wherever I go,
I know my teacher will say,
"Pay attention, Lauren!
We don't have all day!"
Lauren Sforza, Grade 5
St Mary's Prep School, NJ

When I Think of Winter
When I think of winter
I think of ringing bells
Snowmen being built
And the sweetest of smells.

Christmas trees up
Stockings being hung
Winter is amazing
Oh, what fun.

Breezy blizzards blowing, burr!
Oh, how cold
Cookies to be made
Stories to be told

Snow covers the trees
Like a warm blanket
Winter is amazing.
Christian Cicilia, Grade 4
James A Dever School, NY

Snow
It is white and cold.
It falls fast or slow.
It can cover a house,
Or cover a mouse.
It can take an hour
To snow a shower
Of white, beautiful snow.
Bundle up when you go outside,
If you don't you'll want to hide,
In a warm house with cocoa at your side.
Maura Casey, Grade 6
Sts Peter & Paul School, NY

Bicycle
As I ride the wind mops my hair back
I feel unstoppable with the wind in my face

My feet pumping hard start to ache
I say to myself, "Be free.
Do what you want to do"

As my heart pumps quickly
The bad thoughts fade away

I crush the leaves as I keep pedaling
And ride down the street
Like I'm gliding on ice
Alexa Goldfarb, Grade 4
Norman J Levy Lakeside School, NY

This Is the Season
This is the season
When all leaves are iridescent;
Scorched with red and orange
This is the season
When strong winds billow.
Leaves shower down in a
Flurry of colors.
But one leaf holds on;
Bearing the storm.
This is the season
When that leaf
Decides to finally
FALL
Maressa Park, Grade 6
St Rose of Lima Academy, NJ

Poppy
The red flower sheds its petals like tears,
Crying with sorrow for the soldiers.
The soldiers who made sacrifices,
Died for freedom,
Our freedom.

But in the midst of destruction,
Sprouts of hope
Grow in remembrance
Of the brave,
Of the faithful,
Of the people celebrated,
Of hope.
Katie St. George, Grade 4
Raynor Country Day School, NY

Wings
Butterfly wooshes
Going flower to flower
Drinking some nectar
Vanessa Van Bodegon, Grade 4
Catherine A Dwyer Elementary School, NJ

Sunset

The colors
The rainbows
The sun falling down
In the sky
Purple,
Red,
Orange,
And yellow
The bright blue sky
Becomes a rainbow
A rainbow of colors
Unimaginable
Too pretty to
Believe in

Adriana Guarascio, Grade 5
Jacob Gunther Elementary School, NY

Books

Books.
An endless world,
Of Imagination.
You create the world,
You create the characters.
Turn the pages,
And grow fonder,
Of this flowing river,
Of creation.
The high mountains of this adventure,
Bring happiness.
As well as the low valleys,
Of sorrow.
Books.

Paulina Karagianes, Grade 5
Martin Avenue Elementary School, NY

Life

Life is not just
Fun and games,
It is filled with
Troubles and blames.

Sometimes life is good
And sometimes it is bad
Life will leave you happy
And sometimes even sad.

Life is what you make it
So try to make it swell,
If you do most things
For you will turn out pretty well.

Danielle DiSclafani, Grade 6
Willow Grove Middle School, NY

A Special Day

Flowers open in the morning
Dew dries, birds talk
I go outside, the sun rises
I look at everything
It is so amazing
It's noon and everything is active
Then dusk falls.
Flowers wilt, birds stop singing
As lovely as it is, I need to go to sleep
I put my head on my pillow
I think about the world in peace.

Chandler Edbauer, Grade 5
St Aloysius Regional School, NY

Fall

In the season of fall,
Leaves will fall.
As I walk outside,
I breathe in the clean, crisp air.
My hands turn numb,
So I go inside to get some gloves.
But as I step outside again,
I notice the colorful leaves of the trees.
Squirrels gather nuts,
And birds chirp.
This, is the season of fall.

Andrew Yoon, Grade 6
Slocum Skewes School, NJ

Christmas Is Near

Christmas is near, can't you hear?
Children laughing and bells ringing,
Carolers singing Happy New Year
Christmas is near, can't you see?
People skating, buying, and getting
ready for sleigh riding.
Christmas is near, can't you smell?
Cookies, cake and don't forget cupcakes!
Christmas is near!
Christmas is near!
Christmas is near!

Christine Brower, Grade 5
Hawthorne Christian Academy, NJ

Snow

Snow spins and spins around
Gently landing on the ground.
Spreading out a sheet of white
And turning water into ice.

Each tree is covered with a blanket of snow
Giving it a warm winter glow.
When spring comes the snow disappears
I can't wait until winter next year!

Alexis Armbrust, Grade 6
Regina Coeli School, NY

Family

Mother, father,
Sister, brother,
All basic people
you all know.
Some pass away,
Some stay alive,
All of them love you,
All are sublime.

Maybe menacing...
Or even warmhearted.
Guiding the way
Through your life

Giving you shelter,
Food to stay healthy...
And alive.
Loving you,
Taking care of you.
Take care of them,
As they do for you!

Gisselle Battaglia, Grade 5
Dickinson Avenue Elementary School, NY

A Stroll

As I walked
Beside the boardwalk,
I felt the sand
Trickling in my feet.
I heard the
Waves crashing,
And saw
Only Peace.
As I walked on,
I saw the mountains
Having a contest
Who is taller?
And I saw
The falls rushing down.
I heard nothing,
Only Peace.
The serene environment,
Led me to rise;
To experience
Blissful Peace.

Rishab Bhatt, Grade 5
Millstone River School, NJ

Christmas

Christmas
Colorful, joyful
Laughing, talking, giving
Spending time with family
Holiday

Myasia Leccese, Grade 6
Caroline G Atkinson School, NY

Hands

Hands working hard and fast,
homework, projects, special tasks.
Who would have thought these little things
are a big part of what life brings?
Fiona Simoni, Grade 4
Holy Family School, NY

Fall

Lonely time of year
Season of reading, ghost book
Cool, windy weather
Anthony Jeong, Grade 5
Bartle Elementary School, NJ

Fall Leaves

Crinkling orange leaves,
Every step makes crunchy sounds,
Autumn is now here.
Andrew Xie, Grade 5
Bartle Elementary School, NJ

Surprising Spring

The snow is melting
The wind's blowing through your face
Why is Spring so great?
Samantha Crossan, Grade 4
Catherine A Dwyer Elementary School, NJ

The Forest

Bears come rampaging
Birds are tweeting in midair
In the big forest
Noah Skorupski, Grade 4
Catherine A Dwyer Elementary School, NJ

The Tropical Rain Forest

Water rustling
Trees growing like a human
Leaves falling like rain
Nicholas Cicchine, Grade 4
Catherine A Dwyer Elementary School, NJ

Clouds

Drifting high above
Floating to and fro, white puffs
Play in the blue sky.
Maggie Sullivan, Grade 6
Great Meadows Middle School, NJ

Our Home Star

Hot and dangerous.
Lights up the sky every day.
Full of hot gasses.
Joey Chabala, Grade 4
Catherine A Dwyer Elementary School, NJ

Black

My mother's hair is the prettiest shade of black in the whole world.
Mrs. Prakapas's shirt is a beautiful shade of black.
I love when I see gorgeous dolls wearing black clothes with black hair.
When I'm at home, I take out a fat black marker and draw on a big black piece of paper.
Black bears have a very nice fur coat especially in the winter.
Every day I wear a different shade of beautiful black.
My black glasses look stunning in the sunlight.
I love the black patches on the soccer ball as it comes straight for my face.
The black words in my book look wonderful as I read it.
I love the way the stars sparkle in the black night sky.
Every day I make sure I wear some black in my shoes and socks.
I love black buttons when they are on things and are not.
When I see a black rock on the ground,
I always think it's amazing like super heroes.
I love seeing people on TV with black teeth.
Dark black holes in the ground look cool to me.
Little black animals look so cute.
Black eyebrows look incredible on people.
Black purses are good for holding black things,
The best color in the world.
C'era Joe, Grade 4
Roosevelt Elementary School, NJ

Boating on Dorchester Lake

Many a ripple indicates a boat floating on the water.
Two figures dwell upon this boat, father and son.
A fish line floats in the air, lands on the water, is reeled in — nothing.
Float, land, reel, nothing.
Float, land, reel, nothing.
Float, land, reel, nothing.
The boat lurches forward to a bank with fallen trees, and thick with plant life.
Stop. Cast. Into the weeds. Reel in. No fish.
Cast. Into the weeds. Reel in. No fish.
Again. No fish.
Then the long row back to shore.
On the bank, a family awaits their arrival.
A lunch soon after.
In a short time, the figures are back on the water.
Floating as if weightless upon the water.
Upon this second trip without a rod, without a hook,
Everything but nothing,
Except the two figures.
Father and son.
Declan Houlihan, Grade 5
Chenango Forks Elementary School, NY

Make the World a Better Place

I will make a better place by helping the animals all around the world.
I will help the animals by taking them for walks, playing,
and feeding them as well as making sure people don't kill them.
I'll tell people to buy or adopt a pet or animal that is safe for the house
and give them love and a good home.
The owners will be very good to their animals.
They will not be bad owners. That is how I will make the world a better place.
Cecilia Morales, Grade 4
New York Institute for Special Education, NY

My Bedroom
Blue, small
Watch TV, do homework, play a board game
I love my room
Quiet space.
Phillip Tran, Grade 4
Ethel M Burke Elementary School, NJ

Soccer
Happy, hurtful
Running, kicking, scoring
Trying to get a goal
Spanish football
Brian Kolacz, Grade 4
Ethel M Burke Elementary School, NJ

My Top
Fancy, glittery
Washes, cleans, shines
Wearable art!
My purple shirt
Krishna Patel, Grade 4
Ethel M Burke Elementary School, NJ

Thunderstorm
Lightning, lightning flashing bright!
On a weekend night,
With thunder crackling by
The clouds open to see the bright sky.
Jaydon Mott, Grade 5
Hillside Elementary School, NJ

Strawberries
Yummy, delicious
Eatable, breaks, drips
Great juicy treat!
Fruit
Justin Delgado, Grade 4
Ethel M Burke Elementary School, NJ

Reviving a Car
Car's engine is broke
Rolls down hill like a barrel
But can be restored
Scott Pfeifer, Grade 5
St Aloysius Regional School, NY

Ocean
Big, blue
Rumbles, ripples splashes
Huge like a bear
Water!
Hirah Sattar, Grade 4
Ethel M Burke Elementary School, NJ

Winter Snow
Winter is full of snow
While all the snowflakes blow

Santa leaves presents for parents to enjoy
While all the boys and girls enjoy their toys

Forget all about the turkey and get perky with the new holiday season
While all friends and family gather around the Christmas tree

They sing Christmas carols with lots of glee because they know about the glittery snow
But, when the night comes…

Wait and listen you will hear Santa's jingling bells nice and clear
And if you look out the window you'll see Santa and his reindeer

Fa la la la la fa la la fa la la.

Arianna Baez, Grade 6
Westampton Middle School, NJ

What's in the Woods
I was running through the woods
I was out of breath and tired of running
I kept going…crunch, crunch, crunch
I heard them coming, I ran faster
"There is no way I'll make it out of here in time…or alive" I said to myself
I could hear them still coming, my heart beating out of my chest
I was out of breath so I stopped, knowing I was going to be dead
The things were feet from me, I could see their scarred faces
Then I drew my sword from my sheath
I took one big slash but hit nothing
The creatures had run to get help, so I ran farther
Some of the creatures had come after me but I could see the clearing
The light was so bright in the darkness
I was so close but the monsters were blocking the path
Somehow I made it past them and arrived at the castle
Relieved I was still alive.

Noble Graham, Grade 6
Westampton Middle School, NJ

Holidays
The car breezes by as we cross the mighty bridge
My family and I near closer to my cousin's house, I can smell the stuffing and turkey.
Next thing I know it is December and it is time for Hanukkah
Fire on candle melting, waxy watery
Presents wrapped in colorful paper
Kids in my family rip and tear, I can hear the wrapping paper screaming
ahhhhhhh as it gets torn apart into happy pieces

It is September now
Jewish New Year creeps closer
There are feasts, toys, and it is a lot of fun
Yom Kippur
My grandparents and I travel to nearby creek, we throw bread in the creek
Bread resembles our sins
Haden Levine, Grade 6
Harold D Fayette Elementary School, NY

Fall Day

Fall is here and we can see
where leaves become multi colored
like flaming red, dazzling orange, and glowing yellow.
These radiant autumn colors are key.

Fresh pies are baking in the oven
and the house feels warm.
It's filled with the delightful smell
of pumpkin pie and sweet corn.

It tastes delicious
and easy to slice.
We cut it into small pieces
that look like velvety orange dice.

Outside we go to play with the crinkled leaves.
It's chilly and cold and so hard to believe
that Christmas is near.
Ho—Ho! I can almost hear
the ringing sleigh bells in my ear.

Arianna Amato, Grade 6
Slocum Skewes School, NJ

Wings

Gliding, swirling, perfection,
Orchestrated flight.
As graceful as an acrobat,
Soaring at great heights.
Wings open on the air,
Brightly colored like a rainbow.
Wings go pitter-patter, flitter-flatter. Whoosh!
Then they stop to take a rest.
Others decide to build a nest.
Tweet! Tweet! I hear them by my window.
I quietly sneak over so they don't hear.
Flying away as I draw near,
Intelligent creatures adorn the sky.
I wait to take another peek.
Pecking the ground with their beaks,
Desperately seeking something to eat.
In the summer they stay cool,
Using my water fountain as a swimming pool.
Calling to each other using the sky as their playground.
Gliding, swirling, perfection

Alana Thompson, Grade 6
Westampton Middle School, NJ

Winter

Winter is white
As white as the snow
Winter has snowflakes
As frosty as an ice cream.
Winter is God's most very wonderful season,
And is also a reminder of His wonderful creations.

Annie Chang, Grade 5
Hawthorne Christian Academy, NJ

The Mime That Cannot Rhyme

I walk across the city, trying to find something amazing
I'm getting tired, losing hope
There in the distance, I don't know what it is
Perhaps a person of some sort
Black and white with a little hat
Standing there lonely
I walk over and watch, he says nothing
I say hi, but he still says nothing
Then he looks up and sees me
He waves and smiles
Next he puts his hands in front of him
Then to his sides
Finally above him
I ask him what he is doing
He locks his lips and throws the key away
He will not talk
What's this, a mime you say?
He is trapped in a box and cannot speak
I give him a tip and walk away
On my way back I think
If he can't speak, can he rhyme?

Tessa McCormick, Grade 5
Little Falls School #1, NJ

War

War.
Brutal combat,
side against side;
fighting until a winner emerges.
It's win or lose,
live or die.
Taking away what matters most.
Tearing families apart.
It's sad to find out that a relative is being sent off to war,
but it's even sadder to find out that they won't be coming back.
The Earth cries out,
"If all men are created equal, you're practically killing yourself!
This bloodshed has to stop."
And as one side emerges victorious,
cries of victory ring out,
and then the battlefield is silent.
But how can there be a winner, when countless lives have been lost?
Because it's the brutal,
horrible,
devastating,
war.

Jeremy Sass, Grade 6
Saw Mill Road Elementary School, NY

Nick

N ice
I ntelligent
C ool
K ind

Nicholas Brasmeister, Grade 5
Tecler Arts in Education Magnet School, NY

Dario D'Iapico

Win a soccer game
No school
In the summertime
Play in the water
Dario Diapico, Grade 4
Catherine A Dwyer Elementary School, NJ

Swimming

Swimming in the morning
Play with friends
And brother
Ride my cool blue bike
Juan Vargas, Grade 4
Catherine A Dwyer Elementary School, NJ

Summer

The summer is fun
Playing with my friends
All day
Excited for fall
Pavlo Pencak, Grade 4
Catherine A Dwyer Elementary School, NJ

Flowers in the Spring

Flowers have petals
Flowers are very pretty
Rain, rain
Help them grow
Elly Enright, Grade 4
Catherine A Dwyer Elementary School, NJ

Honey Bees

Honey bees are sweet
Honey bees can
Sting you badly
The Queen bee is mean
Arlie Guida, Grade 4
Catherine A Dwyer Elementary School, NJ

Winter

Snowy, icy
Freezing, crunchy, cocoa
The winter is always so cold,
Christmas
Emilee Teran, Grade 5
Catherine A Dwyer Elementary School, NJ

Ocean

Big, stupendous
Makes waves, moves, gives
Fun salty swimming!
Ocean
James Marengo, Grade 4
Ethel M Burke Elementary School, NJ

Thanksgiving

Thank you
For all my eyes can see
White puffy cotton balls linger in the crystal blue sky
Brandy trying to eat leaves as they fall from trees that tower over houses
Tables filled with chairs are a long football stadium waiting for people to sit and eat

Thank you
For all my ears can hear
Brisk winds whispering secrets to the amber leaves
Gobble gobbles of turkeys running from ovens are as loud as a screech of an owl
Children laughing as they play outside in the crisp chilly air

Thank you
For all my tongue can taste
Tender, juicy turkey followed by smooth, thick, sweet gravy on Thanksgiving
Cold or hot cider that drops down your cheek with each tasty sip
Delicious apple pie resting on your tongue as if you don't want the taste to end
Emily Monahan, Grade 6
Oakdale-Bohemia Middle School, NY

Your Mother

A person who is always there for you
No matter what happens or what you do
She finds a way to help you
And taps on your shoulder and leads you through,

A person with a heart filled with forgiveness
That never wants to depress you
She only does it for your own good
And doesn't want anything bad to happen to you,

A person with unbelievable wisdom and amazing skills
Who doesn't leave any part of your heart until it's filled with happiness and thrills,

A person who is no other
Than your beloved, kind mother
And no matter what you do
It can never repay your mother for what she did for you.
Isra Arbab, Grade 6
Al Ghazaly School, NJ

Thanksgiving Feast

T hanksgiving is here! I can't wait to
H ave turkey
A nd pumpkin pie.
N ow it is time to start cooking!
I help my mom set up nap **K** ins.
Then we make a lot of cranberry **S** auce for Thanksgiving.
Ding dong! Oh **G** ood, my cousins are here.
I am so happy all the food is ready.
Red **V** elvet cake sits on a tray waiting for us to scarf it down.
I ce cream is in the fridge getting ready to be scooped.
N ow it is time to eat the turkey.
But first, we give thanks to **G** od for this wonderful feast.
Oscar Lopez, Grade 6
Riverside Middle School, NJ

Bronx

The loud Bronx is where I am from.
Music loud,
I can't sleep.
Loud Jamaicans on my block never stay quiet.
Bronx is where I'm from.

Loud gun shots is what you hear.
It goes boom, bang,
and people screaming mostly every day.
Bronx is where I'm from.

I hope where I'm from is a better place.
I wish it could be.
I'll give it another day.

Bronx, Bronx is where I'm from.
Bronx is loud and terrifying for all of us.

Kean Finlay, Grade 5
The Bronx Charter School for Better Learning, NY

The Best Time of All Is Fall!

Fall is a great time of the year
When children share a feeling of fear
When pumpkin pie is a treasure to all
This is why I love the season fall

With turkey and ham and stuffing and pie
Food piles up as high as the sky
Ghosts scream "Boo!" as trick-or-treaters run
But to me, Halloween is just plain fun

You can hear the drip-drop on a rainy day
Fall's just a season where you have fun and play
Leaves change to red, orange, yellow, and brown
You can ride a hay ride in a different town

Jump into the huge pile of colorful leaves that stand tall
The best time of all is definitely fall!

Shianne Cooke, Grade 5
Buffalo United Charter School, NY

"Thanks to Thanksgiving"

T hanksgiving is here, but there is so much to do,
H arvest we shall, to make some delectable stew.
A ssuredly, there will be turkey,
N ow, doesn't that make you perky?
K nives, forks, spoons, and plates have to be set,
S o don't forget to bring a dish for your pet.
G iving thanks is what this is all about,
I know this without a doubt.
V ulnerable clothes should be worn,
I n the end you don't want them to be torn.
N evertheless, we will have a great time,
G etting to do this will be worth every dime.

Amanda De La Roca, Grade 6
Riverside Middle School, NJ

Winter

Getting up in the morning
Hey, there's snow outside
Quickly getting dressed with a coat, hat, and mittens, oh so nice
Going outside, feeling a cool breeze on my face
Going sledding down a hill, wow what a race
Climbing up, going down, climbing up again
Keep doing it all over again
You're getting tired
It's getting late
You are thinking of your time; it was great
Walking home that night
You notice something to the right
It's your friends, siblings, and neighbors
Wow, what a sight
Now you notice they're throwing snowballs at you
You raise your sled, but it's too late
You're covered with snow from head to toe
Going inside for some hot cocoa
Going to bed to do it all again tomorrow

Michael Spencer, Grade 6
Sts Peter & Paul School, NY

Laughter

Laughter is a song
Something you can't get rid of
It will play over and over again in your head
Once you start you cannot stop

Laughter is a memory
Something you never forget
You make a memory every time
Always cherish the moment

Laughter is golden
It makes you one of a kind
Every time you laugh you're like a star
That won't stop smiling back at me

Laughter is a precious gift
That you will always enjoy
Nothing will ever rise above it
Just keep laughing until the end

Shea Prouflias, Grade 6
Great Meadows Middle School, NJ

Hawaiian Happy-Faced Spider

They're creepy and they're crawly
and they smile too
If I saw one
I don't know what I'd do

If you see one don't think that their amount is poor
If you just go exploring
You'll find many more

Arielle Nogueira, Grade 4
Deerfield Elementary School, NJ

A Cloud

a cloud is puffy,
it is so tempting to touch it,
it looks like a cozy blanket on a cold winter's night,
a cloud is white,
as white can be,
the whitest color you have ever seen.
a cloud has many different shapes,
it could be any size
a bird, cat, even a mouse,
there are many different clouds,
more than a trillion in the whole world,
clouds like to roam in the sky,
and go really fast,
the chances of seeing the same cloud is one in a zillion
a cloud looks light,
but it holds a lot of rain,
people also think clouds are like trampolines,
to jump on and have fun,
but if you try to jump on it,
you will fall through.

Lilliana Zakrzewska, Grade 6
St Stanislaus Kostka Academy School, NY

The Four Seasons

Every season is one of a kind,
And there is no telling what you might find.
Winter, spring, summer, and fall,
Every day can be a ball.
During the cold winter days,
Step outside and be amazed.
A white blanket of snow covers the ground,
And your ears are filled with Christmas sounds.
When spring arrives and melts the snow,
It's a clear sign winter has to go.
Pretty flowers pop up near the pond,
And it looks like the work of a magic wand.
When the days get very long,
You wake up to the birds' summer song.
The cool ocean washes up beneath your feet,
And you have fun with the people you meet.
When the apples in orchards are falling from the trees,
The last of the pollen is collected by the bees.
This means fall is here,
But very soon we will have a new year!

Annie Podedworny, Grade 6
St Stanislaus Kostka Academy School, NY

Christmas Food

I love Christmas because of the delicious food.
When I eat it I get in the Christmas mood.
My favorite food is the tasty ham.
I do my best to avoid the yams.
I end my meal with ice cream and cake.
How could you dislike it for goodness sake?

James Schoneboom, Grade 5
Hillside Elementary School, NJ

The Best Season of All

Fall is a great time year,
There is so much to do and it's filled with lots of cheer.

This is when warm weather goes away,
And there is less and less sunlight every day.

It is also the beginning of school,
And everybody knows, that is not cool.

There are many things in the fall to do,
Playing football and soccer are just two.

Autumn is the time with colorful leaves in the sky,
It also has the World Series, then baseball says goodbye.

Halloween brings out many ghosts and goblins on the street;
Thanksgiving brings us many good things to eat.

When the trees are bare, autumn is coming to an end.
That is when we know winter is right around the bend.

Anthony Paradiso, Grade 6
St Rose of Lima Academy, NJ

Nature

Nature is all the trees giving shade,
Where the animals get cooled down.
Nature is all the leaves that are falling in autumn,
Making a colorful carpet on the ground.
Nature is all the birds that sing,
The rabbits that hop and the small bushes.
Nature is all the green grass covering the Earth,
Making a huge, green, healthy blanket.
Nature is all the insects and animals,
Fighting and working hard to survive.
Nature is the desert and its animals,
Snakes slithering, hawks soaring,
All trying to get water in the harsh weather.
Nature is also the poles,
With penguins waddling, reindeer roaming,
Trying hard to stay alive.
Nature is the rain forests, savannas, and grasslands.
Sadly, global warming has affected these places.
Almost everywhere is nature and it's very important,
All we have to do is keep it alive!

Hannah Donnelly, Grade 6
Great Meadows Middle School, NJ

Gymnastics

Flipping, jumping all around,
Making a giant sound.
Front handspring here and there,
I love doing them everywhere.
When I feel down,
I do a handstand to make the opposite of a frown.

Victoria Kenney, Grade 5
Hillside Elementary School, NJ

March

March
Warm, rainy
Laughing, playing, blooming
A special celebration day
Saint Patrick's Day

Alyssa Cruz, Grade 6
Caroline G Atkinson School, NY

Flower

Flower
Beautiful, colorful
Growing, blowing, glowing
They make me happy
Rose

Roselor Pierre-Paul, Grade 6
Caroline G Atkinson School, NY

Christmas

Christmas
Cheerful, fun
Exciting, talking, laughing
We get many presents
Holiday

Jason Sandoval, Grade 6
Caroline G Atkinson School, NY

Santa

Santa
Fat, jolly
Caroling, eating, giving
Santa eats the cookies
Christmas

TaFari Simpson, Grade 6
Caroline G Atkinson School, NY

Dessert

Dessert
Eat your dessert
Pumpkin Pie and Dream Pie
I got an awful stomach ache
Yummy

Benjamin Miller, Grade 4
St Aloysius Regional School, NY

Baseball

Baseball
Fun, active
Running, hitting, pitching
Derek Jeter is amazing!
Yankees

Jennifer Perez Pimentel, Grade 6
Caroline G Atkinson School, NY

The Whole World

Because "homeless" people and "foodless" people need shelter.
I will give them shelter
I will give them food
I will give them lots of stuff to keep them busy for a while.
The people will be happy. They will have hope inside themselves!
They will live!
I did something right
I would feel proud because lots of people do not have homes, they could die
If I could give the whole entire world a chance to have everything they need
I would keep them safe!

Adrien Hungria, Grade 5
New York Institute for Special Education, NY

My Mom and My Family

My mom makes my world a better place
by calming me down and letting me talk about my feelings.

She always listens to me when I am sad.
She also does fun things for me like buying me DS games and Wii games.

My father also makes my world a better place because
he loves me so much and he is always there for me.

There are many people in my life who love me and make my world better.

Kevin Araujo, Grade 5
New York Institute for Special Education, NY

Solo

The curtain opens
I am alone center stage
I feel the intense heat of the spotlight
This feeling is what I live for
A plethora of voices chant "Sing!"
My mouth opens to reveal a voice as sweet as honey
The song ends
The curtain closes
The spotlight is off
Tearing myself away from center stage, I feel an emptiness inside my heart

Kayla Simmons, Grade 6
Westampton Middle School, NJ

Poppy

Poppy is my grandpa's name,
His real name is Sal.
Poppy is funny, cool and plays silly games with me
He makes me cards for my birthday and puts money in them as a gift
He makes the best snacks for me when I get home from school,
Usually pasta or soppresata and cheese!
On Sundays, we have dinner with him at his house.
When we are all sitting at the table he makes funny jokes
And uses weird words and makes us all laugh!
My poppy is really cool!

Guiliana DiBernardo, Grade 5
New York Institute for Special Education, NY

Halloween Fun
The green witch's face
As green as leaves on trees in the summer.

The flowing wings of an angel
As white as clouds on a cool spring day.

Jack-o-lanterns glowing in the dark
Like the sun in the early morning.

The pirate boy had a beard
As black as the darkest night.
Gianna Brucato, Grade 5
Ridgeway Elementary School, NJ

Halloween Fright Night
A bag filled with candy
As heavy as a colossal pumpkin

Going up to a door knocking loudly
Like a woodpecker on a tree

Rows of decorated houses
Like haunted houses from movies

Eating your Halloween treats
As if you were a shark consuming a fish
Basil Preston Meehan King, Grade 6
Ridgeway Elementary School, NJ

An Adventure
More than words
More than pages
More than a title
The sound
Of music
The feeling of home
The page flips
Ever so gently
An adventure
Bigger than the solar system,
Books
Annie Zomback, Grade 5
Saw Mill Road School, NY

Fall
Fall is near,
It's almost here.
Summer's almost gone,
And school's just begun.

Fall is near,
It's almost here.
The days are shorter,
And Halloween's around the corner.
Gail Cabahug, Grade 6
All Saints Catholic Academy, NY

Thanksgiving
Oh, how the hunters hunt for turkey
I think they taste like jerky
People think they're swell
so eat them I might as well.
The yams are really yummy,
and ham does fill my tummy
It could someday be a hit,
because it doesn't taste like spit.
I really like cabbage,
because it doesn't taste like garbage
Thanksgiving is my favorite holiday,
but I wish it were held in May.
Sincere Ervin, Grade 5
Hillside Elementary School, NJ

Pie Time of the Year
When I opened my eyes,
I saw three pumpkin pies!
I saw running deer,
Which meant fall was near.
I had a twitch in my eye,
And saw four apple pies!
I saw the changing leaves
Right by the bare trees.
I was wondering why
As I saw six coconut custard pies!
Now I couldn't believe my eyes
As I saw a turkey pecking at my pies!
Joseph Manno, Grade 6
St Rose of Lima Academy, NJ

Angels
When you sleep, the angels wake.
Their day is just beginning.
When you fall asleep in bed,
The angels start their singing.

They make you feel so peaceful
And give you fantastic dreams.

But when you yawn and rise from bed
And open your weary eyes,
That's when angels disappear
But are always at your side.
Charlotte MacKay, Grade 6
Regina Coeli School, NY

The Fish
I lower the hook into the water.
Then I feel a tug so hard,
It pulls the boat.
I pull back as hard as I can.
I reel it in quickly.
I just caught myself a salmon dinner.
Charlie McElwee, Grade 4
Lincoln Park Elementary School, NJ

Bicycle
I feel free
Just riding my bicycle
Not worrying about anything
As the wind mops my hair back.

Easily pedaling
Clenching on tightly
Never losing grip
Legs starting to ache
But never going to stop.

Heart beating
All good thoughts absorb like a sponge
Bad thoughts fade away.

Silence wraps my street like a present
Winds rushing
Fierce breezes blanket everyone
Leaves crumpling, dispersing in tiny pieces
I take a short glimpse at what's around me
Never wanting to stop
Savoring this moment forever.
Emma Gold, Grade 4
Norman J. Levy Lakeside School, NY

Pasta
Pasta, pasta
Ooh-la-la
In a French Café
Twirl it,
Swirl it,
It dances in my belly
Like a ballerina.
Bring more with cheese.
I could eat a million plates
As beautiful as the Mona Lisa.
Carolyne Chang, Grade 4
Concord Road Elementary School, NY

My Mom Is Baking!
My mom is baking
Oh my, oh my
Is it cookies?
How about a cake?
If I eat too much
I will end up with a
tummy ache
Is it pie?
Oh, I would just die!
Is it chocolate candy?
Oh so divine!
My mom is baking
So sweet and tasty
I love her baking!
Bre'Anna McQueen, Grade 6
Graham Elementary School, NY

The Big Softball Game

Softball is my favorite sport,
together we are a formidable force.
Crack, the ball hit the bat,
never seen something quite like that.

Balls flying high, as tall as the trees,
here they come one, two three.
Running, running, running through the bases,
the runner never stops through her paces.

"Hooray! Hoorah!" says the crowd
as the runner touches the plate, it sure is loud.
The players on the field all drop to their knees,
As they see the runner past base three.

"We won! We won!" said the team.
The others thought they were just being mean.
"Good game. Good game" the winners say.
"We can all play again another day"

Kiaraa Fulton, Grade 6
Westampton Middle School, NJ

Friends

You make me smile,
When I was about to cry.
You always go the extra mile,
Instead of walking on by.

You make my life complete,
But, what have I done for you?
You are the people, who make my heart still beat,
Even when there is nothing for you I can do.

You are the one that keeps me going,
When I want to stop.
I hope our friendship keeps on flowing,
I don't want our friendship bubble to pop!

I don't want you to leave me,
And I will not leave you.
We are friends, because that is what is meant to be,
I hope we stay friends forever, just me and you!

Samantha Miscedra, Grade 6
Regina Coeli School, NY

Fall

In the woods are scary trees
We are looking in the night
What is it that my dog sees
I can't even find a light
So I went to turn right
With a big fright
But I found another dog in the night
And I finally found a light

Noah Tatun, Grade 4
R.J. McNulty Academy for International Studies and Literacy, NY

In Flanders Fields

In Flanders Fields the poppies grow,
In big holes in the ground.
Cheering up soldiers, the poppies let them know,
They're here for them.
The birds sing proudly while guns blow loudly,
The poppies let soldiers know,
They're here for them.
The poppies burst colors, red, black and yellow.
The soldiers feel the pride they have,
And burst it out,
Boom! Boom! Bang!
Guns blow, losing soldiers.
Other soldiers carrying on the torch.
The poppies still grow, row by row.
More pride bursts out.
The guns stop,
The birds are heard,
The yelling stops.
The poppies still grow in Flanders Fields.

Deanna Kelly, Grade 4
Raynor Country Day School, NY

The Shift

He jumps out of the bench,
His skates hit the ice,
The player skates hard to the play,
Skates are cutting through the ice.

A pass hits his stick,
The puck rolls off his stick as he makes a pass,
The crowd is cheering loud.

The puck gets taken,
He plays defense,
Now skating backwards,
Aggressively he steals the puck.

The player skates fast up the ice,
Avoids two defenders,
Confidently takes a shot on the net,
The powerful shot is stopped by the goalie,
The referee blows the whistle and the shift ends.

Charlie DiPasquale, Grade 6
Sts Peter & Paul School, NY

A Day with My Grandpa

I can't wait for my papa to call;
Maybe we'll go play some ball.
He makes me happy when I fall.
Maybe we'll go to the mall.
He would get me anything,
Even if I wanted a diamond ring.
I love my papa every day.
I can't wait until we can go outside and play.

Steven Valad, Grade 4
Holy Family School, NY

Ornament
Blue, sparkly
Swings, bounces, shines
Brightens up my Christmas tree!
Glass ball
Kaila Corgliano, Grade 4
Ethel M Burke Elementary School, NJ

Nail Polish
Sparkly, purple
Splatters, washes, dries
Hands look pretty for days!
Finger paint
Waliya Rahman, Grade 4
Ethel M Burke Elementary School, NJ

Zain
Nice, tall
Playing, talking, picking
Has black hair
Friend
Purvish Patel, Grade 4
Ethel M Burke Elementary School, NJ

Poinsettia
Red, beautiful
Grows, lives, soothes
Flowering at Christmas!
Plant
Jean Fernandez, Grade 4
Ethel M Burke Elementary School, NJ

Maxine
Fluffy, smooth
Jumps, digs, barks
Snores like my mom!
My dog
Julia Falchetta, Grade 4
Ethel M Burke Elementary School, NJ

Trees
Brown, tall
Gives out oxygen, moves, grows leaves
Very cool looking!
Bush
Firas Nasir, Grade 4
Ethel M Burke Elementary School, NJ

Fall
The old earth is changing,
The seasons turn 'round.
The autumn leaves flutter,
Their way to the ground.
Gian Mission, Grade 6
All Saints Catholic Academy, NY

Life
Life is a glass pane,
Occasionally, it falls on its own onto the dark, cold floor of death,
And occasionally, it gives in to the howling thunderstorm of the night.
But sometimes, the greedy will strike it down with the mortal hammer,
However the glass cracks, it is no longer there in the window pane.

Life is a pillar,
Atop the pillar sits our mind, our soul, our hearts, and our will in one large dome.
The lone pillar is as strong as all of the forces,
It will forever hold the dome safely, and lift the values inside away from attackers.
It can give the dome a chance to stand tall and defiant for the whole world,
And when the dome becomes concave and implodes,
The pillar crumbles, once and for all.

Life is a flame,
The flame is started when needed,
Put out when not needed,
And cherished by you and others for the warmth of all.
Jason Russack, Grade 6
Great Meadows Middle School, NJ

Suicidal Thoughts*
I am a boy from Rutgers University
An excuse to make fun of me is because of my diversity
People think I'm mental while others call it perversity
I don't know how God lets me go through this terrible adversity
Today I feel so very bad
I couldn't tell anybody not my mom or my dad
Why do people make fun of me just because I'm gay
Every person is different in their own different way
Somebody posted that video and I know who did it
Now it's on the internet and I can't get rid of it
People make fun of me on my Facebook account
I'll write a post so that people will find out
It'll read "Today is the day that I will die"
While the people that bullied me think "Why, Why, Why!?"
Soon I will jump off the George Washington Bridge
I'll post this so people will know I wasn't crazy when I fell off that ledge
Nevyn Duarte, Grade 6
Woodrow Wilson School, NJ
*Dedicated to Tyler Clementi

The Maud Abrams Band
The long clarinet easily squeaks in a loud music room.
A little class performs perfectly every Wednesday.
The Christmas concert happily entertains on the stage!
A talented music teacher carefully demonstrates every day.
The shiny keys softly click once in a while.
A massive song nicely flows outside of the room.
The fast fingers on the trumpet swiftly move at 8:00 am for a morning practice.
A silver flute of a practicing child quietly peeps in the bedroom.
The giant trombone painfully moans on the floor.
A sturdy music stand joyfully helps in the practice room, and
The gold saxophone quickly blows in a spring concert.
Lily A. MacDonald, Grade 4
Maud Abrams Elementary School, NJ

My Spring Time
When spring called me forth
That time came for new life to come,
My life!

Her eyes were waiting for the exact moment
The moment I was born.
Spring came into both of our eyes.
Love and peace were in her soft, warm arms.

We bask in the sun
Our lives had intertwined
Like a perfect morning sun
Our lives have gone on

Spring has left us
When dark clouds obscure the sun
Her light shines forth
I remember my spring time.

Michael Bellion, Grade 5
Buckley Country Day School, NY

The Good Old Days
Sometimes I remember the good old days.

Making buildings out of multicolored blocks
in fantastic Kindergarten.

Shark's cartilage as squishy and flexible as a bean bag,
reading nonfiction in second grade was enjoyable.

Running around as fast as a cheetah and playing tag
all through the years in Duffield.

Creating art masterpieces using greasy oil pastels,
messy paint, and colorful markers.

Composing music performances in groups
with our marvelous singer Mr. Nagle.

I still can't imaging anything better than that!

Dylan Macejko, Grade 5
Helen B Duffield Elementary School, NY

Winter
I see the last leaf on a tree,
As it slowly starts to fall,
The others are as empty as a hollow log,
The weather becomes bitter and I really start to shiver,
All the leaves are gone,
And it slowly snows at dawn,
The ground is a white baby blanket.
All the children play,
They don't forget that day,
That winter came to town.

Evan Chaladoff, Grade 5
Hillside Elementary School, NJ

Silent Prisoner
I shiver and I shake
I can't sleep, I stay awake
The scratches on my feet burn
Freedom is what I yearn
Why do people treat me bad?
What did I do wrong to be so sad?
It's not fair that I can't speak
It's really just kindness that I seek

I'm a prisoner that's never free
A lone soul without a family
I cry and whine, though it does no good
I might never be understood
I believe that being treated well is right
Everyone should believe in fairness, not fight

I'm an animal but I have feelings too,
Treating pets humanely is what people should do
Shelters can help me find a second home
Somewhere I don't stay in a cage, a place I can roam
Adopt an animal at the shelter today,
Find a home for a pet to stay

Nicole Chiang, Grade 5
Pine Bush Elementary School, NY

Changing the World
No more bullying,
Bullying hurts.
No more teasing,
Teasing gives people low self-esteem.
No more fighting,
It's very harmful.
No more stealing,
It makes people worried.
No more lying,
It's not trustworthy.
No more hatred!
Why can't we all get along?

Rayvonne Acosta, Grade 6
New York Institute for Special Education, NY

Stars at Night*
11 stars shine so bright.
To me it's a spectacular sight.
Wonder how you look so beautiful.
Makes me feel so wonderful.
Whoosh! Whoosh! The wind blows hard.
You look like you could blow very far.
That land! That land!
Gets good breeze and the ground is sand.
I love your painting.
Thank you for inspiring me,
Vincent Van Gogh.

Kailah Turner, Grade 5
Roosevelt Elementary School, NJ
*Inspired by "Starry Night" by Vincent Van Gogh

Wolves

Wolves are giant dogs
Meat-loving canines in woods
Wolves, dominant dogs
Jordan Thompson, Grade 4
Catherine A Dwyer Elementary School, NJ

Birds

Chirping loud at dawn
soaring through sky high or low
Lots and lots of birds.
Alexia Symak, Grade 4
Catherine A Dwyer Elementary School, NJ

Spooky Owls

It sleeps during day
It hunts and eats at nighttime
A nocturnal owl
Nicholas Miller, Grade 4
Catherine A Dwyer Elementary School, NJ

Birds, Birds Everywhere

Birds fly to the sky
Birds can be different colors
Birds tweet and kaw-kaw
Tyler Johnson, Grade 4
Catherine A Dwyer Elementary School, NJ

Summer Heat

Summer heat scorches
Melting the freezing ice cubes
Get them while they last
Thomas Foody, Grade 4
Catherine A Dwyer Elementary School, NJ

Summer

Watch the green, green grass
in the slow, cool summer breeze.
I love the summer.
Isabella Doherty, Grade 4
Helderberg Christian School, NY

Birds

I see a few birds.
I see blue, brown, and black birds.
Birds chirp, peep, and squawk.
Maxim Nikolovski, Grade 4
Catherine A Dwyer Elementary School, NJ

The White Board

We have a white board.
We write sentences on it.
Then we erase it.
Anthony Rufa, Grade 4
Helderberg Christian School, NY

Bravery

Bravery is sacrifice.
Sacrifice is willing to give your life for someone else.
Sacrifice is putting your life on the line for other people.
Sacrifice is putting yourself in danger to help others.

Bravery is independence.
Independence is not being afraid to stand up for yourself.
Independence is doing what you want and not giving in to peer pressure.
Independence is liking what you want and not what others want you to like.

Bravery is perseverance.
Perseverance is not backing down when it gets tough.
Perseverance is ignoring obstacles in your way.
Perseverance is helping others when the situation looks difficult.

Bravery is strength.
Strength is helping others.
Strength is accomplishing things that the normal human cannot do.
Strength is following your heart even in the toughest situations.
Eddie O'Melia, Grade 6
Great Meadows Middle School, NJ

Dancing in the Wind

I spotted a peppery red smooth leaf.
It gracefully dances with the wind doing a couple of
impressive flips and somersaults.
I follow it around wondering where its next destination will be.
I carelessly step on multicolored pieces of old
wrinkled-up paper, hearing the crunch with each step I take.

I feel the breezy wind reach my skin with a frigid sharp strength, freezing
my whole body. I fill up with excitement, wondering if this is now a great
adventure through a windy forest, wondering where the leaf will take me.

I taste the piercing cold air in my mouth. I continue to follow the quick
flying leaf. As the wind starts bursting, I spring to catch up to the leaf as it
continues to gracefully dance.

As it takes me into the busy town, I was able to smell the
cinnamon-apple-scented bakery. Now
tired of all the dancing, the peppery red leaf falls and joins the
multicolored mountain of leaves.
Phoebe Richiez, Grade 6
Slocum Skewes School, NJ

What America Means to Me

What America means to me
We live in the land of the free, a place where it's okay to simply be me.
A place where dreams are made to come true,
A place that's free for me and you.
Our troops fight for our freedom every day,
We need to give thanks in every way.
Thank you for my freedom and opportunities galore,
I'm going to do you proud and much, much more!
Devin Ramos, Grade 6
Westampton Middle School, NJ

My Bike

I can't wait to get home
I want to ride my bike
School's finally done
I can't wait to ride with my friend Mike

Mike and I have a race
Down the street we go
We look like zooming cheetahs
As we pass our good friend Joe

My bike is black with the word Spit-Fire
With little blotches of red
When you see my bike coming
My friend will be up ahead

Some people think my bike is fast
Some think that it is slow
I often get a little confused
I guess I'll never know
Jack Jones, Grade 4
Little Falls School #3, NJ

Anticipation

Going on vacation
Yay! Can' wait
I'm so excited
It's going to be great

I'm packing up
Got everything I need
I'm going to the Bahamas
This trip is guaranteed

There's going to be water
And a lot of sun too
Can't wait to go
I have so much to do

I'm ready
It's going to be a good day
I'm in the car
Hooray!
Elizabeth Kapelevich, Grade 4
Little Falls School #3, NJ

Boys…

They make you laugh,
They make you cry,
They make you smile,
They make you fly,
They make you feel special,
They make you want to die,
They make you fall,
Till one day they just say bye bye.
Jesenia Cueto, Grade 4
Terence C Reilly School #7, NJ

Poppies

Poppies growing in a field,
In a foreign land.
Soldiers in a far off place,
Sailor on the sea.

You left your home to make the world
A better place for me.
Poppies waving in the breeze,
In a foreign land,

Soldiers and sailors want to fight
So we could take a stand.
Today, I wear a poppy
To say thank you that I'm free.
Alexander Smith, Grade 4
Raynor Country Day School, NY

Bicycle

As I fly through the wind
Like a cheetah charging to its prey
I'm unstoppable
I'm invincible
And no one can catch me
Faster than the speed of light, I race cars
Quicker than a blinking of an eye
I pass people
Cars seem as slow as tortoises
Like a ninja, I keep my balance
I look right
I look left
Before I know it
I'm home in the blink of an eye.
Max Abramowitz, Grade 4
Norman J Levy Lakeside School, NY

A Spring's Day

During spring there's always one day,
That is the best of them all,
The sun is out,
The weather is just right,
The animals are out,
Birds are chirping,
Plants are growing,
Everyone is happy and excited,
Many people pick flowers,
Also other fruits and vegetables,
People buy air conditioners,
In stores buying clothes,
And getting ready for a new season,
Which is called summer.
Maciej Jablonowski, Grade 6
St Stanislaus Kostka Academy School, NY

Stress

I must confess,
This feeling of Stress.

I feel like a mess,
With this feeling of Stress.

I feel like taking a rest,
From this feeling of Stress.

Should I feel like a guest,
To this feeling of Stress?

Or should I go on a quest,
To stop this feeling of Stress?

I HATE this Stress,
I said as I confessed!
Freya Peters, Grade 6
Willow Grove Middle School, NY

Exception of Life

Life is like a big balloon
you don't know when it could pop.
In other words it could be good
and then your life could drop.
But it's okay as we say
stuff isn't always right.
You can be glad or even stay mad.
But know, "That's just life."

We laugh and cry and scream and sigh
but most of time we smile,
But don't let sadness overcome you,
happiness should be your style.
So if your life's plans don't turn around
don't let life get you down,
Hold your head up and lose the frown
and know, "That's just life."
Maiya Holmes, Grade 6
Westampton Middle School, NJ

His Winter Day

He fell in the snow
He is stuck, stumped, slumped
He feels angry.
Raging, craving to go wild.
I felt mild when I saw him.
He was ready to blow like a bomb!
I was about to scream, "MOM!!"
He went crazy!
He got up,
Cried, and went inside.
That's how he spent
His winter day.
Emily Plevritis, Grade 4
James A. Dever Elementary School, NY

Jump-Roping
Today I was jump-roping
Clicketty clack smack
Unfortunately I couldn't keep track,
So, next thing I knew the sink I was soaping,
Not jump-roping!!!

Elysa McHugh, Grade 5
Catherine A Dwyer Elementary School, NJ

Blue
Blue sounds like raindrops pouring down everywhere.
Blue is the sight of a blue ball flying in the air.
Blue is the taste of a blueberry yogurt dripping down your throat.
Blue is the smell of blueberry pancakes on a Sunday morning.
Blue is the feeling of waves hitting my feet.

Jonathan Fernandes, Grade 4
PS/MS 207 Q, NY

Aunt Maureen
Neon animal prints delight exotically on her shirt!
Crazy diamonds glow brightly in the sun!
Sweaty gym training provides strength while pumping iron!
Thin hair straightens warmly in the bathroom!
Colorful makeup applies lightly creating art!

Jade DeLuca, Grade 4
Maud Abrams Elementary School, NJ

Thinking of You
Red poppies as a symbol to remember our veterans.
White crosses marking those who have died,
When I see both,
I will be thankful to you,
Our heroes of the red, white and blue.

Brianna Van de Wetering, Grade 4
Raynor Country Day School, NY

All About Dance
Beautiful dance teacher demonstrates gracefully in class
Shining costumes sparkle brightly on stage
Colossal dance studio holds strongly in the ground
Comfortable mat cushions luxuriously in the studio
Wonderful crowds clap blaringly in their seats.

Sara McNeal, Grade 4
Maud Abrams Elementary School, NJ

Bullying Hurts
I would stop all kids from bullying.
We need to teach kids to get along with each other
and use words instead of violence.
If kids have a problem, get an adult to work it out.
If only everyone knew this the world would be a better place!

Daryl Correa, Grade 4
New York Institute for Special Education, NY

A Moment in Time
I sit on the rug while the snow stands there clear
My time is limited, I know it's coming near
I sit, frozen next to a tear,
Not a thought in my head
I'm at the edge of fear
No toe-tapping, finger-snapping music to hear,
Just me and my thoughts, who whisper in my ear.

Lia Barning, Grade 6
Windward School, NY

Seasons
S nowy winter
E ver green spring
A lways sunny summer
S o many leaves in the fall
O h these seasons
N ever
S top!

Ayana Cintron, Grade 5
Tecler Arts in Education Magnet School, NY

Fall
I love baking
And climbing trees
And I love raking
And jumping in the leaves
I love apple picking
I love fall!

Brianna Jones, Grade 4
R.J. McNulty Academy for International Studies and Literacy, NY

Dare to Dream
If you dare to dream, you can do anything.
Just remember, if you can't dream…
You can still do everything and anything with your dreams.
Your parents will set you free to be who you want to be,
And they'll understand and believe what you can be
And be on your side dead or alive.

Alyssa Swartz, Grade 5
Tecler Arts in Education Magnet School, NY

My Mom
My mom is a hardworking woman
She wants to make a good living
She tries to feed me and my brother
I feel that she is a great worker
And that's the story of my hardworking mom

Lorenzo George, Grade 5
Public School 114 Ryder Elementary, NY

Take Off!
Start the propellers
Speed down the long black runway
Take off and fly high!

Nicholas Bertos, Grade 5
Dickinson Avenue Elementary School, NY

Best Friends for Never (Was It Meant to Be?)

She left me in the dark,
Nowhere to go.
Being best friends for 3 years,
Didn't help her know?

Now, when I see her in the hall,
She doesn't say anything at all.
If I'm lucky I'll get a "hi" or the same strange stare.
But that is it.

Trying to reach her through the summer,
She didn't get my message.
What a bummer.
Now, she can suffer.

It's her loss.
So long friend.
You never seem to be fazed,
Until you finally found out there is no way out of this maze.
Goodbye. Forever.

Emily Schindler, Grade 6
Fords Middle School, NJ

Winter, Winter

Winter, winter let it come.
When fall is over it has begun.
With snow and ice and frosty bites,
We dance and sing with pure delight.
Off to the kitchen where mama makes
Our warm hot chocolate for us to drink.
Snowball fights and sledding too.
Down those frosty, white topped hills.
Sleigh rides through the town at night
And white covered trees with a glow just right.
All the animals have built their dens
And lay to rest until winter ends.
With their tummies full and minds on hold,
They lay fast asleep, no effect from the cold.
Winter, winter let it come.
I will be waiting for all the fun.
Please come quick, for I'll still be here.
I would not miss the fun and cheer.
Winter, winter I know you're near.
Pay a visit and I'll see you next year.

Kayla McBride, Grade 6
Holy Family School, NY

Yellow

Excitement,
Yellow like sunshine
A spring daisy,
It brightens my day
And flies through my mind…
Inescapable

Caitlyn Cannon, Grade 4
John G Dinkelmeyer Elementary School, NY

Autumn Is Colorful

A utumn is filled with color.
U npredictable weather.
T ime flies by!
U nlike winter, autumn has color.
M y family and I look at the colorful leaves.
N othing is better than seeing colors!

I like the rainbow of colors of autumn.
S tanding in leaf piles is fun!

C olors like rose red fill the trees.
O ver the trees, all I see is blue.
L ove the rich colors.
O n, the bushes leaves will fall.
R ed, orange, and yellow leaves are so pretty.
F un is jumping in leaf piles;
U ntidy leaf piles now.
L ovely pinks and red below my feet.

A rainbow all around me!

Nicole Cremin, Grade 5
St. Rose of Lima Academy, NJ

Life

Life is definitely a walk in the park,
But picking the right trails is the hard part,
So should I pick the wrong trail and be silly,
Or pick the right trail and be smart?
Some see life as a pretty, wonderful day,
With butterflies and flowers, a beautiful day to play,
But others see life as a thunderstorm; with bolts of lightning,
They don't come out because they think life is very frightening.
The choice is up to you,
A beautiful day or not,
I know it's a big decision,
And it really means a lot.
Just remember we aren't perfect,
And that life isn't a bad place,
Just try to pick the right trails,
But go at your own pace.
It doesn't matter how far you dig yourself in a ditch,
Because you can always get out,
Just believe in yourself and life,
And have no doubt!

Daniella Devaney, Grade 6
Willow Grove Middle School, NY

Summer Winds

The summer winds were blowing and the sand was flying
The water was cold but calm
I swam for hours with only the sound of birds
The waves were dancing with joy
Another joyful summer day went by
And I rested waiting for another great day

Jack Dombrowski, Grade 6
Sts Peter & Paul School, NY

Camping

I love sitting around the campfire.

The tent is thin as a pretzel stick
rolling side to side
On the blowup end, under the blanket
cozy and warm
I sink into my pillow.

Morning breakfast on the griddle smells of
greasy bacon and sizzling eggs
I love the sound of the crackling fire
and
the smell of the chocolate melting
between hot marshmallows
as the marshmallows oooooze out of graham
crackers…s'mores…yum!

I LOVE CAMPING!

Danielle Corrao, Grade 4
Norman J Levy Lakeside School, NY

Life

Do you sometimes
f
  e
   e
    l
you're doing something wrong
but
it's right?
I mean the
sharp, edged knife
that stabs
you in the back
every once and a while.
The glass your foot
steps on
Is not always fair
Not everyone gets…
Life

Jada Nunez, Grade 6
Graham Elementary and Middle School, NY

Oc-snow-ber

Once happy jack o' lanterns on the church lawn
Were now wearing white caps with the rising dawn
Icy snow had blown in
Tragically wiping off jack's grin
Those round orange pumpkins hoping to be sold
Were now sad faces shriving in the cold
Oh, what fun they could have brought
If only they had been bought
We thought we could have had our pick
But Mother Nature played a Halloween trick!

Katie Weikl, Grade 6
Slocum Skewes School, NJ

Fall to Winter

Fall days filled with color
Never seem to change to winter
Raking leaves is coming close
To nights where fireplaces burn all night
From fall to winter comes the bitter cold change
Along with days growing short
Waiting for the first sight of snow
Ready to build a snowman
The thrill of winter around the corner
Knowing the holidays are near
All the excitement that fall is here
Until it comes around next year

Krissy Weikl, Grade 6
Slocum Skewes School, NJ

Marshmallows

M aking s'mores
A t camp
R acing with friends
S torytelling
H iking in the woods
M aking shadow puppets
A ll together
L istening to campfire songs
L ooking at the stars
O ff to our tents
W earing pajamas
S leeping in sleeping bags

Ivy Dulysz, Grade 5
Tecler Arts in Education Magnet School, NY

Fall

Today is a fun day.
I see lots of leaves.
Maybe I have football practice on Monday.
That's a very huge, colorful tree.
I am worried about Sunday.
We'll be playing against an awesome team.
I can't wait until Monday.
Sometimes I get nervous it seems.
Tomorrow I am going out raking.
The leaves are crunching.
Tomorrow my mom is baking.
And cookies I will be munching.

Michael Henderson, Grade 4
R.J. McNulty Academy for International Studies and Literacy, NY

Winter!

W inter is a time of year when all creatures are in bed.
I n their homes they lay until the sun comes out again.
N ear their homes they have food so they don't die in pain.
T hey love to look at the plain white snow and hope it does not rain.
E ven in the minds of creatures that walk on Earth today,
R emember the time of season when the snow comes out to play!

Aidan Fischer, Grade 5
Dickinson Avenue Elementary School, NY

Happiness

Happiness is a gem that sparkles in the sun
When you feel happy it feels like you sparkle
You feel as light as air
As you skip under the crystal-clear sky.

Happiness is a chest full of mysteries
No one knows why someone is happy
Happiness occurs with no warning
Happiness is a mysterious thing.

Happiness is a magical feeling
When you are happy you feel like flying
Happiness is something you can't control
Happiness happens magically.

Happiness is a joyous thing
Sometimes it comes with laughter
Sometimes it comes with crying
And other times it comes with both.

Zoe Eberhart, Grade 6
Great Meadows Middle School, NJ

Trust

Trust is like a big tree of life,
Many branches reaching out from the core.
Sometimes there are new branches growing,
sometimes branches are snapping.

Trust is like a pillow,
Protecting you from lies.
But it can also be like spikes,
If you fall into too many lies.

Trust is like glass,
It is very fragile.
But if you use it the wrong way,
It will shatter.

Trust is like the American flag,
Waving in the sky with pride.
Because it is so glorious,
It will never divide.

Kimberly Sharp, Grade 6
Great Meadows Middle School, NJ

Starry Night*

The stars are so bright;
it's like the sun itself is shining over the village.
It's a breezy night in the small village.
The crescent shaped moon is
as bright as the stars.
Every person is in a deep sleep
in the middle of the night.

Eric Jones, Grade 5
Roosevelt Elementary School, NJ
*Inspired by "Starry Night" by Vincent Van Gogh

A Broken Heart

A broken heart is walking on broken glass,
it's a struggle to not scream,
it hurts so bad you just want to cry out in pain,
and once it heals, your heart will never be the same.

A broken heart is pie,
as the time goes by,
pieces slowly leave,
then the pie will never be whole again.

A broken heart is a book with pages missing,
you can't tell when it's going to end,
or you miss the best part,
and you can't feel complete.

A broken heart is being Pluto (the dwarf plant),
you feel like a tiny, cold essence,
you are so far away from Earth,
and on the edge of the universe.

Robin Schmeltzle, Grade 6
Great Meadows Middle School, NJ

Ballroom Dancing Is My Dream

Ballroom dancing is what I like to do
Wearing a pretty dress and high heels too
I like to dance in front of a big crowd
Because that always makes me feel so proud

I really like the costumes, the makeup, and mostly the hair
But it takes such a long time to do, I swear
I've been to many interesting places
Like Canada, California and have seen many famous faces

When I grow up I want to be on Dancing with the Stars
To win lots of money and buy some expensive cars
For the world to know just who I am
And for my sister to win a grand slam

In the future after my college days
I would like to go my separate ways
To open a studio and make it the best
And to bring in a pro, a famous guest

Vanesa Falisova, Grade 5
Little Falls School #1, NJ

The Great Orange

On the outside, you look like a round, yellow, orangish sun.
You feel like a soft, comfy, pillow.
When I peel you, you sound like crunchy leaves in the fall.
When I slice you, you sound like juice pouring into my cup.
Inside, you look like veins in my arm.
You smell like my mom's perfume.
You taste like sweet and sour sauce.
Tell me, why do you smell like perfume?

Erikka Chester, Grade 5
Roosevelt Elementary School, NJ

My Bicycle

Suddenly the wind shifts me over
My hair blows over my face
The wheels beneath me glide smoothly on the road

The long road is ahead of me
I feel free and unstoppable
I whisper to myself
Faster, faster, keep peddling, never stop!

Teeth shivering and clanging against each other
Heart beating as fast as a cheetah
Just wanna keep going
Running a race in the concrete jungle.

Brandon Wexler, Grade 4
Norman J Levy Lakeside School, NY

A Colorful Season

Fall is here, so colorful and bright.
The leaves float peacefully on to the ground,
And perfect plump pumpkins are easily found.

They're turned into Jack-o-lanterns so spooky
They light up the night,
And fill kids with Halloween fright.

As children scurry through the dark,
Dry leaves in their path are crunched
While sweet candy is happily munched.
Until a stomach ache appears.
Happy Halloween!

Jason Smith, Grade 5
Liberty School, NJ

Stuffed Up with Stuffing

T hanksgiving is a holiday for peace, and
H aving friends and family over for a feast.
A turkey filled with delicious stuffing, there's
N othing better, I'm not bluffing.
K icking back with lots of food to eat,
S o many courses, then it's time for a special treat.
G ather around for some pumpkin pie,
I feel like I'm going to die!
V arious pies, cakes, and fruit galore,
I nside, my stomach can't fit any more!
N ext year, I'll try to level my appetite my dear,
G ood thing…Thanksgiving comes only once a year!

Karol Ferreira, Grade 6
Riverside Middle School, NJ

The Song's Rhythm

The song's rhythm is like the beauty in the sky,
A husband's wife is like God's angels,
A teacher's students is like a dog who you have told new tricks to,
And a poet's poem is like John Henry's hammers and his railroad.

Gary Robinson, Grade 5
Hillside Elementary School, NJ

Fall

Roses are red
Violets are blue.
I love the fall
and so should you.
I love the fall and I'll tell you why
as long as you promise not to say good-bye.

I love the fall because it rocks.
I also love it because it's my birthday month.
I love to jump in piles of leaves.
Now you see why fall is so fun to me.

Lauren Washko, Grade 5
Dickinson Avenue Elementary School, NY

A Walk Down Winter Lane

Snow is covering the ground
Like a giant blanket

Snow white rabbits searching for food
Like robbers looking for something to steal

Snowflakes hitting against my cheeks feel
Like sharp pieces of cold metal

Decorated snowman on my front lawn looking
Like a million bucks

Christopher Mecca, Grade 5
Ridgeway Elementary School, NJ

Mega Lime

On the outside, you look like a piece of grass on a field.
You feel like a rock I'm gripping tightly in my hand.
When I peel you, you sound like a bean pod being ripped.
When I slice you, you sound like a piece of lettuce being ripped from its ball.
Inside you look like a green orange fresh from growth.
You feel like a napkin that's just been made.
You smell like elegant perfume in a bottle.
You taste like sour gum in my mouth.
Tell me mega lime, do you like when people eat and use you in a drink? How does it feel?

Rogers Prudhomme, Grade 5
Roosevelt Elementary School, NJ

No Drugs

It is incomprehensible that anybody would want to do drugs.
You hurt not yourself but your friends and family.
You might get sick and die.
It's hard to stop.
So don't even try.
Keep Safe.
Join the fight.
Speak up.
Stop Drugs.

Matthew Rottaris, Grade 6
St Stephen's School, NY

Love
Love is a dove
So perfect and pure
It softens cold hearts
And chases away hate

Love is a curse
It hurts the most
To see the one you love
Love someone else

Love is a gift
It brings happiness and peace
Love is hurt
It fills you with sadness
And makes you want to love nevermore

Love can change the way you see the world
It can make your heart black or make it melt
Love can hurt you, love can heal you
You can hate it, you can love it

Love can be simple
It can be complex
But it will always just be
LOVE

Maddie Crisp, Grade 6
Great Meadows Middle School, NJ

So Which Religion Do You Choose?
There are many religions in the world
But God chose one for us to follow
Religion leads us to heaven and many glorious things
But if you want to know what religion I'm talking about, read on

This one religion is Islam
We people believe in it, with all our hearts
There is only one God and his messenger is Muhammad
Trust him, believe in God, because we know you are smart

So which religion do you choose?

Of all religions
The most common ones are: Christianity, Judaism, and Islam
It's okay if you are one of them
Because believing is eman (faith)

So which religion do you choose?

We pray day and night
For ourselves, the poor, and for you of course
We hope to die with faith and not get in the devil's path
For he has a mind no one should have

So which religion do you Choose?

Qainat Kashmiri, Grade 6
Al Ghazaly School, NJ

My Mother
My mother
She cooks,
She cleans,
She drinks,
She sends texts

My mother
She jumps,
She screams,
She laughs,
She cries,

My mother
She cares
She loves people
but most of all…
My mother
is all that matters!!!

Tajahanae Aiken, Grade 6
Graham Elementary and Middle School, NY

The Story of Hanukkah
Why are the kids jumping for joy?
Because they know they are getting a new toy.
But before we gather round the table,
Let me tell you a little fable.
I'll make this story short and not to bore,
Many years ago there was a great war.
The temple of Maccabees was burnt and knocked down,
There weren't any supplies left in the town.
The people were all worried and scared with fright,
As there was only enough oil for just one night,
So when the darkness came they lit the light,
As it burned and burned night after night.
For a total of eight days and nights, wow, oh boy,
Giving the people that last taste of joy.
So today we celebrate like the days in the past.
We light our own candle because just one won't last,
And the kids get gifts and Hanukkah gelt as treasure,
To remind us of how a light could give us so much pleasure.

Jake Temares, Grade 6
Shelter Rock Elementary School, NY

December
This is what December means to me:

D elicious food
E xciting
C hristmas
E lves
M istletoe
B ulbs
E gg nog
R eindeer

Courtney Lalla, Grade 5
Tecler Arts in Education Magnet School, NY

Rubik's Cube

It flosses your brain. It twists your mind.
A solution is what we hope to find…

Red, orange, green, white, yellow, blue
Like a colorful painting on a cube
The designs you can make are unlimited
Twist it, turn it, mix it up like trail mix
Wait, how do you put it back the other way?
Twist right? Left? Top? Bottom?
Does green go on this side? What about red?
Is this even possible?

Hit it with a hammer and you solved it.
BOOM! BASH! Problem solved
Your brain goes *SQUISH* like a sponge
All day you twist it and turn it
At school, on the bus, in the shower, in bed
Don't pull out your hair, you can do it!
Is that it? Blue, yellow, white, green, orange, red…
Got it!

Harrison Tepe, Grade 6
Harold D. Fayette Elementary School, NY

Donations

How do I make our world a better place?
By donating.
My mom and I donate
A lot.
We donate too small clothes and
never been worn clothes.
Boots, shoes, sneakers. Things
that help people in need.

Canned food to the church soup kitchen.
Cakes my mom bakes. Anyone who
is hungry can
get a meal at the soup kitchen.

Once, we donated a car
for charity. "Kars4Kids!"

Let's work together.
Let's donate and
help each other.
L.J. Omar Reid-Yasin, Grade 6
New York Institute for Special Education, NY

Shadow

S hy
H appy
A wesome
D og hater
O dd
W eird

Kristi Greco, Grade 5
Tecler Arts in Education Magnet School, NY

The Moment

The stitched ball releases from the pitcher's hand,
the circular object flies over land.
The ball gets hit, there is a crack,
there is no turning back.
Round the bases, the fast man goes,
there is no hope if he slows.
He'll make it home, he will not fall.
And that's the run that wins baseball!

Ryan Thorpe, Grade 6
Shelter Rock Elementary School, NY

The Five Senses

Seeing is to believing
as feeling brings to comfort
Tasting reveals to mixed emotions
while smell brings to a new dimension
Hearing makes you feel exhausted
while these five senses make you feel confused
But this is all part of nature
and so are you

Antara Ahmed, Grade 6
Razi School, NY

Leaves of Telling

Wind curling around my face
Like a whisper trying to tell me Autumn is here
Colorful Autumn leaves swirling in the air
Like a rainbow after a thunderstorm
The fresh aroma of apple pie
Like the smell of grandma's house
My trusted friend and I raking colorful leaves
Like two peas in a pod

Lauren Lane, Grade 5
Ridgeway Elementary School, NJ

Seasons

Orange leaves sway in the breeze.
Snow falls as swiftly as rain.
Twigs grow from the moist spring ground.
Summer unleashes the sun's full rays.
Fall leads endeavor, preparing for first frost.
Winter leads the end, covering ground in ice.
Spring leads anew, making life and heat.
Summer leads beginnings, as a whole new cycle starts!

Joseph Conforto, Grade 4
Maud Abrams Elementary School, NJ

My Dream

It is hard for me to see,
how someone could change me.
I will never, ever quit, I will never stop.
I will keep on chasing my dream, I will never let it pop.
I'll just keep going forward, I won't ever turn back.
I'll just keep going forward, I will never stop.

Lily Bryan, Grade 5
Hillside Elementary School, NJ

Red, White and Blue
Red!
Hardiness
and
Valor

White!
Purity
and
Innocence

Blue!
Vigilance
and
Perseverance

The
American
Flag

America!
America!
A-mer-i-ca!
Codelia King, Grade 5
Public School 114 Ryder Elementary, NY

Baseball
I hit the ball as far as I can
Until I see the ball in the outfielder's hand.
I look in the stands surprised to see
That everyone is cheering for me.

I take my glove and warm up,
The batter then hits a pop up.
He's hitting it straight to me
I could catch it only if I could see,
I go to dive for the ball
I catch it then I fall.

The crowd's screaming and roaring,
The planes above are soaring.
I go into the dugout so happy,
Then I hear the crowd saying MVP.

I try again and hit it far,
The ball goes over the yellow bar.
We win the game because of me,
Then they announce I'm MVP.
Anthony Paolillo, Grade 5
Newbridge Road Elementary School, NY

A Stormy Night
On a stormy night
People were hiding in fright
As lightning struck the Earth
Drake Testa, Grade 5
Dickinson Avenue Elementary School, NY

My Name
According to the dictionary
Chloe means
Young grass
That is true
I do start out young
And grow
Through the years
But
There is so much more
Chloe means
A dancer who dances
In front of a mirror
Who will take chances
Chloe means one
Who loves nature
Making new friends every day
And
Much more to say
That is what
Chloe means
Chloe Shipley, Grade 4
Saw Mill Road Elementary School, NY

My World
Through the veil
If you look
Then you can see
It all
And if you do
I will welcome you
With opened arms
Come
Join me please
Open up the door
Step on through
With dancing and laughter
With a light heart
All your worries will cease
You will become light
All will happen
If you come
And if you do
I will welcome you
To my world
Brianna Cummings, Grade 6
Holy Innocents School, NJ

Fall
In the fall the leaves start to drop,
I can smell a sweet fragrance in the air.
It is apple pie, it is too hot,
But I don't care,
The fun in the fall,
Is without compare.
William Phillips, Grade 6
All Saints Catholic Academy, NY

Christmas Tree
I can't wait to go
Walking through the snow

Buying a Christmas Tree
No place I'd rather be

Placing it in the hall
Up against the wall

We had lots of fun
Our day is sadly done
Kayla Zelko, Grade 5
Bartle Elementary School, NJ

Bicycle
Riding my bicycle
Feeling the wind on my face
like a fan speeding
"whoosh"
Standing on my bike
pumping pedals
heart pumping
chains clanging
cars zooming by
I look around with eyes wide open
at the beautiful world around me.
Isaac Grama, Grade 4
Norman J Levy Lakeside School, NY

My Little American Doll, Samantha
Brown curly hair
White plain face
Watching me with those lovely eyes

Hugged her while we were in airplane
Bringing her from America
Always played with only Samantha

She is in Korea with my other dolls
Tears rolling down from her beautiful eyes
I miss you and I love you, Samantha…
Jisoo Jung, Grade 6
Buckley Country Day School, NY

Zombies
Zombies, zombies here and there
Zombies, zombies everywhere
Zombies comin' down the hall
Let us hope we don't fall!

Zombies ripping out our hearts
Zombies eating body parts
Zombies running in a bunch
Let's hope we're not their lunch.
Christopher Sabo, Grade 5
Liberty School, NJ

The First Day of School

It was the first day of school.
What should I do?
I had butterflies in my stomach.
I felt very sick.

Who is my teacher?
Is my teacher a girl or a boy?
All those questions were stuck in my head.
What should I do?

By the time it was 8:45, I was in school.
The next thing you know, I was in my new classroom.
Suddenly the butterflies in my stomach started to disappear.
I liked my new teacher, my old school, my friendly classmates, and also everything I was with.

School was fine.
What a fun day at school with my new classmates.
Will this happen next year?
Well I guess not.

Bing Lan Huang, Grade 5
Public School 130 The Desoto, NY

Sense-ational

Thank you
for all the sounds my ears can obtain —
the chatter of business and economy at our decadent Thanksgiving feast
desolate crackling of the campfire on a frosty night with the Boy Scouts
the stimulating crinkling of leaves on a brisk autumn day

Thank you
for the stupendous images which I envision —
the dazzling red and white fire trucks lined up like toys among the brave men that ride them
sunset glimmering on my dog's lustrous caramel coat
the looming shadow of a shark under the murky waters as it pulls my line away

Thank you
for the aromas that seem to last for eternity —
hickory wood smoldering in the fire pit
steam climbing to the sky from a frothy mug of hot cocoa
salty sea mist whooshing and hissing against my face as the boat charges into a royal blue abyss

How thankful I am

Richard Fizzuoglio, Grade 6
Oakdale-Bohemia Middle School, NY

Half an Hour with My Grandfather John Russell Hugill

One afternoon, I went to go see my Grandfather. He was right there where I left him, as he has been there 12 years. I walked through Fairview Cemetery cherishing the moments I get to spend with him. I talk to him, though the sky is between us. His body is below me. I feel comfort when he is near me. Even though I cannot see him, I pour out all my troubles for I know, somewhere, he is listening. I tell him what is happening with my life at school. He patiently listens. He is the only one who I feel can truly listen to my life story. I sit on his permanent memorial not meaning any disrespect, but as the wind blows the grass around me, I wonder, what would he have been like?

Ian Krager, Grade 6
Red Jacket Middle School, NY

Wonderful Orange

Orange is the color of a juicy orange that we like to eat
The color of a jack-o-lantern glowing on a Halloween night
The color of Mrs. Prakapas' pretty shirt
The color of the fat cat Garfield we all adore
The color of a beautiful sunset
The color of some coral reefs
The color of a dragon's flames
The color of an orange marker being used for an art project
The color of sweet lollipops that my sister likes to eat
The color of a basketball that my friends like to play with
The color of the cold, but not warm, western region
The color of Mrs. Prakapas' scissors
The color of a lion's mane
The color of the orange folder sitting by the window
Orange is the color
Etched in my mind for all time.

Dominic Markwant, Grade 4
Roosevelt Elementary School, NJ

The Tree of Mystery

The tree swaying in the brisk wind
Protecting squirrels in its hollow body
The sky darkening
Preparing for the moon and stars
The colorful leaves are jumping from the tree
Plummeting to the green wet ground
The thin branches suddenly
SNAP!
Under the force of the once calm but now gusty breeze
The fierce clear wind chilling the air
Detaching branches like scissors cutting paper
Soon the tree will stand tall and bare
But eventually will grow its little bushy friends
Called leaves and squirrels
The tree wonders why the leaves leave
And thinks it's because he's an old bare boring tree

Robby Tschiember, Grade 6
Harold D Fayette Elementary School, NY

Snow

It falls so graceful.
It's cold and makes me sniffle.

It's white and wet.
It's soft and fun to play in with a pet.

You can make a snow man
With stick hands.

It falls to the ground when a storm hits.
It's time to play in the snow with my warm mitts.

Watch it fall to the ground and make no sound.
I wish it could last all year round.

Kylee Marchena, Grade 6
Regina Coeli School, NY

A Guiding Hand

As the sun comes up I look at the window.
I see the light shining through.
I hear a soft voice calling my name.
I know my mom is there waiting for me.
I go to the breakfast table.
I smell the fresh bread.
I know my day will begin with a smile.
I know my mom is there waiting for me.
My days go flying by and before I know it.
I am on my way to college.
As I prepare to start a new chapter,
I know my mom is there waiting for me.
Four years of college have passed and I am on my own.
I get myself up, prepare my breakfast, get myself out the door.
For so many years I had a guiding hand.
And now I will be alone.

Nicole Rudzikewycz, Grade 6
St Stanislaus Kostka Catholic Academy, NY

Attitude Adjustment

I see frowns that need to be turned upside down.
I don't understand why we're all upset today.
All the bad choices we make,
all the bad things we say,
why are we always so grumpy with each other?

We need to change our attitudes; yeah that's right.
We need to change them and make it right!
I'm sick and tired of the negative vibes we translate all day.

If we change our attitudes, we'll do our best.
If we do our best, we'll past our test.

There's no need to be grumpy because we have friends,
and we should never ever forget our blessings.
We need to turn our frowns into smiles.

Breena Dorsett, Grade 4
Icahn Charter School 3, NY

Thanksgiving

Family is coming over for Thanksgiving
Cousins jump out of gray Toyota
He sees my broad smile
We play football.
Leather ball spirals towards me
I reach and pig skin touches smooth hands
Touchdown!
We go inside. I smell Thanksgiving dinner.
I wash my hands and see cold water rush down drain.
My mouth waters
Turkey, gravy, corn, stuffing, sweet potatoes
Taste sweet potatoes with marshmallows.
Cousins leave, faces turn into frowns
Thinking can't wait until we're together again!

William Kilada, Grade 6
Harold D Fayette Elementary School, NY

Summer

Sun bobbing,
Sand glows
It's summer,
Feel the thrill.
Yeah
Hot, sweating.
Ian D'Angiolillo, Grade 4
Catherine A Dwyer Elementary School, NJ

Family

Awesome, fun
Laughing, hugging, talking
Families are people to cherish
Loving, caring, sharing
Sweet, helpful
Family
Lauren LaRocco-Edwards, Grade 6
Our Lady of Good Counsel School, NY

My Flea

I have a little flea,
He is attached to me,
Everywhere I go,
He always puts on a show.
I hope one day he will find some place new,
Maybe he will even go on you.
Ariel Ingersoll, Grade 5
Hillside Elementary School, NJ

Crisp Autumn

A stonishing autumn leaves
U nique hanging colorful leaves
T errific jack-o-lanterns
U nparalleled trick-or-treating
M arveling Halloween treat
N ice bold leaves
Nicole Morehouse, Grade 5
Helen B Duffield Elementary School, NY

School

S ophisticated
C over Work
H omework
O utstanding
O ver achieving
L ikes work
Jamil John, Grade 5
Public School 114 Ryder Elementary, NY

Snowflakes

Snowflakes tumble down.
Have you ever
Felt the thrill?
Fluffy snow blanket.
Luca Ruskauff, Grade 4
Catherine A Dwyer Elementary School, NJ

Bergeron Family Christmas

C hristmas dinner is always prime rib at Nana's house
H as always been one of the best days of the year
R ed is a Christmas color
I s one of the days Sammy comes from Virginia
S tockings full of candy
T orn wrapping paper all over the floor
M aking Christmas cards is awesome
A ll different colored stockings
S hopping is what people do on Black Friday

P iles of presents under the tree
R eady to open and give presents
E very Christmas morning I wake up to the smell of cinnamon rolls in the oven
S anta Claus is fat
E very Christmas my family and 20 cousins go to Nana's house
N ever boring
T he gift exchange is always fun

Zachary Bergeron, Grade 6
Great Meadows Middle School, NJ

Bravery

Bravery means strength
A soldier fighting for his country has to have courage
His family worries about him all the time and misses him a lot
He never comes home on the holidays because of the war
They write to him every day, and he always writes back
His kids pray to God every night and ask to give him strength to come home
Every day they wonder how he is doing in the war
And they wonder when he will ever come home
He barely comes for a visit
His kids always wonder
Has he perished or will he come home?
They send supplies for him and his soldiers
Gum, meat, toothbrushes, deodorant
They will cherish these items forever and use them wisely
They also send new pictures of them to him
Will the soldier ever come home?

Dylan D'Ambrosio, Grade 6
Great Meadows Middle School, NJ

Moment of Fall

F eeling cozy inside with the heater and chilly outside with the shivering wind
A pple picking will always be one of many favorites
L eaves brown like Kit-Kat in my trick-or-treat bag, or red like a cherry pie
L ots of leaves crunch under my feet when I take a step

I can hear the howling cool wind, blowing hard against our brick house
S ometimes I'll have to wear a fluffy warm coat when I go outside

F resh, moist air is what I can smell from the air out in the dark, frosty sky
U nder the bushes or on the grass is stuffed with a
N ew layer of floor covered by nature's colorful leaves

Fall is the moment to feel the cold, dry, and frosty air with autumn's rich-colored leaves
Annie Wang, Grade 6
Slocum Skewes School, NJ

Rocks and Minerals

For billions of years,
Rocks have been here,
I don't think they'll disappear.
Rocks to climb with your best buddy
Rocks are really cool to study.
Under all of those boat docks
There are oh, so many rocks.
Sometimes you might see a mineral
But not in your Kellogg's cereal.
Rocks and minerals here and there
Rocks and minerals everywhere
I don't think that they are dumb
I just wanna know where they come from!

Jaydah Edwards, Grade 4
Roosevelt Elementary School, NJ

Love

What is love?
It can be many things.
Sometimes people hide their feelings
From their loved ones.

If you love someone
You have to let it go
If you hold it in
You are not going to feel any better.

If you want to be loved
You have to love, first.
That is love.

Nikkita Louis, Grade 5
Public School 114 Ryder Elementary, NY

Report Card

I got my report card today
At lunch my friends told me

F stands for Fantastic
D stands for Did awesome
C stands for Could have done worse
B stands for Better luck next time
and
A stands for Awful

I can't wait to
show my mom because
I got all F's!

Yonathan Reyes, Grade 5
Dickinson Avenue Elementary School, NY

Fall

Leaves are falling down
because fall is coming here
yellow, red, and orange.

Mia Charles, Grade 4
St Mark School, NY

Land and Sky

When Land sees all the majestic birds go,
Sky looks down and sees the sparkling snow.

When Land gets bathed in gentle raindrops from Sky,
Sky gets covered in a gray, soft blanket from which rain falls by and by.

When Land grows thirsty and weak and feels the ray of a thousand fires,
Sky looks down and sees Land with cracks like wires.

When Land peers up and sees wind sway tall, brilliant trees,
Sky glances down and there are magnificent different colors to see.

Claire Whipple, Grade 5
Hillside Elementary School, NJ

The Season of Fall

The season of fall, with its bright colors and squirrels running in the streets
The wonderful colors of orange and yellow,
Create gardens of heaven on earth
This will be the place
Where peace, love, and dreams come true.

A butterfly flies from leaf to leaf
Working with much effort to make the leaves fall
They want the next season to come
It will come with different effects
And things from nature

Paula Rodriguez and Valentina Gonzalez, Grade 6
Shelter Rock Elementary School, NY

The Poconos in the Winter

Speedy tube slides quickly down the long hill.
Warm car steams quietly in the cabin driveway.
Bitter winter freezes quickly while people snuggle up with their family.
Cozy cabins warmly provide shelter while snow falls outside.
Zooming snowboard soars gracefully in the blue sky.
Fluffy snow falls gently on the log cabin roof.
Mammoth steep hills scarily dare people at the snow tubing place.
Loving families laugh loudly in their warm cabins.
Blinding fireplace crackles beautifully in the dimly lit room.
Scary ski lift precariously carries families and friends up the big hills.
And exhausted children collapse in bed after having a fun day at the Poconos.

Destiny Price, Grade 4
Maud Abrams Elementary School, NJ

Chocolate

C reamy and delicious
H onestly, chocolate is exquisite in taste
O bviously the other desserts seem tedious compared to chocolate
C hocolate flows into people like silk
O nce you taste it you are addicted
L uckily chocolate was discovered, if it was not what would people do?
A ll the other desserts are jealous of chocolate's goodness
T ears sometimes roll down people's faces when eating it
E veryone loves chocolate

Kamerin Correa, Grade 6
Westampton Middle School, NJ

Summer

Summer is the best
Kids and adults
Having fun
School is over now.
Summer rocks!

Trevone Green, Grade 4
Catherine A Dwyer Elementary School, NJ

California

California
Large, west
Surfing, eating, playing
I love this state
Los Angeles

Justin Lennon, Grade 6
Caroline G Atkinson School, NY

Soccer

Soccer
Fun, physical
Exciting, laughing, learning
It is the best
Futbol

Jose Mejia, Grade 6
Caroline G Atkinson School, NY

Bill

There once was a guy named Bill
He worked at a big mill
Bill got in a muddle
By slipping in a puddle
It wasn't really quite a thrill!

Sean Lux, Grade 4
St Aloysius Regional School, NY

Bunny

I once had a bunny
who chewed up all my money
I was very mad
and she was very bad
I think the bunny thinks it is funny!

Evelyn Smith, Grade 4
St Aloysius Regional School, NY

Christmas

Christmas
Cake, presents
Snowing, eating, singing
Spending time with family
Holiday

Elizabeth Capellan, Grade 6
Caroline G Atkinson School, NY

Summer

Oh, I loved when it was summer
Then school started and it was a bummer
When you had those days to relax and sit back
Watching TV, while drinking a soda and eating a snack

Going on vacation and having lots of fun
Laying on the beach and getting a tan from the sun
Stopping at the carnival going on a ride
As your mom won't stop taking pictures while she's watching from the side

Taking a stroll to the park on your bike with your sibling
Then you get ice cream and it starts spilling
Summer is awesome, it's really the best
As soon as it starts you get so obsessed

Summer is something that all kids enjoy
All of them every single girl and boy
I always hope that summer never ends
It makes you so happy just like your friends

Gabriella La Rosa, Grade 4
Little Falls School #3, NJ

A Rainbow in the Fall?

All around me I see them flying above me while the wind blows;
The site of a rainbow.
Red like a ripe, juicy tomato
Orange like a plump pumpkin
Yellow like the bright, warm sun
Green like freshly cut grass

Then what do I see before my eyes?
The most beautiful brown leaf.
It was as brown as the bark on a newly grown tree.
No holes, no damage, just perfect texture.
It was the first brown leaf I ever saw.

As the wind blew, the leaves kept falling.
Then I turned around and I saw a tree full of brown leaves!
It was like a giant woven basket. It was a beautiful sight. All shades of brown:
tan, sepia, raw sienna, burnt sienna, and the greatest color of all, Brown

It really was a rainbow in the fall!

Alexa Dischler, Grade 6
St Rose of Lima Academy, NJ

It's Beginning to Look a Lot Like Christmas

Blizzard blows crashing through snow.
Snowballs shooting around while bells jingle in the background.
Cocoa, cookies, candy, winter wonderland dandy.
Lying on the ground looking snowmen spying like spies around town.
Reindeer roughing rooftops, kids in sleds.
The best part is going home to your warm bed.
It's beginning to look a lot like Christmas.

Henry Renelus, Grade 4
James A Dever School, NY

The Sun

As the moon disappears from the night sky
And the stars start to fade away
It rises up in the morning
To start a brand new day

It peeks out of the darkness
It lightens up the day
It turns night into morning
So I can go out to play

It is up all day
It glistens and it gleams
It warms the whole earth
With all of its strong beams

And when the day is over
The sun will go away
It will hopefully rise up tomorrow
To start a brand new day

Emily Hyde, Grade 5
Little Falls School #1, NJ

My Vacation

We got off the plane and looked around
Mountains you could see from miles away
I couldn't take my eyes off of them
I would like to reach the top someday

When we got out of the airport
We went out to lunch
It was very delicious
But it was more like a brunch

About a few days later
We went in the pool
The hot tub was hot
But the pool was really cool

I couldn't believe it
The week went by so fast
I did have fun and
I've been to Colorado at last!

Lauren Hamilton, Grade 5
Little Falls School #1, NJ

New Dawn

As I looked upon the new dawn,
my foolishness having gone,
a wisdom came upon me,
and I was able to see,
that a new light will shine upon the world,
and the demons shall be curled,
in corners of purgatory,
begging to be admonished.

Adam Ilgin, Grade 5
Our Lady of Mercy Regional School, NY

Poppies in Flanders Fields

You served with the poppies,
The poppies served with you.
In Flanders Fields,
The blood splatters all around,
You are blue.
The dead soldier in front of you,
You are blue.
You finish the war,
And the poppy stands by you,
In Flanders Fields.

Jacob Wen, Grade 4
Raynor Country Day School, NY

Games

Games are fun,
They are for all ages,
Some are violent,
And some are nice,
Like Mario and Sonic,
And the violent ones,
Have zombies and guns,
But, if you don't like these games,
You can try board games,
Because they are all lots of fun.

Trevor Rauscher, Grade 6
St Mary's Prep School, NJ

Oooo Food!

Food is the best!
It can't be beat.
So let's sit down
And start to eat.
Pass the chicken, pass the pie.
Hurry up, or I might die!
When your plate is empty,
You might be sad.
But is was a great meal,
So why not be glad!

Giana Franklin, Grade 6
St Mary's Prep School, NJ

Do You Not See?

Look, do you not see?
Look, that is your Lord
Do you not see what they do?
They strip Him of his clothes
And beat Him with a whip
Do you not see?
Do you not see Him carry his cross?
Do you not see?
Come and see what the Romans have done
Do you not see?

Brittany, Grade 6
Holy Innocents School, NJ

Spring

Off came my boots
Off came my coat
I'm so happy
I can just float

I can take off my hat
I can put on my cap
I can take out my ball
And I can take out my hat

The snow is gone
The shovels are away
The beautiful leaves
Are coming back
On the trees today

The children are out
The sun is too
We're having fun
With everything we do

I guess you're wondering
What time of year
This brings my favorite season
Everybody it's spring

Leonard Cottle, Grade 6
Public School 138, NY

Seagulls of the Beach

You taunt us and tease us
And attract us with food
But we're just so tired
Of being chased and shooed

We are the seagulls
Living at the beach
We're just sick of humans
And now we're going to teach

We are living things
And we get exhausted too
So don't chase us around
Because we don't chase you

Don't taunt us with food
Cause we really want to eat
Don't force us into water
Cause it freezes our feet

If you now know
What keeps us off your land
We ask you to let us be
Because this our sand!

Zoë Weigele, Grade 5
Little Falls School #1, NJ

Winter

Winter is the season of snow, people watch their dim fires glow,
They tell stories from long, long ago, and grandmothers continuously knit and sew.

Out everyone goes to play and to run, making snow angels and having great fun.
Inside, people sip cocoa, their faces warm up and smiles start to show.

Marshmallows roasting, music flowing.
Outdoor lights glowing, cold winds blowing.

Children make snowmen and snowballs galore, having a great time and wishing for more.
They slip and slide as they skate to and fro, and speed down hills in sleighs shouting "Heigh-ho!"

Children waiting impatiently for presents under the tree, one for each, an extra one for me.
Santa and his reindeers prepare to take flight. Ho, ho, ho! They will be very busy tonight!

Ten, nine, eight, excitement fills the air, there is no time to spare!
Even dogs and cats have to cover their eyes, everyone is waiting for the big surprise.

Christmas comes, and then it's gone. It will be a new year before too long.;
But winter continues, icy and cold. Everyone feels it, both the young and the old.

Then finally one day, it comes to an end. We knew it would happen eventually, my friend.
Snow turns to rain, then rainbows appear. Winter is over, spring is here!

Anna Westfall, Grade 4
James A Dever School, NY

The Seashore

In the moonlight the sand glistens like dew on the grass,
In winter the snow blankets the beach like a soft, down comforter,
In the summer the sun heats the sand so hot it feels like your feet are on fire,
In the spring, storms whip around the sand that pelts you so hard you tingle.

The high tide brings the water way up that will wash away all of your sand creations,
The low tide pulls the water back revealing the ocean shells,
The hurricanes and bad storms create the biggest and the angriest waves of all,
The calm and serene summer days make the ocean water look like a slow, rolling breeze on the prairie.

Fish in the ocean are a box of crayons, the colors are a sight to see,
Seagulls can be found high in the sky or chasing waves, always keeping an eye out for something to eat (your lunch),
Crabs so tiny and little, we can give you quite a mighty pinch,
Dolphins look so beautiful jumping through waves, as they surf the coast.

All the many colors and designs of beach umbrellas will decorate the beach on hot and steamy days,
Lifeguards' whistles can be heard from beach to beach during bad rip tide conditions.
Fun can be found body surfing, boogie boarding, and diving into the coolest waves.
Smells at the beach can be alluring, from the tropical smell of suntan lotion, to the delicious boardwalk delights.

Hannah Applegate, Grade 6
Great Meadows Middle School, NJ

Making the World a Better Place

I would make the world a better place by making sure that there is no littering and people would pick up behind one another. I would make a sign saying, "Litter at Your Risk!" I would paint the sign red; and on it I would paint people picking up trash. If you do litter, you will have to pay a ticket and you will go to jail for a month. You should not litter, it makes the air we breathe and the neighborhood where we live dirty!

Heaven M. Denson, Grade 4
New York Institute for Special Education, NY

Nature

I love the sight of nature
The trees dancing in the wind
as leaves come floating down
The water on the beach crashing
down on to the wet, moist sand
The air sipping through the world like worms
slipping and sliding through wet, moist mud
The outdoor fires burn logs into crisp ash
I know nature is my brother

John Benson, Grade 5
Jacob Gunther Elementary School, NY

Lemon Lime

On the outside, you look like a small green egg.
You feel like a soft rock I would find on the beach.
When I peel you, you sound like a gentle lion growling!
Inside you look like a green sun shining above the sky.
You feel like wet lines they would use to divide
the bad waves in the beach.
You smell like a nice perfume.
You taste like sour patches.
Tell me lime, how does it feel like to be sour all the time?

Andre Souza, Grade 5
Roosevelt Elementary School, NJ

Green Kiwi the Lanterner

On the outside, you look like a dog's foot.
You feel like a hairy leg.
When I peel you, you sound like someone whistling.
When I slice you, you sound like reading with no noise.
Inside you look like a stage with people around it.
You feel like an ice ring.
You smell like an orange.
You taste like a banana.
Tell me, why do you need the hair?

Steph Stelus, Grade 5
Roosevelt Elementary School, NJ

My Cats

M essy
Y oung

C lumsy
A mazing
T errific
S cratchy

Robert Martinez, Grade 5
Tecler Arts in Education Magnet School, NY

The Meadow

The meadow is a beautiful place
As the sun rises and sets
When the light shines upon the meadow,
I stop and think "Wow, this is a beautiful place."

Mariah O'Connor, Grade 6
New York Institute for Special Education, NY

What Makes Me Happy!

What makes me happy is…
Playing sports!
I love
Floor hockey,
Basketball,
And football!
Especially when I am with
My family!
They are my cheerleaders!

Jean Pierre Viri, Grade 4
New York Institute for Special Education, NY

Rocks and Minerals

Did you know
that you live on the biggest rock in the world?
It's the Earth!
Mostly everything is made of rock
which is made of minerals.
Some rocks are formed by pressure.
Minerals are made of simple chemicals.
The names of some minerals are:
clear quartz, milky quartz and rose quartz.

Daunté Hinton-Sturdivant, Grade 4
Roosevelt Elementary School, NJ

Starry Night*

The *Starry Night* with the tall dark green grass.
Starry Night with the village that lights up in the
dark during the night.
Starry Night with the yellow stars.
Starry Night, what's
your favorite
Sight of
The Village?

Anthony Power, Grade 5
Roosevelt Elementary School, NJ
*Inspired by "Starry Night" by Vincent Van Gogh

Fall

Leaves we are raking.
I jump in the leaves.
My mom was baking pie.
I went inside to eat.
There was a storm.
This morning was sunny.
It was fun to play.

Alondra Mateo, Grade 4
R.J. McNulty Academy for International Studies and Literacy, NY

Fall

My mom made fall dinners
And it's my turn to help with the turkey.
We hunt for a turkey
And found one just right!

Carmelo DeAngelo, Grade 4
R.J. McNulty Academy for International Studies and Literacy, NY

Ernie

Ernie is my dog.
he is a playful and happy dog.
We all love Ernie.
I love my dog very much.
He loves his food.
Ernie barks at the doorbell.
My dog is a lover.
My dog stand on a red stool.
His food is called "Moist N' Meaty."
My dog is the best.
Madison Engelhardt, Grade 5
St Mary's Prep School, NJ

America

I'm proud to be an American,
I'm just proud to be free.
To live among my neighbors,
Who will always reach out to help me.
Proud to live in the 50 states,
Individual, but one.
One heart,
One mind,
One home.
I'm just proud to be me.
Alexa Setteducate, Grade 5
Forrestdale School, NJ

Snowflakes

Snowflakes gently coming down,
Softly landing on the ground.
White as foam that's in the sea,
Landing on my nose and knee.
I wonder how it feels as one,
So I go out and have some fun!
My friends and I have a snowball fight,
We drink hot cocoa and stay up all night.
I love the snowflakes coming down,
Softly landing on the ground.
Elizabeth Kelson, Grade 5
St Mary's Prep School, NJ

How I Feel About Christmas

Christmas, Yippee!
I can't wait for that Christmas tree
Christmas, Hooray!
I just can't wait for that day
Christmas, cool!
I get a week off of school
Christmas, that's not all!
We still get to throw snowballs
Christmas, that's not the fun
It's about Jesus' birth, then we're done!
Danny Rittinger, Grade 5
Hawthorne Christian Academy, NJ

Glass

When light hits
it bends in sheets of color
reflecting off the marble floor.

Fragile
and delicate
as a butterfly drifting in midair.

Like a million
diamonds pressed
out on one big sheet
it glistens in the
morning sun.
Sam Moskowitz, Grade 4
Norman J Levy Lakeside School, NY

It's Halloween

I t is time to go.
T he children are not moving slow.
S piders are all over the house.

H orrifying and fun costumes and a mouse.
A ll the streets are full of children.
L ots of tricks and treats.
L ots of laughing on the streets.
O range pumpkins with carved faces.
W e went to many places.
E verything looks so scary.
E specially my cousin Mary.
N othing is more scary.
Robert Cincotta, Grade 5
St Rose of Lima Academy, NJ

Monsters

My mom says monsters aren't real
My dad says they are no big deal
I don't believe them one tiny bit
'Cause monsters are sitting where I sit
There are monsters under my huge bed
Monsters aren't just in my head

There are monsters hiding in my room
Monsters are on my swings, I assume
There might be monsters eating my lunch
At school I will have nothing to munch

I don't like monsters one little bit
Sydney Rosen, Grade 4
Hillside Elementary School, NJ

Flyers

Fantastic, very good
Watch on TV, skating, checking
Exciting when they score!
Mark Rosato, Grade 4
Ethel M Burke Elementary School, NJ

Starsky

I love my dog Starsky.
When you look into his eyes,
You'll feel completely comfortable.
You'll be hypnotized.

I love my dog Starsky,
He's as white as a cloud.
Whenever I pet him,
I feel perfectly proud.

I love my dog Starsky,
He tells me everything.
Let's hope he never ends,
Because he's not like anything.
Maya Cohen, Grade 4
Concord Road Elementary School, NY

Going to the Park

It's time to go to the park,
So we can play until dark.
We'll have so much fun,
As we run and play in the sun.
We will go on the swings,
And feel like birds with great wings.
Let's hit the ball really far,
And take off faster than a car.
Scooters, rip sticks and bikes everywhere.
There's no place better anywhere.
So believe me when I say
The park is a fun place to stay,
This is where I want to be,
Come join me today and you to will see.
Alexandria Hungreder, Grade 6
St Stanislaus Kostka Academy School, NY

Red, Blue, and Purple

Red is one of my favorite colors
It describes love, power, blood, and pain
But that doesn't make me evil

Blue is one of my favorite colors
It describes peace, kindness, and calmness
But that doesn't make me a hippie

Purple is one of my favorite colors
It describes royalty
And it's a mixture of red and blue
But that doesn't make me full of myself
It just makes me
Well, me
Gospelline Fenelon, Grade 5
Public School 235 Janice Marie Knight, NY

Train
A train
So fast and noisy
Carrying people
Who had a long day
But brings fresh
New people for another day
John Berry, Grade 5
Martin Avenue Elementary School, NY

Winter
Cold
and shivering
hands as red as can be
frostbite on your nose
snow in your shoes
snowflakes on your coat
Robert Caulfield, Grade 5
Dickinson Avenue Elementary School, NY

My Dog…
P layful all day!
U nbelievable every second of the day!
G reat at being a BFF!
G oes all around outside!
L oves you all day!
E very day super excited!
Sarah Flood, Grade 5
Dickinson Avenue Elementary School, NY

Snowflakes
Filmy sheets, something mysterious
Delicate like glass
Not handmade, always unique
Dark December days coming on
Crying in despair while melting away dying
We sighed as we went inside
Shannon Morgan, Grade 4
James A Dever School, NY

Dancing in the Stars
Dancing is magic
Hypnotized with the rhythm
Dancing is my life
I won't stop dancing
I can do it all day long
It's my goal in life.
Lauren Louis, Grade 6
Holy Innocents School, NJ

Erasers
Pink, rubbery
Erases, bounces, shreds
Really helps when you make a mistake
Pencil topper.
Lindsey Burleigh, Grade 4
Ethel M Burke Elementary School, NJ

Islam: It's a Way of Life
You're having "fun..."
Then, you spot a person opening a book,
Guess what's he's reading?
The Holy Quran.

You're hearing music...
Then, you hear a beautiful voice,
Guess what this is?
It's the Athan.(Muslim call to prayer)

You're watching televison...
Then, you see your brother going somewhere
Guess where he is going?
He is going to the Mosque.

You're eating your favorite desert...
Then, you see a person making duaa (supplication)
Guess what their supplication for?
They pray that you never forget to make a supplication before eating.
Rema Damedi, Grade 6
Al Ghazaly School, NJ

Summer
Summer is flying a kite, fishing, or just taking a hike.
Summer is sitting on the beach in the sun.
Oh, summer is just fun.
Summer is swimming in a lake.
Or swinging from a tree.
Yeah, summer that's what it means to me.
Summer is camping in the woods, or riding a horse in a show.
Summer is a new theme park, or an ice cold Pepsi dripping down your lips.
Summer's days are longer, nights are shorter, and it's a whole lot warmer.
Oh summer, where do I begin?
Summer is bugging my sister, hanging out with my friends,
Or running down a giant hill.
Summer is when bees come out, and people like to play.
When it is summer, where do we begin?
By eating ice cream, sleeping in, or using the computer.
How about sailing on a boat, or flying in a plane.
That's what I'd do if I were you.
Oh summer, where do we begin?
Jenna Stapp, Grade 5
Hawthorne Christian Academy, NJ

Football
Orange kicking tees hold the football flawlessly when the second arrives for opening kickoff.
Hard pads defend when it's time to play football.
The huge stadium fills quickly on a sunny afternoon.
The big flashing scoreboard displays the score brightly over the gigantic field.
The loud fans shout thunderously inside the dome.
Every delighted cheerleader cheers and dances during half-time.
Useful coaches always encourage on the field turf.
Team players helpfully collaborate under every circumstance.
Green grassy fields provide dirty cleats every time somebody steps on the field.
Nico Castellano, Grade 4
Maud Abrams Elementary School, NJ

My Mom Makes Me Happy!
My mom makes me happy!
She is also very funny.
She is cool, she teaches me to cook.
She is the best mom!

Paula Morejon, Grade 4
New York Institute for Special Education, NY

Expressed!
My words are expressed with drawings
my drawings are expressed with colors
the colors move gracefully across the paper
and fill in the blanks that have no excitement!

Kirstin Goodlad, Grade 6
South Side Middle School, NY

Mother Forever
Love is love,
Hatred is hatred
It comes and goes,
Between us both.

You treat her bad,
She's the only one you had,
You will forget,
And go back to the day you have met.

See what she did for you,
What you thought of is true,
All you think of,
Is that she gave you love.

Use my idea,
And you will see for yourself,
She always made sure
You were in good health.

You drove her crazy,
Just because you were lazy,
She worked so hard,
To protect you like a bodyguard.

Do not show hatred,
Always show love.
She is your mother forever,
No matter what happened, whatsoever.

Nourhan Elsayed, Grade 6
Al Ghazaly School, NJ

Birthday
Birthday
Fun, big
Laughing, eating, talking
Best party ever had.
Bash

Antanasia Allen, Grade 6
Caroline G Atkinson School, NY

Coco
She is very playful.
She likes to chase a laser.
Hits her ball around.

She lays in her bed.
She likes to lay in her perch;
Curls up in my bed.

Claws as sharp as knives.
Paws as soft as cotton balls.
Her whiskers are long.

Likes to watch the birds.
She likes to lay in sunlight;
Watches cars go by.

Lays around all day.
She sharpens her claws a lot.
She snores when she sleeps.

Sees us at the door.
She swats at my dog Ernie.
Lays on my dad's lap.

Plays with lots of toys.
She cleans herself by licking.
My cat is Coco.

Matthew Bryan Engelhardt, Grade 5
St Mary's Prep School, NJ

Martin Luther King Jr.
Martin Martin Martin
White and Black together
Even though he was in jail
He still was a good fella

He talked and talked and talked
Made decisions forever
They fought and fought and fought
Until it was forever
Revenge, revenge, revenge
We post signs together
Stop hanging us like this
We will be free forever.
Love, children hand and hand
And free at last
Free at last.
That was Dr. Martin Luther King Jr.

If he were here today and
Bullying happened today
He would talk and talk and talk
Or even go to people's schools
And talk to them

Gary Queen, Grade 6
Public School 138, NY

Flowers

They bloom ever so brightly
In the warming heat
Tilting ever so slightly
Brushing against me
They perk up as they arrive
With their beautiful wings
So happy and alive
In the morning
What's that they see?
A beautiful pattern
Oh please come here bee
Bright as a lit lantern
Oh no! Oh dear! Look at that!
So transparent and clear
Drops of rain sprinkling about
I just want to cheer!
Twist and turn and finally
I'm picked by you
Put in your hair so elegantly
What adventures I have been through
Nuha Syed, Grade 6
Benjamin Franklin Middle School, NJ

Halloween

We run up the steps with much joy,
So much fun for a girl or boy.
We see ghosts painted on a jar,
As we wait for our candy bar.
Hoping we get King Size,
That would be the ultimate prize.

Our pillow cases feel like bricks,
We feel like pulling off some tricks!
Orange and black on every door,
Ghouls and goblins roam the floor.
There's a fake hand in the candy bowl,
Joy and excitement in every soul.

I see Jack-O-Lanterns here and there,
I see candy everywhere!
The dead may rise again tonight,
Oh, Halloween is such a fright.
Christmas and Easter are also fun,
But Halloween is Number One!
Stephen Cracchiolo, Grade 6
Avenel Middle School, NJ

The Earth

The Earth is round and big
It has water and lands
From Europe to the United States we go
Hills, valleys, and plateaus we have
With everyone recycling
We can make the Earth cleaner and greener
Justin Cardenas, Grade 4
Holy Family School, NY

School Rules

S leep early
C ome to school early
H oly Family School rocks!
O pportunities to learn!
O pen your eyes and learn;
L earn with all your might!

R ead, write, learn,
U nited States of America.
L ook and understand the work.
E very day is time to study!
S tudy every day!
Danica Sindo, Grade 4
Holy Family School, NY

Christmas

Snow falling…
Carols playing…
People laughing…
Ornaments hanging…
Manger standing…
Cookies baking…
Reindeer flying…
Trees glistening…
Children wishing…
Angels singing…
CHRISTMAS
Cara Hackford, Grade 6
Sts Peter & Paul School, NY

Fall

Fall is when the leaves fall by,
Fall is when the wind blows high.
Cats and critters hide away,
The sun is shorter day by day,
If we could it's not a crime.
We should see summer one last time.

Fall is when Halloween comes by,
Fall is when the moon is high.
Trick-or-treat is everywhere,
Don't forget to do your hair!
Angelique Balmori Buensuceso, Grade 6
All Saints Catholic Academy, NY

I Love My Mom

I LOVE my mom
in all my heart
she was the one
who took care of me
when I was born
I should thank her
for all the things
she's done for me.
Karen Morocho, Grade 4
Public School 112 Lefferts Park School, NY

My Drug-Free Role Model

My drug-free role model is Responsible
Reasonable
Drug-free
And that is what I would like to be
She listens to me
When no one else does
She never overdoses
Nor takes too many in a day
She's always by my side
Through thick and thin
The person I trust
My nurturing mother
My guardian
My loved one
Isabella Panepinto, Grade 6
St Stephen's School, NY

Song

Crickets are crying in sadness
The leaves are still blowing in madness
But when it comes singing
The joy it is bringing
Is just indescribable
Peace
The tune it is singing is
Really too happy
The sound of it is
Really too sappy
But when I come there
The forest
Its lair
Is the property of the bird.
Anna Salvatore, Grade 4
Toll Gate Grammar School, NJ

Penguins

Flippers waddle on the ice,
Some iced fish would be nice.

They get front seats for the northern lights,
They cuddle together on icy nights.

The egg must stay above their feet,
For it will hatch within a week.

Soon you'll learn to swim for fish,
And give the chicks a tasty dish.

"HONK, HONK," they talk all day,
That's cause they can't fly away!
Tien Servidio, Grade 5
Hillside Elementary School, NJ

Amazing Fall

Fall is when you go pumpkin and apple picking
Leaves fall, littering the ground
People get dressed up for Halloween,
To go trick-or-treating, waiting to eat their candy the next day
They go food shopping for Thanksgiving,
Waiting for their meal
And once that day comes their meal will be gone
All the little boys and girls will jump in a pile of leaves,
Making their parents rake the leaves again
All the little kids will make their Christmas list for Santa,
Hoping they don't get any coal

Caitlin Castel, Grade 6
Slocum Skewes School, NJ

Wonderful Winter

When winter comes I feel snug under my blanket
Like a bear in hibernation

A fine snowflake drifting through the air
As delicate as a butterfly's wing

During the harsh snowstorm I sleep
Like a newborn

To make it through the freezing winter you need to be
As smart as an owl

Christina Pender, Grade 5
Ridgeway Elementary School, NJ

The Moon

It sparkles in my eyes.
The silver knights guard it in the sky.
It's big, and round, and white.
It has a big smile all night.
Sometimes you see it, sometimes you don't.
The little knights in the sky are silver and white.
And they're always looking up for a fight.
When the sun goes down, he comes up to play.
I hope to see him again.
No matter how small, no matter how big,
I'm glued to this big piece of land.

Haleigh Morris, Grade 5
St Mary's Prep School, NJ

R Is for Reading

Reading is so much fun
You can have fun too
Fun at the zoo
Fun in a castle
Fun in a kingdom
Fun in a school
You can have any kind of fun

If you just read a book

Bailey Chard, Grade 4
Good Shepherd Regional Catholic School, NJ

Thanksgiving

Thank you for all my hands can hold
The warmth of the hot apple cider
From a large mug
White blankets
As fluffy as a pile of feathers
Dry, crispy grass about to die

Thank you for my family
My brother and I watching the parade
My parents' voice calling me to wake up
All of us together
Stuffing our tummies at Thanksgiving dinner
Like a child tasting candy for the first time

Thank you for the mouthwatering meal
Soft steamy mashed potatoes
The golden brown tender turkey
And the warm toasty pumpkin pie

Liza Aquilino, Grade 6
Oakdale-Bohemia Middle School, NY

Luke

My mom went to the hospital, had a cute baby boy.
When I held him, my heart filled with joy!
We brought him home, we named him Luke.
Everything he ate, he would start to puke.
Only six weeks old, he was so sick.
I wanted him better, and I wanted it quick!
You could see his ribs, he kept losing weight.
To take him to the doctor, we didn't hesitate!
He couldn't lie down, Mom held him tight.
She never let him out of her sight!
Just thinking about him, made her cry.
Thinking thoughts, "He might die."
He had an operation to fix his belly.
Now he eats peanut butter and jelly!
He makes me so happy every day.
Anytime I'm home, he wants to play!
He is so priceless, love that can't be earned.
Life is so fragile and precious, I learned.

Sierra Fezenko, Grade 6
Great Meadows Middle School, NJ

Fall

The leaves change as they fall from the trees.
Kids playing, laughing and screaming.
People inside all cozy by the fire.
People raking up the mess,
flowers dying aren't the best thing.
Kids dreaming of jumping in a pile of leaves,
while other people are enjoying the breeze,
wishing for fall to never end.
Fall is not too hot or cold
but it's perfect for both young and old.

Amanda Harrop, Grade 4
Eugene Auer Memorial School, NY

Wintertime

Snow is falling to the ground,
I'm loving the delighted sounds.
Beautiful sounds of jingle bells ringing
And some carolers singing.

I love the wintertime,
You can hear the beautiful chimes.
You can have a snowball fight
Because the time is just right.

I love the wintertime you see,
It's a winter wonderland for you and me.
You can drink some tasty cocoa,
With whipped cream or chocolate mocha.

Wintertime is a wonderful time,
It's where I can drink some tea with lime.
You don't even have to pay a dime
Because it's free all the time.

It's a wonderful time,
I can listen to the chimes.
While I drink tea with lime,
And I can rhyme all the time.

Taylor Buckley, Grade 5
Tecler Arts in Education Magnet School, NY

The Dream

I lay in bed wondering what it would be like to fly,
to soar through the sky like a hawk.
Then I close my eyes tightly and see clouds and an endless, blue sky.
I look down at the trees, animals of all kinds and people far below.
I smell the pine trees of the forest and feel the wind blowing
against my feathers. I feel happy and free.

But then I hear a screech above me. An eagle has seen me.
Suddenly I am frozen with fear and I cannot move my wings.
I come soaring down into the trees and find a hiding spot.
There it is — a bush next to a big tree.
I wait and listen.
Nothing.

I come out from the bushes and realize I'm hungry.
I take off into the air to search for my dinner.
Below I see a little brown mouse running across the
snow. I dive straight down and grip him with my
sharp talons. After my dinner, I begin to get sleepy. I find a nest in a
tree and settle down for the night.

I open my eyes and find myself under my blanket with my dog
snuggling next to me. I realize who I really am. I can't fly, but
I can run, and that is just fine.

Ayla Haik, Grade 5
Dickinson Avenue Elementary School, NY

Change

If I could change the world...
Everything would be perfect
It would all be my way
I'd make the sun rise high and bright
The word "bad" wouldn't exist
Everyone must be sweet, nice and neat
OR
There will be a penalty
They would have to obey me
These are the changes I would make...
The biggest change of all would be...
That I would be the Queen!
The leader, the one you must obey!
The one that will bring the world
Victory, Love and Peace!

Jennifer Luna, Grade 5
New York Institute for Special Education, NY

Sterling Hill Mine

We studied rocks and minerals, and we got on the bus,
We went to Sterling Hill Mine and had a great time.
We went in a tunnel, I'm glad we didn't use a shovel.
I went down deep, and the only thing that got wet was my feet.
It was hot, but not a lot.
It was chilly, but not freezy.
It was very fun with the sun.
We went rock hunting,
and went all around and walked on the ground.
I was scared, but I didn't care.
When we went to lunch
my friends shared with me.
I was glad to go to the trip with teachers and friends, too.
I love going on trips
and having fun with the rocks and minerals.

Viviana Arbelaez, Grade 4
Roosevelt Elementary School, NJ

Winter

The snow fell silently onto the white ground.
It laid there and laid there without a sound.
The evergreens were covered with a white sheet of snow.
This made it seem like the trees has a glow.

A wreath hung on the door with joy,
While inside the snow globe was a little drummer boy.
He seemed to be drumming a sweet little tune,
Underneath the glistening moon.

Outside the pond was covered with ice,
It made the scene look ever more nice.
I looked out my window with delight,
And what I saw was a wonderful sight.

Elizabeth MacKay, Grade 6
Regina Coeli School, NY

Myrtle Beach

Myrtle Beach is quite a sight
Sometimes the waves though can be a fright
The sand on the beach is nice and hot
That's why I go to the beach a lot

Now we're on our way to Broadway at the Beach
We walked to the rides and heard people screech
My mom and I are on our way to the store
The manager greeted us as we walked in the door

We go home for the night and go right to bed
I would actually rather stay up instead
We woke up in the morning and laid on the couch
My mom and dad are like Mr. and Mrs. Grouch

I helped dad make pancakes and bacon too
Now I have to clean up and that's a lot to do
I run to my room and start to get dressed
Then I think to myself Myrtle Beach is the best

Nicole Mokray, Grade 5
Little Falls School #1, NJ

Ice Skating

It's time to go, I'm on the ice
Music plays and spreads all around
I start to move, to jump, and spin
I hope I land all of my jumps on the ground

I start right away
With spins, edges, and some jumps
I go straight for a leap in ballet
All I hope is that I don't get bumps

I go to do my spin
I start to spin in the T shape
I'm almost done with my program
I suddenly fell and saw a huge scrape

Not feeling so great with myself
I get off the ice with a small smile
I always thought I would have done better
But at least I still have skating style

Rachel Schneider, Grade 5
Little Falls School #1, NJ

My Dog

His color is like shining gold.
His fur is like a hood over his eyes.
It's as soft as a pillow of clouds.
My dog's fur is the fluffiest thing in the world.
He whimpers trying to bury his ripped, stuffed raccoon.
When he cries he goes whee! whee! through his nose.
He yawns as big as a mountain.
He puts his paws on me when I am joyless.

Lucas Koenig, Grade 4
Concord Road Elementary School, NY

Snowy Halloween

Two days before Halloween
The color from the town had drained.
All of a sudden, it started to snow.
It was all white and fluffy.
I sprang outside to touch it.
It felt smooth and slushy.

On the day of Halloween, there was splashing and sloshing.
The snow was still frosty and cold.
I enjoyed the fresh and piney smell.
We took our baggies and then got dressed.
We raced to every house on the block and
Chimed to the people, "Trick of Treat!"

When I got home I dumped my candy.
I couldn't believe how much I had gotten!
The sweet smell made me want to eat them right away.
These couple of days felt like a dream.
I wish this could happen once more!

Mar-tina Karaiakofoglou, Grade 6
Slocum Skewes School, NJ

What Is Thanksgiving?

Thanksgiving is the time of year,
To say thanks to the people who give you cheer.
To be with your family full of love,
And pray to God, our Lord above.

Thanksgiving is a joyful thing,
A time to play and laugh and sing.
A time to cook and then to feast,
It's my turn to eat the turkey beast.

Thanksgiving originated long ago,
The feast lasted three days we know.
Pilgrims and Indians ate and ate,
The friendship that was born was really great.

Thanksgiving is only days away,
I'm glad we still celebrate this holiday.
Then when Thanksgiving time is done,
Black Friday sales, here we come!

Shannon Miller, Grade 6
Great Meadows Middle School, NJ

Fall

The pumpkins are orange and bright.
The thunderstorms have lightning.
I love a cool fall night.
Fall storms can be frightening.
I like apple pie.
Today was fun.
I look at the sky.
It is a bright sun.

Hunter Korona, Grade 4
R.J. McNulty Academy for International Studies and Literacy, NY

Friends

Friends are
everything

No matter what you do
they're by your side

You tell them your secrets,
they tell theirs

Friends are in
your life forever!
Taylor Gilchrist, Grade 5
Dickinson Avenue Elementary School, NY

Florida's Beauty

The ocean shimmers
like diamonds dancing over it.

The waves come crashing down
like a tornado towering over your house
before it falls apart.

The sand as hot as an oven.

As I walk on the hot sand back to the house
I think about Florida's beauty.
Lindsay Feldherr, Grade 4
Norman J Levy Lakeside School, NY

Books

I love to
read books
it's my favorite
thing to do

If I had one
wish in the
world I'd
choose to
have every
book in the world
Andrew Infranco, Grade 5
Dickinson Avenue Elementary School, NY

Playing Baseball

Baseball baseball is so much fun
Sweating in the summer sun
Swing my bat, hit the ball — CRACK!
Stretch my neck and throw my bat

Reach each base before the chase
Ball in play — should I stay or race?
Heart pounding so eager to reach third
Ball drops…HOME RUN could be heard!
Jonathan Laudani, Grade 6
Our Lady of Good Counsel School, NY

Songs = You

A song is a soul
Personalized by you
Creative and talented
In it's own way.

A song is a story
Telling of time past or present
With as much truth as false
It raises your feeling and pulse

A song is a rainbow of notes
Majority of color and voice
Collecting your completely as one
The genre is now your choice

A song is YOU
Varieties in soul and story
Your own rainbow of notes
And it can call itself YOURS!!
Lillian Corman, Grade 6
Great Meadows Middle School, NJ

Strength

Strength is a tornado.
Destroying the land in its path,
Coming harsh and unexpectedly.
Never ending till it has done its duty.

Strength is a fireplace.
Always warm and comforting,
Keeps you from getting cold,
Burning until it turns to ash.

Strength is time.
You're always running out of it.
Precious and wanted,
Never ending; infinite!

Strength is a cloud.
Delicate and calm,
Drifting through the sky,
Letting the wind blow it along.
Emily Wilson, Grade 6
Great Meadows Middle School, NJ

September 11

Roses are red
Violets are blue
We will never forget
Heroes like you
You saved lives
Gave pride
Some were lost but
Never lost in our hearts
Andrew Erato, Grade 5
Helen B Duffield Elementary School, NY

The Leaf Who Grew

Fall leaves frolic through the wind
as they flutter down from a slowly
going bald tree. As they change
their colors from green to red to
brown like my mood as it goes
up and down from bright to dull.
They gather me and crunch me up
and jump on me. But when winter
comes I will have no place. Just wait
'til next year when I come again.
When the whole cycle goes from
start to end.
Michelle Muhammad, Grade 5
Bartle Elementary School, NJ

Summer

Summer fun stands for…

S oaking wet
U nder the sun
M agnificent weather
M inor tan
E xtra sun
R un

F ast runners
U nderestimated weather
N O SCHOOL!
Hayley Farraye, Grade 5
Hawthorne Christian Academy, NJ

Petey

Very cute and
Very crazy
He also
Barks a lot! Mostly at the
Birds
He also loves the pool,
We take him out,
He jumps right back in!
He swims and swims for a while
He does the
Doggy paddle across
The whole pool!
Joseph Giardina, Grade 5
Dickinson Avenue Elementary School, NY

Fall

Fall is cold and people are raking leaves.
Halloween has come.
People are going to spooky houses at night.
Wind is blowing making people scream.
Things jumping out.
Getting candy.
Sabrina Salvadori, Grade 4
Eugene Auer Memorial School, NY

What I'm Thankful For

Thank you for all my ears can hear
The crunch of leaves under my feet
A kitchen timer going off as loud as a marching band
My cousins and I giggling about jokes we tell each other

Thank you for all my nose can smell
Maple leaves falling to the ground
The aroma of fresh pumpkin pie baking in the oven
Juicy turkey roasting on the stove waiting to be eaten
As if he were still alive

Thank you for all my eyes can see
My brothers playing football in the backyard
Going to school every day and seeing my friends
Visiting my cousins in other states

Olivia Drennan, Grade 6
Oakdale-Bohemia Middle School, NY

The Corn Maze

The crisp air blowing on my face.
The smell of apple cider donuts from the shop.
The corn maze and the hay rides in the fall air
Were wonderful while we sit in the cold with layers of clothes.

We can see the train coming from a mile away,
With the thick black smoke blowing in your face.
As you hear the little children cheer,
You know the train here.

The bouncy house is so much fun.
When I play all day in the sun.
It is finally night when we go on the adventure,
When we succeed we will come again.
When fall strikes again.

Julianne D'Amico, Grade 6
Slocum Skewes School, NJ

Change

You know you had change
When you had love to the heart.
Love is exactly change, hallelujah.
Yes, I had change to my heart.
The bittersweet memories rub against my mind,
But my personality is not the reason I wrote this poem.
Change is real.
Please change, as in set me free,
Let me go to thrive high.
Start with yourself.
You should be lucky to have change,
To have such a thing feel your heart and your inner self.
Feel change, feel love.
Open your heart like open doors.
Love change.

Chassity Pacheco, Grade 5
Tecler Arts in Education Magnet School, NY

The White Blanket

Shoveling snow in my driveway, feeling
As strong as an ox.

Snowflakes falling throughout the night
Like white confetti blanketing my neighborhood.

Trudging through the light snow, it felt
Like running through a room full of soft pillows.

Slithering into my bed, huddled under the covers feeling warm
Like a snake in the Senora Desert.

Emily Kurilla, Grade 5
Ridgeway Elementary School, NJ

Fall

In fall the leaves change colors,
The air becomes crisper.
In fall Halloween comes around,
Halloween is filled with ghosts and ghouls,
Masks and candy
On Halloween the air is filled with trick-or-treats,
And the laughter of children everywhere.
Fall starts the school year,
And seeing your friends.
Fall starts new friendships!

Marialuisa Berghela, Grade 6
All Saints Catholic Academy, NY

Elements of Nature

The sky is gray
The air is crisp
The water is cool
The wind is gentle
The Elements of Nature can be kind to us but
It can be harsh
The sky deeply foreshadows danger
The air is that of evil
The water is black
The wind is trying its hardest to knock us down

Siarra Ingram, Grade 5
Westampton Middle School, NJ

My Mom

My mom, the home of my heart
The sprinkles of my cupcake
The light of my heart
When I see you, I feel like a cupcake
Your voice is like Michael Jackson's voice
Your baking smells like the perfume of the sky
You're beautiful like a sunflower.
You're the moon of my brain
I love you mom
Just the way I love myself.

Ahmad Lo, Grade 6
Al Ghazaly School, NJ

My Midnight Wish

In the sky, I see a light
I made a wish that very night.

"Star light, star bright, first star I see tonight,
I wish I may, I wish I might
Have the wish, I wish tonight."

I wish for peace for my mom and dad,
Then the star took the wish I had.
Without further talk, I went to bed,
I went to sleep, and rested my head.

The very next day my wish came true,
I thanked the sky, so very blue.

James Orr, Grade 5
Public School 114 Ryder Elementary, NY

My School

I love my school.
It has helped me in many ways.
It has helped me with reading.
It has helped me with writing.
It has helped me stand up for myself
And be more confident.
It has helped me make new friends
And not be afraid.
O yes, my school has really helped
Me.
Now if only it would help me
Write a poem.
I love my school.

Jessica Karim, Grade 5
New York Institute for Special Education, NY

Fall

The wind in my face, the red on my nose
These are all signs that fall is coming close
My hair is blowing in the air, going crazy all around
Fall is coming close, I can tell by what I've found

Orange, red, and yellow is all I see
Fall is coming close, it's got to be
The smell of a fire warms the soul
It's a part of me that makes me whole

Bethany Kudisch, Grade 5
Hawthorne Christian Academy, NJ

Power Rangers Samurai Are Making the World Better

The red ranger is the best at Kung Fu and at being a leader.
The world would be gone without him and his team.
They're a good example of people who make the world better
because they want to keep people safe and out of danger.
They would never pick a fight with innocent people.
They only want to protect people.

Nicholas Chimelis, Grade 4
New York Institute for Special Education, NY

N.Y.I.S.E.

On my first year
When I got here
I was shy
I don't why
I would cry
But, I wouldn't go back
Because this school has changed me

Hey you can't blame me!

I can't deny
Yeah that's right, I was shy!
But now I shine in the sky
If it wasn't for the school
I wouldn't be as cool
I love the NYISE

Hey you can't blame me.

Esmeralda Chavez, Grade 5
New York Institute for Special Education, NY

A Penguin

A penguin sliding down
A snowy hill.
The penguin's life
Must be a thrill.
I watch him swim
With lightning speed
And catch a fish
For a delicious feed.
But then a seal shows up — Oh-No!
The penguin jumps up on the snow.
The seal gives up and swims away,
The penguin continues on his way.
He sits right down upon the ice.
A penguin's life must sure be nice!
He picks up the fish and swallows it whole
Then he slides away on the ice, on the ice,
Of the North Pole.

Emily Maiello, Grade 5
John G Dinkelmeyer Elementary School, NY

Fall Leaves

Leaves fall in the air day and night,
Some leaves are yellow and orange, crisp and bright,
Others are mostly green and dark brown.
Some people have a frown
Because the leaves are falling down.

All leaves are multicolored in the fall
In a pile of leaves it is fun to crawl.
My brother and I toss them up and down.
We'll jump until they're all around
Autumn's quilt is covering the ground.

Kevin Murphy, Grade 5
Liberty School, NJ

Starry Night*
You pop out at me,
Bright sky.
You are colorful,
Blue sky.
Your colors are wavy,
Colorful sky.
You're a wonderful painting,
Little town.
You make me dream,
Nice buildings.
You're as tall as a giant,
Tall tree.
Tell me, what are you,
Starry Night?

Griffin Keat, Grade 5
Roosevelt Elementary School, NJ
*Inspired by "Starry Night" by Vincent Van Gogh

Ode to Jonathan
Jonathan is a dufus; he's my big brother,
Or should I say my big BOTHER,
Jonathan is a dufus; his hygiene is poor,
I think he has the same gym clothes from the year before,
Jonathan is a dufus; why does he have to live with me?
He's so annoying; he has no empathy!
Jonathan is a dufus; I wear optimism on my shirt,
From head to toe and every day I'm treated just like dirt.
Jonathan is a dufus; he's rather cretinish,
Getting rid of him is my only wish!
Jonathan is a dufus; his mind bubbling with stupidity,
I hope you know how I feel,
To be his brother is filled with humility.
But I have gratitude for the times he tries,
To be kind and caring, until the respectfulness dies.

David Ramirez, Grade 6
Willow Grove Middle School, NY

Football
It is time for the kickoff
We kick an onsider,
We get the ball back.
Our team marches down the field
Our QB hands it off to the running back and he scores,
Our team has to kick it off.
Again we get the ball back.
The first play is a pass.
Our QB throws a perfect pass,
And the wide receiver catches it,
But he gets tackled.
The next play,
They throw the ball to me.
I catch it,
And score!

Matt Foreman, Grade 4
Lincoln Park Elementary School, NJ

The Sun and the Moon
The sun and the moon
Are two different things,
But they have things in common.
Like they both are round,
They both are beautiful,
They both are in the sky.
But most of all, they shine on me and you,
And make our lives a little sweeter!

Sandra Zelaya, Grade 5
Tecler Arts in Education Magnet School, NY

Band
My square music book helpfully provides on my stand.
The large trombone painfully emits notes.
The short trumpet carelessly beeps on stage.
The clunky sax gratefully soothes on the street.
The circular French horn sweetly buzzes in the house.
The long clarinet squeaks easily outside.
Humongous piano tweets gracefully in the studio.

Nicky Arpa, Grade 4
Maud Abrams Elementary School, NJ

Starry Night*
It is bright as the sun
Darkness and brightness combine together like
night and morning
It's as beautiful as a daisy
Colorful as a rainbow
Do you think the same?

Jada Davis, Grade 5
Roosevelt Elementary School, NJ
*Inspired by "Starry Night" by Vincent Van Gogh

Art
Neon paint flows smoothly across the paper.
Bright oil pastels paint creatively on the blank table.
Empty drawing paper lies quietly on a shelf.
Crazy drawing beautifully shows amazing colors on canvas.
Razor-sharp scissors viciously cut paper into halves on the art desk.
Creative stencils beautifully trace dolphins onto blue paper.
Talented art students joyfully express their feelings in different ways.

Delaney Cluff, Grade 4
Maud Abrams Elementary School, NJ

Dreams
The one thing that will stick with you throughout life
A story of you that will never change
No one can take them away from you
They push you to keep trying
Your inspiration to do your best
The things that keep you running
Your motive in life

Luis Nieves, Grade 6
Saw Mill Road Elementary School, NY

My Name Means…

The dictionary says
Nathan means
A gift from God
That is true
But
There is more

My names means
Athletic
An animal lover
Daring and energized
Fast
Unstoppable

There is more
To my name
But there is not enough
Room on this page
That is what Nathan
Means to me

Nathan Rosen, Grade 4
John G Dinkelmeyer Elementary School, NY

Creature of the Night

The obscure creature in the dark
Dart or it may want to make its mark
The sight of the teeth that hang like daggers
Just one look and you will stagger backwards
Threadlike tendrils encircle its victim
Attaches to one's body to restrict him
The dark creature's blood lust is uncontrollable
When it's starving, it's inexorable
Many that face darkness are unperturbed and think it's an illusion
But when it attacks, they are filled with confusion
It's dark, daring, and disrespectful to others
If provoked enough, it will force you to go against another
Its eyes are as piercing red as rubies
And it wastes no time with stories
Suddenly, a strip of pink lights the sky
If this creature doesn't flee, he will die
Up lights the sky and the wind gusts
All of a sudden, the monster turns to dust
The victim sprints out of woods with all his energy
Never again does he want to see that dark entity

Vanessa Rivera, Grade 6
Westampton Middle School, NJ

A Better Place

People fighting every night
I just want to sleep.

Robbing and killing every day
I just want people to get along.

Stealing and lying
I just want people to do like they usually do
Go to work, go to school, go to the store
Just be honest.

Drinking and driving
I just want people to be safe.

Smoking and drugs and beer
I just want all those things to be closed down

I'd be happy if all these bad things had never been created.
So I'd be happy if they would all just
GO AWAY!

Joshua Gonzalez, Grade 6
New York Institute for Special Education, NY

School

A nother day of moaning and groaning
B etter hurry up
C ome on let's go
D own in the dumps are
E ndless children
F ighting for a spot on the dreadful school bus
G oing to class after class
H our after hour
I t goes on and on but
J ust never seems to end
K ids shrieking and screeching
L unch time is here
M y head is about to fall off
N othing tastes quite as bad
O n my not so very merry tongue than a
P ile of peas and broccoli
Q uizzes are being passed out
R eady or not, here it comes
S till as glum as a kid could get
T il I wake up the following day to find out it is Saturday

Garrett Gualtieri, Grade 5
Roosevelt Elementary School, NJ

My God

When I am by the sea, I feel great relief
As I sit on the sand, I know that I have peace at hand
While I look up in the rain, I want not to use God's name in vain
I always know He's at my side, in doubt, in pain, and when I cry
While He loves me I love Him back, He stands there right at my back
My hope my life lies in His hands, my lord is the most peaceful man.

Peyton Kellner, Grade 6
Sts Peter & Paul School, NY

Halloween

Halloween is a scary night
And you know what makes it scary?
The moon!
Have a great fright soon.
Halloween happens in the fall
On a dark and spooky night.

Peter Rivera, Grade 4
R.J. McNulty Academy for International Studies and Literacy, NY

The Universe

In times of happiness,
In our troubles and worries too,
We always think
of the universe.

You can blame it,
Or thank it as well,
But,
If you're completely self-centered,
You'll curse it.

No matter what you think of the universe though,
It's always going to be here.

The universe comes up all of the time,
Especially in that eternal human debate,
"Why are we here?"

Maybe because of some unknown scientific occurrence?,
Or perhaps we evolved from tiny micro-organisms floating in space?

Well,
I think we're here because of just a single reason.
The universe.

Brian Massoni, Grade 6
Saw Mill Road Elementary School, NY

My Name

In the dictionary Alyssa means rational
Yes, that is true but Alyssa means so much more
Alyssa means loving and kindhearted
Always blooming
Trying to reach the top
And much, much more

Alyssa loves poetry and writing a lot
Art and singing along to tunes

Others say that I am fast and like to run
But honestly, Alyssa means
One who doesn't run through life

The girl who watches everything
Alyssa is one who fears failing
Or dying
Or just feeling blue

But most of all, Alyssa means
Determined
One who never gives up
And much, much more

Alyssa Dioguardi, Grade 4
John G. Dinkelmeyer Elementary School, NY

Beyond

Beyond the sky and the stars up there
I see change
A bit more light every time I look up
Beyond the depths of the water I hear
A clink of the golden penny
Beyond my clear mirror one scratch appears
Soon to make it harder to see
Beyond that blade of grass
I touch an atom the smallest particle
Beyond the future
I see the past making this day even here
Beyond one weakness
There is a certain strength
To have its own personal dream
Beyond a being there is an invention
Used to serve a being
Beyond the infinite universe
I see me

Only myself

But trying to see beyond the ends
Which I never seem to find

Kavya Borra, Grade 4
Village School, NJ

Midnight Monster

My eyes have no power.
The clock ticks twelve,
Yet I am awake.
The chilling air crawls throughout my body,
Like a spider with hairy legs.
I sense something coming up from the bottom of my bed.
It growls,
My heart skips a beat.

I whimper as something breathes heavily on my face.
The wooden floor makes a creaking noise.
A screeching sound comes from a turning doorknob.
Nails scratch the floor,
Sending a chilling shiver down my spine.

The warmth of my blankets is my only support.
But my lips still twitch,
And I still fear.
All of a sudden,
There is no movement nor sound.
All is dead but me.
The Midnight Monster has left,
Leaving fear in my heart.

Hetal Lad, Grade 6
Iselin Middle School, NJ

The Chilly Days of Autumn

Whistling wind
Like an orchestra, playing a song

Rustling leaves swirling
As if they were a funnel of a tornado

The chilling breeze against my skin
Like icicles piercing my cheek

Bright colorful leaves surrounding me
As if I were being trapped in a box of crayons

The glowing moon in the sky
Like a gleaming Jack-o-Lantern

Autumn will soon fly away
Like the birds heading south for the winter to come

Elisabeth Hudak, Grade 5
Ridgeway Elementary School, NJ

Dancing Stories

Feeling the beat
Moving your feet
Your dancing is telling a story to the world
Every move resembles a word
Dance as though no one is watching
Dance as though you will never dance again
Leaping in the air
Spinning in the atmosphere
The crowd reads your movement like a book that never ends
Your life story unfolds through your dancing
All of the sorrow, pain, and defeat
Your dance shoes are battered
They went through a lot
The late night rehearsals
Dancing on the spot
Dancing is your life and you will never stop
These are your dancing stories

Kiah Champion, Grade 5
Westampton Middle School, NJ

My Family

Sometimes we fight,
But we get along,
We love each other no matter what,
We stick with each other through thick
And thin
But at the end no one wins
We think about all the troubles
We go through
We hug each other and say "I love you"
Every day I think about my wonderful and precious
Family
My brothers, mom and dad too, I
Wrote this poem just for you
And I want to say I love you
Just remember when we fight
Think about the poem and stop the
Fight

Sierra Peters, Grade 6
Intermediate School 61 Leonardo Da Vinci, NY

Don't Judge Me

Am I uglier than you?
You made a face
Different teeth, different hair, different size —
Does that matter?
Does that really?
Are you depressed when I am not?
I will do my best to make you smile
Please don't judge me
I might have the autograph of the person you hate
Now will you judge me?
Would you, would you really?
You are a singer, and I am a dancer.
Does that matter?
I don't think so — everyone is different
I am the short one, and you are the taller one
Do you really want to judge me now?
Do you?

Courtney Gesior, Grade 6
Holy Innocents School, NJ

Smile!

I love to smile I really do,
But I also love to Moo!
People smile with joy, laughter and awesomeness.
I love to smile when people tell me funny jokes!
My smile smiles with might not fright.
So Just Smile!
I love to smile I certainly do,
But I love to laugh too!
Lots of people Smile!
I smile when I hear something funny.
When people smile I smile with joy.
!Just Smile!

Diane Tapia, Grade 4
John E Riley Elementary School, NJ

Canals

A canal is a manmade waterway,
You can use it to ride from bay to bay.
Some people use it for transportation,
While others use it for irrigation.
If you live in a dry area you don't have to worry,
The canal will bring you water in a hurry.
That was a pro and here is a con,
Soon the water from the bay could be all gone.
Some canals in the U.S are the Erie, Cape Cod, and Cape May,
They take water where kids might play.
They also take water from state to state,
Wow, canals sure are great!

Kate Setteducate, Grade 5
Forrestdale School, NJ

The Beatles

Beatles
Loud, awesome
Rocking, playing, thinking
Drums, guitar, bass, songs
Calming, amazing, performing
Practice
Band

Emilie Bills, Grade 5
Bartle Elementary School, NJ

Colors

Blue is the sky,
Green is the soft grass we walk on,
White is the puffy cloud,
Red is the apple on a tree,
Yellow is the sun that shines bright,
But best of all is…
Pink — the color of my bedroom walls.

Brianna Kehoe, Grade 5
Dickinson Avenue Elementary School, NY

Toby

Toby is my best friend.
He is a plump cat.
He is so puffy,
I could hug him
Until the world ends
Toby is my best,
Four-legged friend.

Ashley Cheung, Grade 4
Concord Road Elementary School, NY

The Guitar

Strum!
I can play the guitar.
It sounds like birds chirping.
I love the guitar.
When I play it's the only thing in the world.
I can play until the world stops moving.
Playing it is like speaking.

Elisa Shah, Grade 4
Concord Road Elementary School, NY

How Should I Feel?

How should I feel?
Should I feel sad, glad, or mad?

Now I feel sad.
Now I feel mad.
But, now I feel glad.
How do you feel?

Erin Edgley, Grade 5
Dickinson Avenue Elementary School, NY

When I Hug You

When I hug you…
I feel I can conquer everything in your arms…
I feel like nobody can hurt me your "protection shield" around me…
I feel like the luckiest person in the world…
To have known and loved someone like you…
You make me feel special…
Having a really close relationship with you…
Most of all you make me realize I love you…
I want to be with you forever

Alicia Etwaru, Grade 5
Lawrence Middle School, NY

How I Would Make the World a Better Place

I would make the world a better place by recycling,
cleaning up the beach and not cutting down the trees.
I would take care of the animals and keep the planet clean.
I would save energy, save the weather and clean up after myself.
I would recycle garbage, use less paper napkins, and smile more often.
I would say a prayer, save the Earth and give it away.
I would recycle furniture, recycle electronics, maintain motor vehicles, and turn off lights.
Finally, I would have more people lend a hand in our community
and I would brush my teeth without running the water and wasting it.

Alize Garcia, Grade 4
New York Institute for Special Education, NY

Fall Is Here

You know Fall is here when the leaves start to change
You know Fall is here when the cold air is in your range
You know Fall is here when the hay rides come to town
You know Fall is here when you're trick-or-treating in your Halloween gown
Fall is fun, fall is cool,
and I know this Fall will really rule!

Skylar Jeffries, Grade 6
Sacred Heart School, NY

The Talbot Family Goes Apple Picking

It was shining bright
The cheerful sun was playing with us.
I saw the happy family having fun picking apples; I smelled the nature all around me.
I hear the honking birds flying south for winter,
I can taste the ripe, red apple crunching in my mouth,
And I can touch the smooth, round apple.

Caitlin Clark, Grade 6
Harold D Fayette Elementary School, NY

The Trip South

Birds flying south as the frost settles down on a barren wasteland like icing on a cake.
As the leaves fall, they take to the air in search of a warmer land.
Flying in a "V" shape, taking turns cutting the cruel winds
Squawking overhead.
Looking for a place to rest their sore wings and settle for the winter.

Elan Isaacson, Grade 5
Bartle Elementary School, NJ

Figure Eight

I kick off the ice and glide.
I zoom through ice and twirl.
I fall,
But I get back up.
I don't stop gliding.
I do the biggest figure eight.
The crowd goes wild.
They announce the winner of the competition,
And I smile.

Ava Biasco, Grade 4
Lincoln Park Elementary School, NJ

Beautiful Leaves

Colorful leaves falling from the tree
Like confetti at a football game.
Smooth to the touch
Like the comfy blanket on my bed.
The rustling sounds as you walk through them
As if someone were crumpling paper.
The aroma of the fall leaves
As hearty as a pine tree.

Ana Jones, Grade 5
Ridgeway Elementary School, NJ

The Seasons' Best

Children's bright red cheeks
Like Rudolph's scarlet nose.
Autumn leaves falling off the trees
Like colorful feathers floating to the ground.
Bright flowers popping through the soil
Like popcorn in the popper.
Refreshing ocean breeze as refreshing
Like lemonade on a hot summer day.

Chloe De Los Reyes, Grade 5
Ridgeway Elementary School, NJ

At the Door

I heard a knock at the door who could it be?
Could it be the postman delivering a gift for me?
Could it be a bill for my mom? I wonder who it could be.

I heard a knock on the door could it be a surprise for me?
Could it be my sister from Florida
Could it be my best friend coming to play?
I wonder.

Kenneth Louis, Grade 4
Public School 114 Ryder Elementary, NY

Fall

Oh, what a beautiful time of year.
I'm surrounded around everyone so dear.
The colors of the leaves are
red, yellow, orange, and some are still green.
It's the most beautiful time I've ever seen of the year!

Lauren Stephenson, Grade 6
St Stanislaus Kostka Academy School, NY

Just Here

My floating reflection hands
Reaching out to touch the fish
My eyes sad and happy just looking into the
Heart and eyes of the pond and reflection eyes,
My reflection eyes looking into the heart and
Eyes of me
Me diving into the water and looking up and still
Seeing me on land and my reflection looking up
At the water and land
What did I become just then?
My ghost, my mouth is speaking in my head
But my reflection can hear
I come out of the water
It is still
There I am
Which one is me?
Happy that I will always have my reflection and
My reflection still follows me, just in my head
Was I the one with the reflection?

Genevieve Onorato, Grade 4
Central Elementary School, NJ

The Mine Trip

We went to school,
And we got on the bus.
When we saw Sterling Hill Mine,
We were pumped up with FUN!!
Students and teachers all hopped off,
And ran over to the helpful guide.
We went on a rock hunt,
What an amazing time!
Then things got quiet,
We were all ready for that mine.
When we walked in,
The floor seemed to go down.
Then we went 1,000 feet,
And it was time to go out.
Soon gift shop time came.
We explored the wonderful museum,
And before we knew it, it was bus time again.
As soon as we got to school,
We wanted to go back!!

Ashley Evans, Grade 4
Roosevelt Elementary School, NJ

The Meadow

As I feel the breeze through my hair.
As I feel God reaching down to me.
As I feel the clouds coming down to me to bring me towards the sky.
As I feel the grass floating me up in the air.
As I get closer and closer to happiness.
And Have more joy and peace.
I found a place that is for me.
I know that the meadow is where I should be.

Arielle Blatt, Grade 6
Pelham Middle School, NY

Spring!

Snow melts quickly off the ground
It seems the weather turned around
The freezing cold winter seemed so long
But now birds sing a lovely song

April showers bring May flowers
Nature seems to have special powers
The grass is green, the sky light blue
The trees grow high, and flowers, too!

Many plants start sprouting
No one should be pouting
Because when you hear the bluebirds sing
You know that it's beautiful, wonderful spring!

Emily Bubel, Grade 6
Regina Coeli School, NY

Life

Life is like a road trip.
You don't know which way it will take you.
All you know is that it will be long, not quick.
You honestly don't have a clue.

Life will take you this way and that way.
You might choose the way you go.
Please be careful, if you may.
Don't always pick the same way though.

So, go live your life.
Remember these words of wisdom.
Always be careful, follow the light.
Good-bye old friend I'll see you again.

Olivia Grogan, Grade 6
Regina Coeli School, NY

Halloween

Halloween is a time for a good spooky scare!
There are ghosts and creepy old ladies rocking in chairs.
The sun goes down and werewolves come about;
The children get into costumes and all go out.
They go trick or treating while parents watch close by,
Unaware of the ghosts flying high in the sky!
The ghosts swoop down, one by one, and scream scary boos,
Knocking the children right out of their shoes.
The monsters are kind and don't want to scare,
But, the way that they look, the children can't bare.
Their paws are quite big and so are their faces.
They wear shoes on their fingers and, on their ears, they wear laces.
So, when you go trick or treating, the night of Halloween,
Don't be surprised if no one is seen.

Emily Schum, Grade 6
St Rose of Lima Academy, NJ

The Clouds' Emotions

I've decided to make friends with the clouds.

I am really not sure why,
they are up in the sky.

Whenever they are extremely happy,

they become puffy and white
and seem to disappear at night.

Whenever they get really mad,

the world becomes gray and dark,
even the Sun seems to lose its spark.

Every so often they let go of weather.

The clouds are crying, rain.
The tissue that wipes away the clouds' tears falls apart, snow.
It is so cold that teardrops freeze, hail.

But in the end we know,
the clouds will never bail.

Claire Grande, Grade 6
Academy of the Holy Names Lower Middle School, NY

A Dream Deferred

Where does a dream go once deferred?
Does it become a distant memory on a wall
Or is it just pieces left on the ground
Waiting to be picked up?
Is it something you would die to do
Or something you do not desire upon?
Some say dreams can never come true
For they are ones no man or woman has ever accomplished.
Some doubt you but what they fail to realize
Is that the key to unlock the door to your dreams
Is right in front of you
You just have to wait until the time is right.
You cannot rush a dream deferred for
Everything happens for a reason.
A dream deferred is like a FLOWER
It grows a little bit at a time.
You cannot tell what kind or type it is
But when it starts to bloom and is fully developed
It becomes very clear.
Once your dream has BLOSSOMED, you can take the key
And unlock the door to your dreams.

Valicia Browne, Grade 6
Prep for Prep, NY

A Natural Beauty

Gently falling towards Earth
fluttering down, down, down.
Light and minute,
it makes up for size in personality.
A bright red flame licks its rough, curved edges.
Not too radiant
but never dull,
best describes its hue.
Its brethren, rustling in the breeze above,
cheering him on to touchdown.
Always smelling only sweet and fresh,
like a ripe, fuzzy peach.
Crinkled and rough, yet at the same time smooth and silky,
but still a bit uneven.
When looking at such a beautiful picture one shall never grieve,
the one the only, the leaf.

Alyssa Ferdinand, Grade 6
Slocum Skewes School, NJ

The Day Nothing Went Right

The clouds were foggy.
I felt dull and groggy.
I just knew it was going to be a bad day.
There was nobody in the streets.
And I had a very bad pain in my feet.
I arrived at school all soaking wet.
I then thought I was finally set.
Along came the principal saying I was in trouble.
I was talking to my friend and it turned into a big bubble.
The teacher gave us a big project.
And we had to use more than one object.
I didn't have any lunch.
I felt like my stomach just got punched.
Then I prayed.
That's all I could practically do for the rest of the day.
I was just hoping for the next day.

Luke Bauer, Grade 6
St Stanislaus Kostka Catholic Academy, NY

Turkey Taking

T hanksgiving is my favorite
H oliday because I get to kill the turkey for Thanksgiving dinner.
My dad couldn't hunt this year because he is sick.
He is making the **A**pple pie.
I get to use my shotgun to kill the biggest turkey.
The mother turkey hides in her **N**est every year, but not this year.
I walk up and she is huge like an elephant.
I **K**ill it!
Now, I rub lemon**S** on the turkey and put it in the oven.
We cook it until it is really **G**olden brown.
I eat the pumpkin pie with whipped cream.
The apple pie is **V**ery good, also **I**s the stuffing. It is really tasty.
The e**N**d has come,
Happy Thanksgivin**G** !

Michael Monteiro, Grade 6
Riverside Middle School, NJ

Thankful Thanksgiving

T ic toc went the clock as the
H ours went by.
A fter the turkey was finished,
N obody was hungry anymore.
K ids were eating desserts while the adults watched the
S miles on their faces grow with each yummy one.
G etting ready to do a craft is so much fun.
I nteresting posters made by children hang on the wall,
"**V** ery interesting posters," said grandpa Joe.
I 'll always remember the wonderful Thanksgiving
    filled with arts and crafts, dinner and dessert, but I'll
N ever forget about one wonderful thing…
G iving thanks to all in need.

Samantha Davan, Grade 6
Riverside Middle School, NJ

A Different World

The world would be a better place
If people would help the homeless
And give money to the needy.
If teens chose not to do bad things
Like dropping out of school.
If people did not litter our streets
Our streets would be clean and healthy.
If people were not broke
They could buy what they need.
If people did not kill each other
Families would never cry or feel depressed.
I would be a happy boy
If the world was a better place.

Raheam Steed, Grade 5
New York Institute for Special Education, NY

Surfing in Cape May

Immense waves crash roughly on the sandy shore,
Hawaiian surfboard glides smoothly on the surface of the waves,
Black leash connects securely from my ankle to my surfboard,
Waterproof wetsuit comfortably warms my entire body,
Remaining wax sticks firmly on the fiber glass,
Sharp fins helpfully support the weight on my board,
Runny sun block constantly covers sensitive skin on the beach,
The cold ocean often pleases the tourists, who come to Cape May,
Peaceful waters lay calmly on the coral below.

Emma L. Golden, Grade 4
Maud Abrams Elementary School, NJ

A Smooth Wind

A smooth wind flying past me
A smooth wind that makes me fly far away
A smooth wind that drifts me off to a sweet dream
A smooth wind that lets me soar high up in the air
A smooth wind that takes me away to a distant country
A smooth wind that lets me run with it
A smooth wind that makes me smile

Daniel Woo, Grade 5
Hawthorne Christian Academy, NJ

Technology

What happened to just a simple book
Now we have all that right on a nook
Don't forget about the iPod and iPad
Today both of these are the latest fad

Now people use a Mac that's really thin
Constantly going on Facebook because that's what's in
There's always going to be something new
And people are going to be asking "who knew"

So now let's talk about a cell phone
Ones that use touch are very well known
Why not get a droid
They say you'll never be annoyed

What happened to a phone that can flip
Now that's not even close to being hip
All these computers and phones dazzled and pearled
So is technology taking over the world
Nicholas Martinelli, Grade 6
Little Falls School #1, NJ

My Final Testament

A blond girl walked into the shoe store
I screamed, "Pick me, I can't take this anymore"
I was an Osiris, colorful and bright
She tried on a size six, but it was too tight

The girl picked me up, I was a size six and a half
She tried me on, it tickled, I let out a laugh
She said, "It's perfect" and was asked if she's paying in cash
She said she would and then left in a flash

The very next day I went to her school
But she stepped in some gum and I felt like a fool
After school her dog Fluffy decided to attack me
My day wasn't too pleasant as you can see

The next day she wore her flip flops instead
As I sat sadly right next to her bed
I may have been the latest trend
But I got chewed up by the dog and that is the end
Tara Daly, Grade 6
Little Falls School #1, NJ

Fall

My mom is basting a turkey
It smells so delicious already
My little sister Emma is very perky
We are racing toward a leaf pile
I'm baking a cake for Thanksgiving
I decorated my lawn with hay
My yard needs to be raked
It's so much fun to bake
Kayla Sondrup-Velez, Grade 4
R.J. McNulty Academy for International Studies and Literacy, NY

Winter

The sound of winter is in the air
As the snow falls down everywhere
As the grass gets covered in a blanket of snow
More love and joy will start to grow
Even though it won't be here for long
You can still hear it sing its beautiful song
But don't forget that next year
It comes again and spreads more cheer
Don't be sad when it leaves you
Just let your eyes deceive you
Then you will be happy that it came
Because in the end life is a never ending game
Siniah Mitchell-Rios, Grade 6
Westampton Middle School, NJ

Fall

Apples we are picking
For pies my mom is baking
Leaves I like kicking
While I am raking
My favorite topping is crumble
Leaf piles I want to jump
I trip and tumble
When I fall in I make a big thump
I felt a chill
I need to put on a coat
On the big hill
I watch the leaves float
Emily Brittain, Grade 4
R.J. McNulty Academy for International Studies and Literacy, NY

Fall

Mom's inside baking
There go the leaves falling
While I'm outside raking
I hear my mom calling
"The pie's ready!" she said
I saw the leaves float
While my face is red
I put on my winter coat
Fall is my favorite season
Baking bread I love
Fall is the reason
The leaves float above my head
Skylar Grybos, Grade 4
R.J. McNulty Academy for International Studies and Literacy, NY

End World Hunger

I would end world hunger.
I would use US Army planes
to drop food and money for the homeless.
They are hungry and need to eat.
They would feel happy.
The world would be a better place.
Jayel Perez, Grade 4
New York Institute for Special Education, NY

Christmas Eve

You can't wait until the next day,
just begging for an early present
going outside
playing with snow

Then you go to bed and
see if Santa comes
to give you presents!

Raymond Heuser, Grade 5
Dickinson Avenue Elementary School, NY

Words

words are funny
words are fun
words are pretty
beautiful too
words are great
and awesome
words are funny
so are you

James Kong, Grade 4
St Mark School, NY

I Am Baseball

Strike the batter out is my mission
Speeding like lightning I blur vision
Smacked with such force I groan
Simply hoping I find my glove home
Strong fingers handle me with care
Soaring with precision through the air
Soft landings in padded hands
Songs of merriment come from the stands

Eric Hanscom, Grade 6
Westampton Middle School, NJ

Fall

Fall is beautiful
with leaves falling on the ground
of different colors

Alice Yee, Grade 4
St. Mark School, NY

Fall

Fall is a season of
picking apples, looking at leaves
and eating apple pie with your friends

James Adiele, Grade 4
St Mark School, NY

Fall Is a Season

Fall is a season
of falling leaves, cold weather,
apples and pumpkins.

Jonah Adames, Grade 4
St Mark School, NY

Ballet

Ballet is so graceful
I feel like a swan when I leap in the air
I don't need to worry if anybody is going to annoy me
When I turn I feel so free — like I can do anything
It is so graceful I don't need to hear all the noise of the loud sounds around me
It is like a vacation from all the noise in my life
I can just be happy
Ballet is my paradise
I love it
Ballet

Elyse Adams, Grade 6
Holy Innocents School, NJ

Spring

The smell of spring is in the air.
A time of new beginnings is finally here.
Spring rains wash the winter snow away.
The sun becomes brighter with each new day.
New animals are born, ready to explore.
The bears come out of hiding and the geese come back from winter crying.
The flowers are rising and the birds are flying.
Barren trees are growing new green leaves.
Children are cheering because summer is nearing.
The cold begging of winter brings a spring you will remember.

Aleah McNeil, Grade 6
Westampton Middle School, NJ

Lemonade!

Lemonade, lemonade, I like you when you're homemade.
I like you during the day, I like you at night and I like you when I'm in a fright.
When I drink you, I am refreshed and when I'm done, I'm depressed.
Your ice cubes make you colder, it gives me the shivers on my shoulder.
When I first drank you I was happy, not bad, not shabby.
Your sugar looks like a snow, and you taste like a thousand rainbows.
Your lemons make your flavor, and your sugar makes you sweet.
When your ice taps this glass, I hear a zesty beat.
Lemonade, you taste as sharp as a blade,
Lemonade, lemonade, your taste is sweet and sour in many ways.

Mohamed Ahmed, Grade 6
Al Ghazaly School, NJ

Christmas

Falling blizzards scream quickly and furiously with anger
Glittering snow falls gently to the ground with a wonderland of white
Wrapped presents wait quietly underneath the green glimmering tree
Fun toys joyfully provide excitement from all over the world
Glowing lights sparkle brightly from above in the peaceful tree
Brown reindeer swiftly fly through the cloudy nighttime sky
Shiny sled runs loudly with snow flying behind
Green tree slowly scents around the beautiful decorated house
Red stockings hang peacefully waiting to be filled, and
Loving Jesus gives gracefully with love and kindness.

Cain Snow, Grade 4
Maud Abrams Elementary School, NJ

Never the Same

A problem so little and small
to begin hurting a boy named Paul
A parent so rough a parent so mean
his fists are getting keen
Why would he do this to a little teen?

I was shocked when he told me

Later that night with a great big "pop"
The way he was crying, he wouldn't stop

I couldn't imagine the pain
we all knew this wasn't a game
Cops were called and things were never the same…
THEY WERE BETTER

Hailey Swancott, Grade 6
Staley Upper Elementary School, NY

Open Your Eyes

Open your eyes
You don't know what you're missing
Beautiful trees and bumble bees

Pay attention
You don't know what you're seeing
Beautiful skies and pretty lights

Open your ears
You don't know what you're hearing
Cute giggles and the birds' wake up call.

Look around
You don't know what you're missing
The world surrounding us

Zarayli George, Grade 6
Graham Elementary and Middle School, NY

All Gone

I was on my bed all relaxed when I heard the news
My loving great-grandmother
Had a new life in the gold spirits of heaven
It's like somebody pressed a button
that made me shut down for the rest of the day.

Brokenhearted

Thoughts drift through my mind
Like paper in the wind.
The rest of the day was more of a threat
Everybody tried to cheer me up
Everybody tried to get brokenhearted thoughts to go away
But it was a failure
She was gone and never coming back.

Matthew Liotta, Grade 4
Norman J Levy Lakeside School, NY

Misery

The river flowed after a rain of tears.
I have been waiting for many years,
To see what I am meant to be.

The horse had been running wildly,
It comes to where it was finally free.
But now I slept.

The ship sails, but not too far.
It flows with the morning star.
But now it's tied low.

We don't need to let it rule our lives.
It comes in and out like the waves in the tide.
Misery. Misery.

Anna Cappucci, Grade 4
Toll Gate Grammar School, NJ

Colors

Colors are beautiful and vivid
They can be bright
Like the sun on a hot day
They can be dark
Like when the moon curls the night
Colors make the Earth special
Blue and green create the world
Red white and blue create America
Red and purple create royalty
Pink and purple create love
Yellow and green create the creatures of the Earth
Orange and brown create peace on Earth
Blue green red white purple pink yellow orange and brown
Are beautiful colors
Because they make the Earth special

Brooke Kappenberg, Grade 5
Raynor Country Day School, NY

The Season of Winter

White sheets grasped a once colorful world
Grass hides beneath the cold blanket
Trees stand, old, wise and bare
Once covered in red, orange and yellow
Now a rough crystal statue in the open
Hidden away from the wonderland
Evergreen trees wrapped in stars
Accompanied by orbs of red
Mugs of brown warmth with white flowering boats
Bodies huddled in front of a glowing flame
Soon an orange ball of light shines bright
Grass and flowers come out to play
The white washes down below
It hibernates until the next fall
The season of winter

Kristen Lewis, Grade 6
Branchburg Central Middle School, NJ

Fall

Fall is when the leaves fall down,
red, yellow, orange, and brown.
Watching movies with our friends,
the fun will never, ever end.
The apple trees are ready for harvest.
Pumpkin patches are at their largest.
Searching for costumes for Halloween,
I think I might go as a bean!
Now comes the best part, PUMPKIN PIE!
You don't like it? Give it a try.
The weather is breezy but still not cold,
You'll enjoy this season even if you're (elderly) old.
Jack-o-lanterns, on Halloween, sit outside;
This is the best holiday, there's no downside.
Pumpkin seeds baking in the oven.
Look! A bat! I hope you're not frightened.
One of the things I like the most is the scent,
Of freshly fallen leaves on the pavement.
But the fall is almost here, you see.
So enjoy all of its great beauty.

Christina Giambattista, Grade 6
St Rose of Lima Academy, NJ

God Created Me!

The mountains and skies
are all very nice,
but God created me!
The men who play dice,
the field mice,
and God created me!
The song and dance,
the shirt and the pants,
but God created me!
The good and the bad,
the happy and sad,
but God created me!
So when I pray, most everyday,
I give thanks for being me:
The smarty, the lefty,
the feisty and the lazy,
because that's how God created me!

Rebeca Oliveira, Grade 6
Holy Family School, NY

School Is Cool

School is cool.
School is fun.
I also hate it when school is done.
When the first bell rings.
The birds must sing.
We have fun as we play.
Playing is fun, but I can't do it all day.
As I got on the bus.
My heart starts to rush.
Loud and exciting.
It's really quite inviting.
I catch a few z's on the bus ride home,
Where I keep my TV a reasonable tone.
My friends meet at school today.
My friends are so happy and we say yeah.
School is going to be fun always.
School is cool.

Franklyn Stephens, Grade 5
Hawthorne Christian Academy, NJ

My Teacher

My teacher is nice
My teacher is cool
My teacher makes me love school
My teacher is loving
My teacher is friendly
I love my teacher

Kristen Davis, Grade 5
Hawthorne Christian Academy, NJ

Nothing

Feel the blank emptiness of nullity,
Just let your mind grow dim,
Let everything go into nonexistence,
Because everything you know is extinct,
Dark streams of nothingness,
Flow steadily into your mind,
All you can do is let it flow,
And relax your mind instead…

Ariel Ortega, Grade 6
Our Lady of Good Counsel School, NY

Parents

A kind, caring, careful mom,
A playful, encouraging dad,
They are as sweet as candy,
With them I am never sad.
Their love to me,
Cannot be explained,
On happy moments
Love is regained.
To me they are stars,
To me they are God,
We stick together,
Like peas in a pod.
I love them,
They love me,
We will always live together,
We are FAMILY!

Isha Brahmbhatt, Grade 4
Concord Road Elementary School, NY

Oh Winter You're Such a Dream

Frigid flakes falling
To the floor
Tickling my nose,
With a soft cure.

Oh winter such a dream!

Air is a silvery blur
Flakes fluttering to my face
Brrrrrhhhh!

Sights to see
Like the Christmas tree
In New York City!

Oh winter, you're such a dream!

Eisha Nasar, Grade 4
James A Dever School, NY

Horizon

I saw it, I saw it
Where the sea meets the sky
The place where they touch
Where the seagulls soar high.

I'm already there
And yet so far away
But I know I'll get there
Someday, someday.

I know it's just God
Playing a trick on the eye
But I know I will find
Where the sea meets the sky.

Julia Peters, Grade 4
Toll Gate Grammar School, NJ

A Bucket Full of Friendship

To me, friendship means happiness.
I think of choosing carefully,
Because friendships are fragile
To make a friendship stronger
You must bring more happiness,
You must water it with support,
And feed it with trust,
And fill it with love
In order for it to flourish.

Allison Frost, Grade 5
Public School 114 Ryder Elementary, NY

Soccer

Soccer is my favorite sport to play.
It's fun to play soccer.
Playing soccer can help you exercise.
You get faster and stronger
By playing any kind of sport.
Soccer; football.
Exercise is a better way
To get healthy
A way for your body
To get in good shape.

Peter Joseph, Grade 5
Public School 114 Ryder Elementary, NY

Ice Cream

Ice cream is creamy and tasty
It can take you to a different world
Ice cream is in all kinds of flavors

Chocolate is the tastiest of all
Strawberry takes you to a berry world
And the best flavor of all is vanilla

Michael Breeden, Grade 5
Public School 114 Ryder Elementary, NY

Christmas Day

Christmas day is fun
We celebrate,
Friends come to play,
It snows
We took a picture
Then sent it to my aunt
We give toys to all.

Wasam Almulaiki, Grade 5
Public School 114 Ryder Elementary, NY

Fall

Fall is coming now
it is hurrying fast here
with leaves of brown and red

Brianna Biggs, Grade 4
St Mark School, NY

Courage Has a Name and a Face

C areful firefighters saved thousands of people
O ur former students were lost helping us
U nited we all came together
R emember the sacrifices of volunteers
A irplane Flight 93 didn't hit its destination because of our heroic passengers
G rateful for all that were saved and lived
E veryone will remember this day

Erika Jarymiszyn, Grade 5
Helen B Duffield Elementary School, NY

Halloween Costume

What should I be?
A goblin, a can, or a tree;
I must have the best costume in school
If I don't, I may look like a fool.
Everyone else is going to be a ghost or witch.
Wait! Maybe I should be a sandwich.
I want to look cool and hip.
But, if I don't, I might flip.
Maybe a leaf and the colors of pink, brown and green
Or I can be a jelly bean.
I should be a super turtle
That shoots out laser beams!
I fooled you didn't I!
I hope you don't fright.
I can't wait to see you on Halloween night.

Noelle Gregory, Grade 6
St Rose of Lima Academy, NJ

Christmas

Christmas Day
is almost here,
then Santa's sleigh
will be up in the air.
Giving presents all around,
In the chimney he comes down.
Every family happy as can be,
Spreading their joy
On the Christmas tree.
And even though Santa is gone,
he's still saying, "Ho, ho, ho!"
on and on.

Ashli Byfield, Grade 5
St Rose of Lima Academy, NJ

My Comfy Bed

Comfy cozy all evening long
Bunches of blankets keeping me warm
Soft stuffed animals
Singing "Good Night"
To me on my teeny tiny bed
As fleshy as a thermal blanket
It comforts me.

Katherine Georgioudakis, Grade 4
Concord Road Elementary School, NY

Thanksgiving

T hankful for food.
H aving fun with my family.
A t the dinner table we sit.
N ature is so beautiful at this time.
K indness is golden.
S atisfaction for sure.
G enerous to everyone.
I magination grows bigger!
V ery colorful all over.
I love the nice weather.
N eighbors are welcome.
G reatest time of year to me.

Olivia Capasso, Grade 5
St Rose of Lima Academy, NJ

Index